ODOUR PREFERENCES

R. W. Moncrieff, B.Sc., F.R.I.C.

ODOUR
PREFERENCES

JOHN WILEY: NEW YORK
1966

© R. W. Moncrieff 1966

Set in 10 on 12 pt Times New Roman and printed by Neill & Co. Ltd., Edinburgh
on paper supplied by Inveresk Paper Merchants Ltd. Bound by Mansell (Book-
binders) Ltd., London.

PRINTED IN GREAT BRITAIN

Contents

3

List of Figures

The frontispiece is from a drawing of the author's dog, Spindle

PART I

The Search for Trends

A study of the odour preferences of a few people towards a wide range of odours

CHAPTER 1

ARRANGEMENT OF A LARGE NUMBER OF ODOURS BY SEVERAL PEOPLE ACCORDING TO THEIR PREFERENCES

O DOUR PREFERENCES? What did we all know about them?
It was common knowledge that most people liked flower perfumes and fruity smells, and that everybody disliked such revolting smells as bad eggs, bad fish, bad drains and so on. Badness and unpleasantness of odours went hand in hand. It was safe to say that there was a large measure of agreement in the human race about what was pleasant to the nose and what was bad. About the very good and the very bad smells it was plain that there would be very general agreement.

But equally, many differences in liking and disliking of odours were widely known: some people were fussy about the bouquet of wines, others could hardly tell one from another, and some did not like the smell of wine at all. And so it was with ciders, beers, whiskies, gins, teas, coffees and cheeses. The differences are quite real; some people will drink no tea but China, others are nauseated by it; those who regularly take a dry gin with their tonic may dislike the sweeter and more floral odour of some popular brands and conversely those who regularly drink the latter dislike the austerity of the dry gin. The odour differences are relatively slight: anyone sniffing a glass of either would unhesitatingly say "gin", but the differences are quite big enough to change pleasantness to unpleasantness. Some farm smells are honest and wholesome to one observer, and disgusting to another. There are some people, mostly children, who like fruit jellies and trifles, others don't: some women like the smell of cigar smoke, others detest it; some men love the smell of seaweed on the rocks, whilst others think the smell just so much evidence that the weed is decomposing.

Wherever one looked there were differences. Although at the extremes of pleasantness and of unpleasantness there might be a large measure of uniformity of liking or disliking, it was very clear that in between the extremes, there were very many differences

11

indeed. Would it be practicable to bring some order into the scattered and diverse differences? Were there general rules that could be disclosed? Was there a grammar, even an elementary one, of smell?

It was evident that, to begin with, a large number of odours, ranging from what are usually thought of as very pleasant to what are quite revolting, should be offered to a few people, and provided that the group included persons of either sex, of different ages, and perhaps of different temperaments, their reactions to them would reveal some trends and might illuminate the main rules, if there were any.

Accordingly, what we did was to take a large number of odorant materials and to ask a small number of people of various ages and both sexes to arrange them in order of preference. It was hoped that it would be possible to ascertain from their arrangements:

(1) Which likes and dislikes were common to the whole group.

(2) Whether there were any striking differences between the likes (and dislikes) of persons of different sex, different age groups and different temperaments.

Three age groups were considered:

    (a) children below the age of 15, that is roughly before the onset of puberty

    (b) young adults, within the range of 15–25 years

    (c) older people

Temperament was divided on Jung's extrovert and introvert basis; the former class included those who were socially bright, but apparently not much interested in abstract thought and the latter their opposites; although such a classification of temperament is empirical it is easy and there was only one of our group of twelve whom we had any hesitation in classifying appropriately.

Experimental method

A collection of odorants, some natural and others chemical, was made; this comprised 132 different smells. Twelve people arranged the odorants in order of their preference, and four of them did it twice, so that in all there were sixteen arrangements made. Because the tests extended over a period of about two months, some of the natural odorants e.g. fresh strawberries and Emily Gray rose, were not always available, so that the full number of odorants was not always available, but it was never less than 119 for any one experimental run. The average of each odorant was calculated for the whole group and also the average placings for:

(a) male and female observers

(b) children, 15–25 age group, and older people

(c) extrovert and introvert observers.

The times taken to sort out the odorants varied considerably from one person to another. Practised smellers who made the first runs took about a day or a day and a half to make their arrangement and took about as long to make a second arrangement working assiduously and carefully; some of the novices to the art made remarkably quick arrangements sometimes in two to three hours and the practised smellers were sceptical about their accuracy. But after one very quick arrangement on the part of a subject who had no special interest in smell, a reliability check was given. The fast-working subject was persuaded to sit on a stool with eyes closed and then bottles containing two different odorants were held successively under his nose and he was asked to say which of the two he preferred; this was done with nine pairs of odorants, selected so that one member of the pair had been rated by him a few places higher than the other in his arrangement of the odorants. He nearly always gave the right answer, i.e. the one that agreed with his earlier arrangement.

The twelve observers who took part in the test were:

RWM	male	52 years	(2 runs)	
SL	female	17 „	(2 runs)	
ST	female	17 „	(2 runs)	
WG	male	14 „	(2 runs)	
ELM	female	77 „	mother of RWM	
RMM	female	24 „	daughter of RWM	
JET	male	48 „	father of ST	
EMT	female	52 „	mother of ST	
MH	male	12 „	first cousin of RMM	
WMM	female	52 „	mother of RMM	
RO	male	16 „		
ARL	male	10 „	cousin of ST	

Blood relationships are indicated. It will be seen that there were twelve observers and that the first four of them in the list made two runs each; the other eight made one run each.

Results

The results of these tests are shown in Table 1. Along the top are the initials of the observers and in each vertical column are the placings that the particular observer gave to the various odorants. The odorants themselves are named in the first column. Because the smell of natural products, and of essential oils in particular, is liable to vary with their place of origin, the supplier or the source from which the various substances had been obtained is also shown. The kind of smell is indicated in the second column. It may seem a little pointless to describe the odour of parsley as "parsley" and that of onion as "onion", but what better can be done, and the description of the "type of odour" of the less familiar odorants, particularly the chemicals, should be of use. In the "average" column is shown the average placing for each odorant and in the last column its ranking. In order to facilitate examination of Table 1, the odorants in it have been placed in order of preference, so that the most preferred material is at the top and the most disliked is at the bottom. Red rose is liked best and ranked 1st, thiomalic acid is disliked most and is ranked 132nd. Red rose is the first odorant in Table 1, thiomalic acid is the last.

Discussion

There is a lot of information in Table 1 and some of it can be seen by inspection. There are two points that stand out at once and these relate to the effect of concentration and to our preference for natural products rather than chemical or synthetic. These two subjects can be dealt with at once.

Effect of high concentration

Many of the chemicals used in our tests and included in Table 1 will only develop really pleasant smells when they are in dilution; when they are concentrated, their smell, although of the same kind as when diluted, is aggressively strong and often quite disagreeable. Hydroxycitronellal, ranked 73rd, affords one example. Methyl anthranilate has been ranked 95th by the whole group of observers, yet on dilution it smells pleasantly of orange blossom: even when diluted it does not smell nearly so pleasant as does a natural flower but it is much more attractive than when concentrated. The ionones when dilute have pleasant violet odours, but when concentrated although their note is still one of violets, they are unpleasantly strong; the two α-ionones are ranked 65th and 67th and the two β-ionones are ranked 69th and 72nd, which positions do nothing to indicate that they are frequent constituents of violet perfumes. Amyl cinnamic aldehyde, also known as jasmine aldehyde, is rated only 78th by the whole group, although jasmine flowers have one of the most beautiful scents that we know, and although the aldehyde is used in the preparation of perfumes. Phenyl acetaldehyde, which has a distinct hyacinth note is ranked as poorly as 96th. Even the synthetic perfume concentrates such as Rose 2321 and Alpine Violet are ranked no better than 62nd and 63rd respectively by the whole group and yet these are mixtures, probably of both synthetic and natural products, that are sold to perfume manufacturers for dilution and possibly compounding and then for sale.

The concentrates of natural odorous materials, and these constitute the class of substance known as the essential oils, do rather better. They are highly concentrated, but nevertheless they have odours that are not disliked: sweet orange oil is ranked 10th, spearmint oil is 18th, English lavender 19th, French lavender 23rd, ylang-ylang (the Eastern "flower of flowers") 25th: but there are a few even of the essential oils that are disliked e.g. oil of geranium is ranked 64th, citronella oil is 70th and patchouli is 83rd.

Preference for natural products

We have just seen that concentrated odorants are not usually liked, but there is more chance that they will be liked if they are the essential oils that are natural concentrates. These are often fairly well-liked.

Those odorant materials that are the best-liked (Table 1) are the flowers and fruits. As a rule their odours are not very powerful, but many of them are generally considered delightful. All the first eight odorants in Table 1 are natural flowers or fruits and the next dozen or more are mainly derived from natural products; in fact not until we come to musk lactone, which is 26th, do we reach a chemical or synthetic odorant. This preference for natural odours is due, of course, to the inferiority of men perfumers and flavour artists compared with the perfection of Nature's creative artists: and, if we try to analyse this inferiority a little, we soon reach two big points of difference.

(1) Natural products are not as a rule powerfully odorous; flowers and fruits usually only hint at their constituent chemical

TABLE 1

Odours arranged in order of preference

Primary records of results of tests with many odorants and few observers

Odorant	Type of odour	Placing (1 is most liked, 2 is next most liked and 132 is most disliked) of each odorant by each observer.																Average	Odorant is ranked
		RO	ELM	MH	RMM	RWM	RWM	WMM	SL	SL	ST	ST	JET	EMT	ARL	WG	WG		
Red rose, Ena Harkness, flower	Deep rose	—	6	—	1	2	3	6	8	5	4	2	3	4	17	—	6	5·1	1st
Fresh strawberries	Strawberries	—	11	8	6	3	1	1	3	2	16	24	2	1	2	4	6	5·5	2nd
Sweet peas, flowers	Floral	17	1	8	3	5	9	3	1	1	2	4	6	2	18	20	11	7·6	3rd
Rose, New Dawn, flower	Powerful wild rose type of odour	1	1	22	—	4	6	2	9	7	5	18	5	3	16	19	12	8·7	4th
Rose, Emily Gray, flower	Lighter than Red Rose	—	—	—	—	7	10	15	10	6	9	9	—	5	14	—	—	9·4	5th
Stock, double ten-week flower	Floral heavy	5	7	28	4	11	12	—	14	15	11	6	—	7	22	—	37	13·8	6th
Honeysuckle, flowers	Floral rich honey	—	2	55	2	1	2	12	2	3	1	8	1	6	24	57	46	14·8	7th
Wild rose (Dog rose), flower	Pure rose fresh, sweet	—	—	—	—	8	7	—	4	4	43	51	—	9	21	6	3	18·4	8th
Raspberry flavouring essence (ABR)	Fruity very true	10	10	12	32	49	43	28	19	31	46	10	11	22	1	6	3	20·8	9th
Sweet orange oil (RAN)	Orange light and very natural	49	20	3	8	9	11	14	18	13	27	49	38	28	87	1	18	24·6	10th
Lemon flavouring essence (BTS)	Lemon, slightly bitter	45	—	25	28	25	22	—	34	33	—	19	18	—	8	11	32	25·3	11th
Meadowsweet, flower	Rich floral, honey note	14	4	56	11	6	4	—	38	27	6	19	35	—	19	55	45	25·4	12th
P'permint flavouring essence (BTS)	Peppermint	15	14	1	61	19	29	47	57	28	29	33	42	76	13	10	7	26·9	13th
St'wberry flavouring essence 1512 (ABR)	Strawberry, very sweet	13	12	13	61	64	78	27	41	32	37	16	12	24	4	3	5	27·6	14th
Heliotrope, flower	Cherry pie	20	5	54	5	14	14	—	23	11	103	—	—	—	—	—	38	28·7	15th
Lemon flavouring essence (ABR)	Lemon, slightly sweet	50	16	17	7	24	21	17	35	34	79	61	27	33	3	9	—	28·9	16th
Banana flavouring essence (ABR)	Banana	11	38	11	54	56	77	18	44	59	26	15	20	23	5	5	8	29·4	17th

Substance	Odour	Rank	Mean	1	8	6	29	33	45	19	12	17	61	69	55	39	23	21	39
Spearmint oil (RAN)	Spearmint	18th	29·8	39	68	28	10	34	11	30	35	31	10	19	32	9	94	—	2
Lavender oil, English (WHH)	Lavender	19th	30·1	—	—	20	8	7	105	121	16	13	7	16	10	—	—	—	—
Mock orange (Philadelphus) blossom	Floral, but bitter and astringent	20th	32·3	54	64	25	26	8	64	71	10	22	4	30	17	12	26	67	21
Garden mint, fresh	Minty	21st	32·6	9	7	7	34	16	23	28	40	50	8	89	82	29	78	13	9
Vanilla flavouring essence (ABR)	Vanilla	21st	32·6	68	71	47	11	13	17	54	20	7	11	28	33	10	95	36	4
Lavender oil, French (WHH)	Lavender, more fruity than English	23rd	32·8	53	63	23	12	54	46	70	14	21	49	32	23	16	7	—	23
Catmint (Nepeta) fresh leaves	Catmint	24th	33·7	34	37	49	40	28	1	3	38	33	83	8	16	52	92	25	6
Ylang-ylang, essential oil (WHH)	Rich floral	25th	34·1	44	52	32	15	23	28	44	83	52	16	5	12	33	33	22	74
Musk lactone (Muscolactone) 10 per cent in solvent (P & S)	Sweet musky	26th	35·5	24	44	27	51	22	66	40	26	6	21	23	34	88	21	42	34
Cinnamon leaf oil (WHH)	Cinnamon light, spicy	27th	36·2	—	—	—	—	—	50	73	17	40	—	17	27	—	10	—	65
Orange flavouring essence (ABR)	Orange, a shade lemony	28th	37·4	41	49	68	53	9	3	12	36	6	81	25	31	53	71	17	46
Rose absolute, attar (WHH)	Rose, not so fresh as the flower	29th	37·6	10	12	10	32	40	41	74	47	67	32	20	26	65	51	58	19
Citral (ABR)	Powerful lemony, a little sweet	30th	37·8	—	25	15	81	37	76	41	21	11	—	33	62	21	52	19	—
Privet flower	Bitter, floral	31st	38·0	23	28	11	30	29	48	83	44	37	22	24	35	89	38	46	35
Cinnamon bark oil (WHH)	Cinnamon, heavy, sweet spicy	32nd	38·9	52	62	98	—	32	26	47	9	20	26	34	79	14	53	30	—
Bay leaf, dried	Reminiscent of curry, bitter, hint of roasting coffee	33rd	41·6	—	—	74	80	10	97	23	19	26	24	90	21	—	37	3	—
Ribes (flowering currant) fresh leaf	Fresh, green, fruity. Like mint and blackcurrant	34th	42·0	56	38	30	65	47	14	35	45	42	68	47	57	36	6	18	77
Strawberry aldehyde (FLD)	Strawberry with acid note	35th	42·6	19	27	44	41	24	94	34	81	90	52	13	13	34	50	44	28
Musk ambrette (ABR)	Sweet, bland musky	36th	43·0	—	—	—	—	—	67	52	30	29	9	44	37	—	66	—	56
Vanillin 100 per cent ex eugenol (GIV)	Vanilla	37th	43·3	—	—	—	—	—	—	—	—	—	—	—	—	—	—	—	—

TABLE 1—continued

Odours arranged in order of preference

Primary records of results of tests with many odorants and few observers—*continued*

Odorant	Type of odour	Placing (1 is most liked, 2 is next most liked and 132 is most disliked) of each odorant by each observer																Average	Odorant is ranked
		RO	ELM	MH	RMM	RWM	RWMM	WMM	SL	SL	ST	ST	JET	EMT	ARL	WG	WG		
Oil of Neroli, French Bigarade (WHH)	Orange blossom	40	48	72	31	36	26	30	30	18	78	7	56	—	80	36	66	43·6	38th
Geraniol ex Palmarosa (ABR)	Rose, a little lemony	57	77	88	51	15	15	19	64	85	63	34	21	44	33	24	27	44·8	39th
Almondflavouring essence (ABR)	Almonds	8	8	18	87	85	91	80	27	41	33	88	19	25	39	29	—	45·2	40th
Nerol (P & S)	Rose, lemony note	53	78	47	41	18	18	33	49	42	82	21	83	19	43	39	40	45·6	41st
Lemongrass oil (WHH)	Lemonylikecitral but a little smoky	7	15	93	76	22	27	62	55	66	85	44	46	31	12	35	63	46·2	42nd
Isoeugenol (GIV)	Spicy, sour, hint of cloves	33	23	5	19	107	67	34	32	37	110	54	43	47	29	51	70	47·6	43rd
Friar's Balsam (local pharmacy)	Resinous	68	43	2	70	61	37	37	88	71	18	35	15	69	34	69	64	48·8	44th
Eugenol (P & S)	Cloves	76	51	4	38	77	50	58	60	58	92	57	48	39	41	13	25	49·2	45th
Parsley, fresh	Parsley	29	73	29	22	44	39	5	25	46	72	69	92	78	71	54	43	49·4	46th
Terpineol (DIS)	Lemony lilac	92	89	9	58	30	36	31	76	80	20	60	76	21	36	32	50	49·8	47th
Oil of Cananga (WHH)	Floral, slightly spicy	3	37	90	64	83	81	36	61	56	65	29	25	36	79	30	26	50·1	48th
Phenylethyl dimethyl carbinol (FLD)	Flowery reminiscent of terpineol	75	32	35	17	51	70	67	74	70	15	40	69	38	59	47	42	50·1	48th
Amyl butyrate, ex technical amyl alcohol (BDH)	Powerful, fruity	30	59	16	74	69	87	109	77	64	67	72	4	27	35	15	4	50·6	50th
Coconut flavouring essence (ABR)	Coconut	52	39	19	77	72	99	—	71	60	51	58	17	63	9	61	16	50·9	51st
Chives, fresh	Onion but milder and fresher	27	85	70	80	86	59	25	15	24	13	27	95	111	70	21	14	51·4	52nd
Butyl acetate (TSH)	Pear drops, slightly sharp	16	34	67	20	67	74	54	84	76	64	65	87	46	45	23	2	51·5	53rd

Rank	Score	Substance	Description															
54th	51·8	Onion, raw, cut	Onion	15	22	54	110	94	5	7	8	12	20	60	96	81	81	84	79
55th	51·9	Terpinolene (DIS)	Bitter, lemony, hint of hyacinth	20	56	37	43	77	59	62	79	46	38	35	29	59	42	88	60
56th	52·6	Tonka beans, tincture in benzyl alcohol (FLD)	Nutty, sweet, some coumarin	71	77	65	49	86	22	36	49	45	85	31	43	25	39	41	78
57th	52·7	Amyl acetate (M & B)	Pear drops	65	14	38	89	88	73	66	54	56	40	65	68	42	15	45	25
58th	53·6	Heliotropine cryst (piperonal) (GIV)	Floral, cherry pie	35	48	77	35	58	89	86	39	39	29	72	74	26	41	26	84
59th	54·3	Musk natural, 2 per cent tincture in alcohol (FLD)	Musk, sweet, heavy, slightly faecal	75	45	53	77	44	56	38	69	83	51	56	54	24	20	40	83
60th	54·7	Benzyl acetate (BDH)	Flowery, hyacinth note	21	16	56	74	39	74	25	104	92	—	83	65	43	57	53	18
61st	55·5	Ethyl alcohol 99/100 per cent, duty paid (BDH)	Sweet, spirituous	96	112	88	73	67	36	32	25	24	—	54	18	18	24	65	100
62nd	56·2	Rose No. 2321, synthetic perfume concentrate (FLD)	Lemony rose	76	46	60	45	71	116	119	22	5	13	62	53	37	111	27	36
63rd	56·7	Alpine violet, perfume concentrate (FLD)	Strong fresh green odour, also violets	114	83	81	14	57	13	10	43	63	87	80	80	30	36	31	85
64th	58·0	Oil of geranium, Bourbon (WHH)	Rich rose, bitter	69	70	69	16	14	12	57	75	68	98	58	42	94	96	—	32
65th	59·0	α-Ionone (P & S)	Violets lighter and sweeter than β-Ionone	72	107	42	18	73	43	97	82	47	44	57	81	48	30	56	47
66th	60·5	Camphor (CCC)	Camphor	29	31	52	42	114	71	91	57	80	42	45	38	13	101	68	94
67th	60·6	α-Ionone (ABR)	Violets light and sweet but not so light as 65th	60	109	31	13	62	63	90	86	85	73	41	40	49	46	74	48
68th	61·9	α-n-Methylionone (P & S)	Violets, slightly nutty. Softer and more flowery than α-Ionone	33	90	78	55	64	30	55	61	87	95	42	87	84	34	52	43
69th	62·3	β-Ionone (ABR)	Intense violets, slightly woody	28	108	55	20	59	82	89	65	75	56	49	46	72	103	35	55
70th	63·9	Oil of citronella, Ceylon (WHH)	Sweet, spicy, floral	113	43	67	17	55	55	88	62	65	23	93	60	92	98	55	37
71st	65·2	Patchouli, clear resin (FLD)	Bland Eastern odour. Rounder and milder than Patchouli oil (83rd)	86	104	106	54	60	32	49	74	81	84	51	28	44	40	79	71

TABLE 1—continued

Odours arranged in order of preference

Primary records of results of tests with many odorants and few observers—continued

Placing (1 is most liked, 2 is next most liked and 132 is most disliked) of each odorant by each observer

Odorant	Type of odour	RO	ELM	MH	RMM	RWM	RWM	WMM	SL	SL	ST	ST	JET	EMT	ARL	WG	WG	WG	Average	Odorant is ranked
β-Ionone (P & S)	Violets, woody, bitter	67	49	87	40	52	73	91	48	63	59	42	90	37	64	92	92	92	65·4	72nd
Hydroxy-citronellal (GIV)	Lily of the valley, jasmine type but unpleasantly strong	110	102	73	35	39	48	88	69	68	53	79	65	57	58	58	49		65·7	73rd
Allyl caproate (ABR)	Pineapple, coarse and strong	51	62	68	90	59	55	97	79	84	96	107	52	85	26	2	55		66·8	74th
Kewda, otto of Pandanus odoratissimus India	Heavy floral	41	24	107	79	66	52	89	59	77	102	115	36	48	48	50	77		66·9	75th
Ethylene glycol (G & T)	Faint oily	31	98	102	63	108	112	41	72	52	58	31	84	50	72	17	94		67·8	76th
Ionone (Indian mixed isomers) (HFO)	Violets woody	24	33	83	82	45	46	86	86	73	87	62	66	79	66	86	110		69·6	77th
α-Amyl cinnamic aldehyde (GIV)	Jasmine type	82	76	45	91	76	84	99	36	23	77	96	30	67	84	80	74		70·0	78th
Naphthalene (G & T)	Firelighters	90	104	14	104	113	116	79	53	53	14	38	93	112	108	18	13		70·1	79th
Musk Tonkin, natural (FLD)	Musky nutty	81	47	97	15	20	40	66	93	67	76	114	70	52	99	78	109		70·3	80th
Anisaldehyde ex anethole (ABR)	Hawthorn blossom light	72	63	44	95	58	66	53	70	97	75	85	49	62	89	96	62		71·0	81st
Methyl salicylate (ABR)	Wintergreen	93	87	86	—	92	79	59	66	50	84	37	72	102	97	33	30		71·1	82nd
Patchouli oil Singapore (WHH)	Heavy warm Eastern odour cinnamon-like	107	54	91	75	47	82	92	96	87	17	20	26	72	82	79	112		71·2	83rd
Veratrol (P & S)	Like thyme but sweeter	38	57	89	27	97	105	43	108	102	45	39	105	86	—	40	87		71·2	83rd
γ-Benzene hexachloride (BDH)	Earthy	96	95	31	47	98	63	39	101	99	31	70	51	82	75	84	95		72·3	85th

Substance	Description																		
Nitrobenzene (TSH)	Aromatic chemicals. Coarse almondy	95	29	69	86	94	106	100	43	48	42	86	68	71	94	67	59	72·3	85th
Peach synthetic concentrate. (Pêche Pur) (GIV)	Peach	42	100	65	50	110	101	48	95	93	—	90	61	66	57	41	67	72·4	87th
Acetone (BDH)	Nail varnish	69	75	62	46	90	95	77	82	78	22	53	78	91	107	66	97	74·3	88th
Ambergris, best grey natural (FLD)	Suave, round, reminiscent of musk	44	69	84	23	109	113	46	94	92	69	104	107	56	50	105	36	75·1	89th
α-Amyl cinnamic aldehyde (ABR)	Jasmine type	61	28	64	93	71	71	107	62	103	39	87	89	64	102	74	88	75·2	90th
Anisaldehyde ex cresol (RAN)	Hawthorn, rather rough	54	—	48	83	118	114	72	97	94	50	25	41	60	73	106	100	75·7	91st
Anisaldehyde ex cresol (ABR)	Warm hawthorn	59	—	59	108	106	97	65	100	95	24	68	45	61	103	95	61	76·4	92nd
Cigarette ash	Rank, sour	12	—	—	—	119	124	90	78	88	120	84	53	—	110	26	17	76·8	93rd
Ethyl lactate (TSH)	Mild "rum and butter"	97	61	60	55	84	76	35	123	117	60	52	63	93	62	97	99	77·1	94th
Methyl anthranilate (GIV)	Powerful orange blossom type	106	92	49	62	88	75	96	109	107	48	80	31	87	104	59	48	77·6	95th
Phenyl acetaldehyde (ABR)	Hyacinth-like	105	9	115	56	95	108	75	58	72	123	124	103	84	86	34	31	79·9	96th
Benzaldehyde, re-distilled (BDH)	Nutty, almonds	63	60	58	85	111	110	113	28	29	111	91	81	70	115	42	118	80·3	97th
Styralyl acetate (methyl phenyl carbinyl acetate) (ABR)	Intense gardenia type. Very bright	87	64	77	107	50	53	101	107	96	61	81	100	58	63	101	89	80·9	98th
Undecalactone (γ-Heptylbutyrolactone) (ABR)	Ripe peaches, nutty	70	71	63	45	117	111	82	106	105	109	92	101	75	46	85	22	81·3	99th
Toluene, BS 805A (G & T)	Like benzene but a little rubbery	112	99	32	101	100	96	64	73	55	8	47	113	107	109	110	91	82·3	100th
p-Methylacetophenone (WJB)	Reminiscent of coumarin and mimosa, fragrant, nutty aromatic	66	70	112	96	78	61	93	91	98	107	83	80	59	51	76	105	82·9	101st
Skatole (BDH)	Azo compounds, slightly faecal	111	94	27	105	114	104	—	51	51	93	95	102	121	83	53	47	83·4	102nd
Diacetone alcohol (G & T)	Heavy, sweeter than acetone	22	90	61	57	93	98	69	103	116	21	120	99	90	96	111	90	83·5	103rd
Ethyl acetate (TSH)	Fruity	89	80	79	78	70	88	104	111	106	56	102	104	68	91	75	58	84·9	104th

TABLE 1—continued

Odours arranged in order of preference

Primary records of results of tests with many odorants and few observers—*continued*

Odorant	Type of odour	Placing (1 is most liked, 2 is next most liked and 132 is most disliked) of each odorant by each observer																Average	Odorant is ranked
		RO	ELM	MH	RMM	RWM	WMM	SL	SL	ST	ST	ST	JET	EMT	ARL	WG	WG		
Methyl alcohol, acetone free (TSH)	Spirituous, woody	58	83	76	71	91	94	45	102	114	112	93	79	98	95	93	98	87·6	105th
Cade oil	Woody, tarry, hint of kippers and of Russian leather	113	72	99	117	48	38	103	98	89	118	118	50	83	116	72	84	88·6	106th
Paradichlorbenzene (BTS)	Moth balls, a little spirituous	91	86	43	103	115	109	—	89	91	113	111	74	88	124	65	51	90·2	107th
Dimethyl sulfoxide (STP)	Mould, hint of crab	102	101	109	100	63	64	57	129	124	81	113	117	92	61	73	57	90·2	107th
Cellosolve, (2-ethoxy ethanol), (G & T)	Astringent bitter, slightly bloomy and fishy	88	106	85	67	89	115	70	113	113	101	112	82	96	76	60	106	92·4	109th
Sour milk	Sour	—	111	—	116	103	92	63	54	101	80	77	116	104	111	91	78	92·6	110th
Carbon tetrachloride (R & B)	Spirituous, a little naseous, like dry cleaning agents	26	109	82	60	101	100	102	99	90	100	110	85	109	121	116	107	94·8	111th
Rape oil (BTS)	Light oily, nutty	64	97	110	98	75	86	71	104	112	105	123	108	99	113	87	83	95·9	112th
Civet, 5 per cent tincture in alcohol (FLD)	Sweet unpleasant, slightly faecal	86	50	74	97	129	123	117	114	110	127	125	91	94	85	81	73	98·5	113th
Benzylamine (M & B)	Bitter, fishy, sharp	109	91	119	73	102	85	60	124	119	99	108	75	105	100	103	115	99·2	114th
Acetic acid, glacial (BDH)	Vinegarish, sour	121	93	125	113	99	68	111	125	125	68	103	111	118	40	82	104	100·4	115th
Chlorophyll, water-soluble, (Sodium copper chlorophyllin) (RAN)	Hay-like	80	—	80	115	73	103	—	122	115	116	101	118	95	92	100	101	100·8	116th
Hair waving lotion thiovanate type	Sulphidy, very unpleasant	62	107	113	106	130	129	50	118	127	115	78	98	115	101	94	80	101·4	117th

Odorant	Odour	98	82	118	68	131	125	115	105	108	95	106	96	100	114	102	85		
Pyridine (R & B)	Rank, gassy, repellent	104	96	105	69	112	102	55	117	120	104	109	120	103	122	113	108	103·0	118th
Hydrazine hydrate, 60 per cent in water (GEN)	Dull, ammoniacal	73	114	104	99	120	118	110	120	100	117	117	97	101	105	89	82	103·7	119th
Castor oil, medicinal	Oily, nauseating	—	105	121	119	104	107	76	121	111	106	121	115	97	112	88	81	104·1	120th
Herring oil (HBP)	Oily, fishy	99	81	114	114	122	120	112	119	123	108	75	106	119	93	117	79	105·6	121st
n-Butyric acid 50 per cent (TSH)	Sour perspiration	115	66	100	121	105	117	105	132	123	114	98	121	108	90	99	103	106·3	122nd
Chlorophyll, oil-soluble FCAS (SCB)	Rank, unpleasant	108	108	117	66	116	122	74	116	121	98	100	119	114	123	115	111	107·9	123rd
Formaldehyde 40 per cent (R & B)	Formalin, hospitals	116	103	106	102	123	121	108	115	109	128	127	109	117	126	114	93	108·0	124th
Phenyl acetylene (LLT)	Coal gas type	101	113	75	122	132	132	118	112	128	126	130	123	124	127	98	102	113·6	125th
Civet, Abyssinian (FLD)	Unpleasant sweet, faecal	114	112	124	118	128	131	—	110	122	94	99	126	113	—	123	122	116·4	126th
Ethyl mercaptan 0·5 per cent in water (LLT)	Foul, alliaceous	118	116	116	111	121	119	94	131	130	122	119	112	120	120	118	117	116·9	127th
Piperidine (BDH)	Sharp, pungent, ammoniacal	119	115	123	110	125	128	78	127	129	129	128	110	116	118	119	119	117·8	128th
Triethylamine (BDH)	Ammoniacal, organic, fishy	120	117	108	120	124	126	116	126	118	125	126	124	106	125	122	120	118·3	129th
p-Chlorothiophenol (EVN)	Pungent, burnt, sweetish	103	110	120	109	127	130	114	128	126	130	129	122	123	119	120	116	120·2	130th
Carbon disulphide (G & T)	Spirituous, nauseating	117	118	122	112	126	127	106	130	131	124	122	125	122	117	121	121	120·4	131st
Thiomalic acid (EVN)	Pungent, rather like burnt rubber	117	118	122	112	126	127	106	130	131	124	122	125	122	117	121	121	121·3	132nd
Sex of observer		M	F	M	F	M	M	F	F	F	F	F	M	F	M	M	M		
Age of observer (years)		16	77	12	24	52	52	53	16	16	16	16	49	52	10	14	14		
Temperament of observer (introvert or extrovert)		I	E	E	I	I	I	I	I	I	E	E	E	E	E	I	I		
Number of odorants tested in run		121	118	125	122	132	132	118	132	132	130	130	126	124	127	123	122		

NOTES : (1) In the table a dash instead of a number indicates that the odorant in question was not tested in that run; usually because it was unavailable at the time of test. When two runs were made by the same subject, e.g. RWM, SL, ST and WG, they were made on different days.

(2) The sources from which most of the chemicals were obtained are indicated in parentheses after the name of the chemical, e.g. Carbon disulphide (G & T) indicates that the material used for test was obtained from Griffin and Tatlock. Indicative abbreviations for the suppliers are as follows:

TABLE 1—*continued*

Odours arranged in order of preference

Primary records of results of tests with many odorants and few observers—*continued*

ABR	A. Boake Roberts & Co. Ltd., London.	HFC	Hindusthan Fine Chemicals Co., Bangalore.
BDH	The British Drug Houses Ltd., Poole.	LLT	L. Light & Co. Ltd., Colnbrook.
BTS	Boots Pure Drug Co. Ltd., Nottingham.	M & B	May & Baker Ltd., Dagenham.
CCC	The China Camphor Co., Hongkong.	P & S	Polak & Schwarz Ltd., Enfield.
DIS	British Disinfectant Co. Ltd., Tottenham.	RAN	Wm. Ransom & Son Ltd., Hitchin.
EVN	Evans Chemetics Inc., New York.	R & B	Reynolds & Branson Ltd., Leeds.
FLD	Field & Co. (Aromatics) Ltd., Ruislip.	SCB	Strong, Cobb & Co. Inc, Lake Worth.
G & T	Griffin & Tatlock Ltd., London.	STP	The Stepan Chemical Co., Chicago.
GEN	Genatosan Ltd., Loughborough.	TSH	Thomson, Skinner & Hamilton Ltd., Glasgow.
GIV	L. Givaudan et Cie., Geneva.	WHH	W. H. Hobbs & Co. Ltd., London.
H & W	Hopkin & Williams Ltd., Chadwell Heath.	WJB	W. J. Bush & Co. Ltd., London.
HBP	Herring By-Products Ltd., Fraserburgh.		

odorants. Fragrant roses remind us of geraniol or of citronellol or even of limonene, but they smell very much better than any of these isolates do; violets can remind us of the ionones and irones, but they are infinitely more delicate and better-liked; orange blossom can remind us of methyl anthranilate, the former is weak and pleasing, the latter strong and not so pleasing (ranked 95th in Table 1).

(2) Natural odorous materials are nearly always complex. There are exceptions such as oil of wintergreen which is almost pure methyl salicylate, but there are not many of them. Most flower or fruit odours or flavours contain probably some twenty to forty different chemical entities. Most often, we know of only a few of them and when we mix the known constituents we do not get quite the right note, because the natural trace constituents being unknown, are missing from the mixtures that we prepare. The more sensitive our analytical methods become, the more complex are the natural odorants seen to be. We may consider two natural odorant materials examples: jasmine and raspberry, both of which have been thoroughly investigated to illustrate their complexity.

Jasmine. Jasmine is one of the simpler flower scent mixtures known. Pomades are made by extracting the odorous parts of white summer-flowering jasmine; they are heavenly to smell when they are freshly made. It is known that the two most important substances in the odorous parts of jasmine are jasmone, a ketone which was isolated by Hesse[1] as long ago as 1899, and methyl jasmonate. Jasmone has the constitution:

$$\begin{array}{c} CH_3 \\ | \\ H_2C \diagup C \diagdown C \cdot CH_2CH:CHCH_2CH_3 \\ | \qquad\qquad | \\ H_2C \rule{1cm}{0.4pt} CO \end{array}$$

this being established when Ruzicka and Pfeiffer[2] showed that on reduction to dihydrojasmone the resulting ketone was identical with one that had already been synthesized by Staudinger and Ruzicka.[3] Methyl jasmonate is methyl *cis*-2-pent-2′-enyl-3-oxo-cyclopentylacetate and may be written

$$\begin{array}{c} H_2C \rule{1cm}{0.4pt} CH \cdot CH_2COOCH_3 \\ | \qquad\qquad | \\ H_2C \diagdown \ C \diagup CH \cdot CH_2CH:CHCH_2CH_3 \\ \| \\ O \end{array}$$

But in addition to these two main odorous components, Demole[4] has reported the presence of benzaldehyde, vanillin, and methylheptenone the first two of which have respectively odours of almonds and vanilla, whilst the third is a penetratingly odorous ketone which is a constituent of lemongrass oil. Furthermore, discussion has ranged over the possible existence of a keto-lactone of empirical formula $C_{12}H_{16}O_3$ which has been reported as a jasmine constituent by Naves and Grampoloff,[5] doubted by Demole, Lederer and Mercier[6] in 1962 and re-affirmed by Naves and Grampoloff and Demole[7] in 1963. Even the main constituents are in some doubt, but three minor constituents are known and very likely there are others not identified. Indole, methyl anthranilate, benzyl acetate, linalyl acetate, and linalol have all been reported. The impossibility of reproducing from synthetic chemicals the true jasmine perfume in the present state of our knowledge is clear to be seen. And yet jasmine appears to be one of the least complex natural flower odorants.

Raspberry. The raspberry flavour or aroma, and that mostly means its odour, has been investigated with great care by the chemists of Firmenich & Co.[8,9,10] Their investigation started with half a ton of fresh fruit and the final analysis of the extracts and concentrates from it was done by advanced chromatographic and spectrographic methods. It was found that twenty-five non-acid volatile constituents contributed to the aroma; only two of them were present in the fruit in quantity greater than 1 part per million and eight of them were present in proportions lower than 0·01 p.p.m. The twenty-five active chemical entities that were identified were those shown in Table 2. Additionally, earlier work (1961) had shown that the fresh fruit contains 0·1–0·2 p.p.m. of 1-*p*-hydroxyphenyl butan-3-one,

$$HO-\langle\ \rangle-CHCH_2COCH_3$$

or raspberry ketone. It has been described by Stoll of Firmenich et Cie as having a strong smell, not typically of the whole raspberry but of one part of the raspberry; its discovery was looked on as a notable success. This phenolic ketone is not readily volatile; it did not distil over with the volatiles shown in Table 2 but was easily identifiable in the residual fruit pulp.

It can be seen from Table 2 that there are eleven volatile alcohols present and yet before this analysis was carried out in 1962 only

TABLE 2

Volatile flavour constituents of the raspberry
(parts per million of fresh fruit)

More than 1	0·1–1	0·01–0·1	Less than 0·01
Acetaldehyde	Acetoin	Acetone	Diacetyl
cis-3-Hexenal	2-Hexenal	β,β-Dimethyl acrolein	Acrolein
	Hexanal	2-Pentenal	Propanal
	α-Ionone	1-Penten-3-ol	2-Pentanone
	Geraniol	Hexenol	β-Ionone
	cis-3-Hexen-1-ol	3-Methyl-3-buten-1-ol	Methanol
		3-Methyl-2-buten-1-ol	Pentanol
		Butanol	trans-2-buten-1-ol
		Ethanol	

four of them, methanol, ethanol, hexanol and 3-hexen-1-ol, had been known to be present in raspberries and of these four only one, the cis-3-hexen-1-ol, is a major constituent. The other seven alcohols had not previously been recognized in the raspberry. The other fourteen volatile constituents are carbonyl compounds. It is not a matter for great surprise that geraniol with its beautiful rose-like odour, or the violet-smelling ionones, or the green leafy hexenals and hexenol should be present in raspberries, but butyl alcohol with its very powerful and unpleasant odour is unexpected and acrolein with its powerful lachrymatory properties even more so. The Firmenich school in 1963 also identified eleven acids in raspberry oil; their concentrations in the fruit were not indicated but the one present in highest concentration was caproic, and then came formic, acetic, propionic, n-butyric, isovaleric, hexen-3-oic, and caprylic with traces only of isobutyric, valeric and hexen-2-oic. The more refined and sensitive the analytical methods become, the more complex do we find natural odorous materials to be, and the clearer becomes the reason for the difficulty that we have always encountered when we have tried to build up true matches to natural odours from synthetic chemicals.

Of the two cases that we have considered, jasmine and raspberry, the one is relatively simple, the other is known to be very complex, but to build up either jasmine or raspberry, to copy the delights of the natural odours, is quite impossible. This impossibility has been appreciated for a long time and when a raspberry flavouring essence came so high up in the preferences as 9th in Table 1, it was really astonishing. Was it possible that a synthetic flavour could be as well-liked as natural flowers and fruits? The makers of the essence were consulted and they kindly told us that this essence was almost wholly natural, made from the fruit. This explanation does away with the seeming difficulty, but it is, too, a testimonial to the success of the manufacturers in putting the aroma of raspberries into a bottle of essence. It is in fact, so very easy to spoil the aroma by air-oxidation, by metal contamination from the vessels and plant used, and particularly by elevated temperatures which must be avoided, and often by the very process of concentration itself. In their classical analysis of the raspberry aroma the chemists of Firmenich & Co. had found it impossible to prepare a concentrated oil which on re-dilution would recapture the freshness and fine quality of the fruit, or of a freshly made distillate from it. It was, as it so often is in flavour work, impossible to concentrate too far without loss of quality. The raspberry flavouring essence which is ranked 9th in Table 1 must be regarded as an outstanding achievement of the extraction and concentration of a flavour; its bouquet not quite so bright as that of the fresh fruit, but approximating nearly to it.

Rules

As we go through this book in our studies of odour preferences, we shall encounter general principles which we can look on as the rules of the grammar of olfactory likes and dislikes, and these will be stated plainly to give them emphasis, and enumerated to facilitate reference to them. It will be realized that much of flavour is smell and that without the smell contribution, flavours would be nothing much more than one of the primary tastes, sweet, bitter, sour and salt. Consequently, when we speak of raspberry flavour it is the odorous volatile components of the raspberry (its aroma or smell) with which we are mainly concerned.

As with most rules, there will be exceptions, but the rules themselves will embody a lot of otherwise scattered information; they will attempt to generalize it, and present succinctly the main principles of the subject. Those that we can derive from the subject-matter of this chapter are:

Rule 1. Natural materials are the best-liked olfactorily. Synthetics and chemicals are much less liked.

Rule 2. The pleasantness of the odours of natural products is partly due to their complexity. Trace constituents modify and improve the quality of their odours.

Rule 3. It is not yet possible to build up from synthetic materials, copies of natural odorous products which are so well-liked. Always the natural product is preferred.

Rule 4. High concentration of any chemical entity is detrimental to olfactory pleasantness. Odorous materials are much preferred in dilution.

These four simple statements encompass a great deal of the odour experiences and reactions that are common to humanity. The best of the synthetics when concentrated, smell like what they are: chemicals. They carry hints and suggestions of flowers that have delightful smells, but they themselves are pleasant only when dilute. Flowers and herbs and fruits do not usually smell powerfully of their active odorous constituents: hawthorn blossom, powerful as is its odour, does no more than suggest anisaldehyde, most roses only hint at geraniol and citronellol, hyacinths can remind us occasionally of terpineol and phenyl acetaldehyde but no more than that. And so it is with all the others; Nature's complex odours whether in flower, fruit or herb, have been blended by a master, and so far we cannot do so well. We cannot equal such masterpieces. To-day we can still repeat the old Rabbi's prayer[11]

"Blessed are thou, O Lord our God, King of the universe, who with the scent of this lowly herb transportest the soul."

REFERENCES

1. A. Hesse, Ueber ätherisches Jasminblüthenöl, II, *Ber. dtsch. chem. Ges.*, 1899, **32**, 2611–2620.

2. L. Ruzicka & M. Pfeiffer, Über Jasminriechstoffe, I. Die Konstitution des Jasmons, *Helv. chim. Acta*, 1933, **16**, 1208–1214.

3. H. Staudinger & L. Ruzicka, Synthese des Tetrahydro-pyrethrons, des Reduktionsproduktes des Pyrethrolons, *Ibid*, 1924, **7**, 245–259.

4. E. Demole, Sur les composants carbonylés de l'essence de jasmin (*Jasminum grandiflorum L.*), *Ibid*, 1962, **45**, 1951–1955.

5. Y. R. Naves & A. V. Grampoloff, Sur la composition de l'extrait éthéro-pétrolique (essence concrète) de la fleur de jasmin, *Ibid*, 1942, **25**, 1500–1514.

6. E. Demole, E. Lederer & D. Mercier, Isolement et détermination de la structure du jasmonate de méthyle, constituant odorant caractéristique de l'essence de jasmin, *Ibid*, 1962, **45**, 675–685.

7. Y.R.Naves, A.V. Grampoloff & E. Demole, Sur les constituants carbonylés de l'essence de jasmin (*Jasminum grandiflorum L.*), *Ibid*, 1963, **46**, 1006–1010.

8. M. Winter, E. Palluy, M. Hinder & B. Willhalm, Procédé d'isolement des constituants volatils de la fraise et de la framboise, *Ibid*, 1962, **45**, 2186–2195.

9. M. Winter & E. Sundt, Analyse de l'arôme des framboises, I. Les constituants carbonylés volatils, *Ibid*, 1962, **45**, 2195–2211.

10. E. Sundt & M. Winter, Analyse de l'arôme volatils des framboises, II. Les alcools, *Ibid*, 1962, **45**, 2212–2218.

11. B. Greene & V. Gollancz, *God of a Hundred Names*, p. 116, 1962, London.

CHAPTER 2

ANALYSIS OF ODOUR PREFERENCES INTO
SEX, AGE AND TEMPERAMENT GROUPS

IF WE turn back to Table 1, looking at it first as a whole, rather than in detail, what is it that most impresses us? It must be, surely, the high degree of uniformity amongst the different observers in their likes and dislikes, especially the latter.

Agreement between individuals in dislikes

It is our everyday experience that we characterize bad smells unhesitatingly and with certainty. They are bad, they offend us, and quite obviously most of us think the same and what one person thinks is a bad smell, another will do so, too. What we all dislike or detest olfactorily is much the same; Table 1 shows this uniformity very clearly. The last six odorants in this table are all characterized by high numbers; everybody puts them among the most disliked. There are ninety-four placings given for these six (ethyl mercaptan to thiomalic acid), because there were sixteen test runs which would have given ninety-six placings, but two tests, those of ethyl mercaptan by ARL and WMM, were omitted so that we have $(16 \times 6 - 2 = 94)$ placings. Out of these ninety-four placings no fewer than fifty-four are to be found in the last six placings of each individual. One observer (WMM) has found triethylamine and piperidine not quite so bad as the rest, but with this minor exception, every one of the six smells is thought bad by everybody and nobody assigns a placing better than 100 to any of them.

Agreement between individuals about the best odours

If now we look at the beginning of Table 1, where the best-liked odours are to be found, we see a picture which bears some resemblance to the other end of the Table but also a significant difference. Most of the placings are good, but some are apparently abnormally poor. There are seventy-eight placings for the first six odorants, Red rose—Stock, and of these there are forty-three within the range

30

1-6; forty-three out of seventy-eight times the observers have said of these six odours, that they are to be found within the six that they like best. Therein lies the resemblance of the beginning of Table 1 to its end; there is a large measure of agreement about what are the best odours, just as there is about what are the worst.

But there is also a difference, because there are numerous instances where an individual has given a relatively poor placing to an odour that most individuals have liked very much indeed. By way of example: Red rose which is ranked 1st by the whole group is placed as poorly as 17th by one observer; strawberries that the group puts second are rated no better than 16th and 24th by one observer in her two test runs; sweet peas that the whole group puts third have been assigned placings as indifferent as 17th, 18th and 20th by some individuals; stock flowers that the whole group puts sixth has been given placings of 37th and 28th by two individuals. There is something odd here, some considerable and significant departure from the uniformity that characterizes the end of Table 1. Most of the people agree fairly well about the odours that they like best, but there are some of the people who disagree with them quite sharply; yet *all* of the people had agreed very well about the odours that they most disliked. Here is a major difference and in order to find the reason for it, we must analyse the contents of Table 1.

Analysis of Table 1

The analysis is carried out according to sex, age and temperament of the observers, and the results of the analysis are shown in Table 3. A note or two on the new arrangement may be appropriate.

Sex. Clearly into male and female. Because all the children who took part in the test were boys, they loaded the males' odour preferences with the children's preferences. In order to get a clearer comparison of the preferences of males and females, there was also extracted from Table 1 the placings for adult males and their placings are shown in Table 3 in the column "M, Excluding those under 15 years", whereas the column M includes the boys, it includes all the males.

Age. Into children i.e. under 15, young adults 15–25 years, and over 25's.

Temperament. Into introvert and extrovert.

Rankings. In addition to the placings, the order in which they

TABLE 3

Odour Preferences (Table 1) analysed according to sex, age and temperament

Odorant	AVERAGE PLACING									PREFERENCE RANKING (Rank of Average Placing)								
	Sex			Age			Temperament		Whole Group	Sex			Age			Temperament		Whole Group
	M	M Excluding those under 15 years	F None were under 15 years	Under 15	15–25 years	Over 25	Intro-vert	Extro-vert		M	M Excluding those under 15 years	F None were under 15 years	Under 15	15–25 years	Over 25	Intro-vert	Extro-vert	
Red rose Ena Harkness, flower	6·3	2·7	4·5	17·0	4·0	4·0	4·2	6·0	5·1	2nd	3rd	2nd	11th	2nd	3rd	2nd	1st	1st
Fresh strawberries	3·0	2·0	7·6	4·0	10·2	1·6	3·3	9·0	5·5	1st	2nd	5th	1st	7th	1st	1st	3rd	2nd
Sweet peas, flowers	11·8	9·3	3·4	14·3	4·7	6·0	7·8	7·3	7·6	5th	7th	1st	10th	3rd	5th	5th	2nd	3rd
Rose New Dawn, flower	10·6	4·0	6·4	17·3	8·0	3·5	7·5	10·0	8·7	4th	4th	4th	12th	4th	2nd	4th	5th	4th
Rose Emily Gray, flower	10·3	8·5	9·0	14·0	8·5	9·3	9·6	9·3	9·4	3rd	6th	6th	9th	5th	7th	6th	4th	5th
Stock, double ten-week, flower	19·2	9·3	9·1	29·0	9·2	9·3	14·0	13·5	13·8	10th	7th	7th	24th	6th	7th	8th	6th	6th
Honeysuckle, flower	26·6	1·3	4·5	45·5	3·2	4·0	15·6	13·6	14·8	16th	1st	2nd	46th	1st	3rd	9th	7th	7th
Wild rose (Dog rose) flower	12·0	7·5	22·2	21·0	25·5	8·0	5·8	31·0	18·4	6th	5th	12th	18th	14th	6th	3rd	19th	8th
Raspberry flavouring essence, 99 per cent natural (ABR)	16·9	28·3	24·8	5·5	24·7	27·2	24·6	16·0	20·8	8th	24th	14th	2nd	13th	20th	12th	8th	9th
Sweet orange oil (RAN)	27·0	26·8	22·1	27·3	27·3	20·0	15·7	36·0	24·6	17th	20th	11th	22nd	16th	13th	10th	27th	10th

Odorant																		
Lemon flavouring essence (BTS)	23·3	27·5	33·5	19·0	37·3	21·7	28·9	17·0	25·3	12th	22nd	21st	14th	29th	15th	20th	10th	11th
Meadowsweet, flower	29·3	14·3	20·3	43·8	22·0	12·3	27·1	23·2	25·4	22nd	10th	18th	5th	10th	12th	16th	16th	12th
Peppermint flavouring essence (BTS)	17·0	26·3	36·9	7·8	28·8	37·8	24·8	29·7	26·9	9th	18th	8th	3rd	32nd	37th	14th	16th	13th
Strawberry flavouring (ABR)	24·0	41·8	31·3	6·3	33·3	36·2	36·0	16·9	27·6	14th	35th	16th	48th	31st	24th	10th	9th	14th
Heliotrope, flower	28·0	16·0	29·4	46·0	32·4	11·0	17·9	54·0	28·7	20th	12th	23rd	7th	10th	23rd	11th	56th	15th
Lemon flavouring essence (ABR)	21·6	30·5	35·3	9·7	44·3	23·0	24·6	33·7	28·9	11th	27th	7th	4th	18th	36th	18th	22nd	16th
Banana flavouring essence (ABR)	24·1	41·0	34·6	7·3	34·8	38·7	36·9	19·7	29·4	15th	34th	4th	28th	34th	28th	34th	11th	17th
Spearmint oil (RAN)	29·3	49·0	30·4	9·5	28·5	44·7	33·4	25·1	29·8	22nd	46th	6th	6th	40th	17th	24th	13th	18th
Lavender oil, English (WHH)	39·5	21·8	19·3	57·3	19·7	21·0	27·2	34·5	30·1	34th	16th	9th	60th	9th	14th	17th	24th	19th
Mock orange (Philadelphus) blossom	13·3	11·0	45·0	20·0	63·8	9·6	12·4	52·2	32·3	7th	9th	70th	15th	15th	75th	9th	53rd	20th
Mint, fresh garden	30·6	19·0	34·5	42·3	33·3	25·3	26·0	41·0	32·6	25th	13th	24th	39th	23rd	20th	19th	33rd	21st
Vanilla flavouring essence (ABR)	37·1	49·0	28·1	25·3	29·8	40·3	35·9	28·4	32·6	31st	46th	19th	20th	15th	75th	30th	15th	21st
Lavender oil, French (WHH)	44·9	19·5	20·8	70·3	18·7	22·0	28·0	39·0	32·8	43rd	14th	8th	75th	19th	8th	16th	30th	23rd
Catmint (Nepeta), fresh leaves	34·8	33·0	32·6	36·5	31·7	34·0	32·7	35·3	33·7	29th	29th	21st	32nd	28th	16th	28th	26th	24th
Ylang-ylang essential oil (WHH)	33·8	14·8	34·4	53·0	22·2	33·3	34·1	34·0	34·1	27th	11th	26th	55th	26th	16th	28th	23rd	25th
Musk lactone (Musco-lactone) 10 per cent soln. (P & S)	34·4	28·5	36·6	40·3	52·3	15·5	41·2	28·1	35·5	28th	26th	11th	38th	47th	12th	26th	14th	26th
Cinnamon leaf oil (WHH) (P & S)	28·6	28·3	43·8	29·0	45·0	32·2	34·4	38·4	36·2	21st	24th	36th	24th	37th	44th	25th	29th	27th
Orange flavouring essence (ABR)	29·8	36·3	45·0	10·0	49·0	22·0	33·2	44·3	37·4	24th	30th	44th	8th	44th	8th	16th	37th	28th
Rose attar (WHH)	42·5	27·8	32·6	57·3	26·0	36·0	40·9	33·3	37·6	37th	23rd	15th	60th	15th	47th	30th	21st	29th
Citral (ABR)	23·5	26·3	52·0	20·8	52·2	34·7	33·1	43·7	37·8	13th	18th	24th	16th	29th	46th	29th	35th	30th
Privet flower	37·3	44·0	38·6	30·7	34·0	46·4	28·8	45·9	38·0	32nd	36th	31st	26th	44th	26th	44th	40th	31st

B

TABLE 3—continued

Odour preferences (Table 1) analysed according to sex, age and temperament—continued

Odorant	AVERAGE PLACING									PREFERENCE RANKING (Rank of Average Placing)								
	Sex			Age			Temperament		Whole Group	Sex			Age			Temperament		Whole Group
	M	M Excluding those under 15 years	F None were under 15 years	Under 15	15–25 years	Over 25	Intro-vert	Extro-vert		M	M Excluding those under 15 years	F None were under 15 years	Under 15	15–25 years	Over 25	Intro-vert	Extro-vert	
Cinnamon bark oil (WHH)	27·9	30·8	49·9	25·0	56·0	31·0	37·4	40·7	38·9	19th	28th	49th	19th	53rd	22nd	35th	32nd	32nd
Bay leaf	58·6	48·3	24·6	66·3	23·2	40·2	37·0	47·7	41·6	60th	43rd	13th	72nd	12th	36th	34th	46th	33rd
Ribes (flowering currant) leaf fresh	46·4	40·3	38·9	55·5	41·3	38·0	36·0	46·3	42·0	47th	33rd	32nd	58th	32nd	33rd	31st	41st	34th
Strawberry aldehyde (FLD)	44·8	57·0	40·4	32·5	41·5	50·3	51·8	30·7	42·6	41st	57th	34th	28th	33rd	49th	53rd	17th	35th
Musk ambrette (ABR)	27·3	19·5	58·8	35·0	60·2	31·2	39·7	47·3	43·0	18th	14th	64th	31st	64th	23rd	39th	44th	36th
Vanillin ex eugenol (GIV)	50·8	45·7	37·4	66·0	46·8	30·0	34·2	61·7	43·3	52nd	39th	30th	71st	39th	21st	27th	68th	37th
Neroli oil, French Bigarade (WHH)	51·5	39·5	34·6	63·5	34·0	39·2	34·8	56·8	43·6	53rd	32nd	24th	69th	26th	35th	29th	60th	38th
Geraniol ex Palma Rosa (ABR)	35·0	27·0	54·6	43·0	59·0	31·8	39·7	51·4	44·8	30th	21st	56th	42nd	60th	24th	39th	50th	39th
Almond flavouring essence (ABR)	41·3	50·8	48·6	28·7	47·3	51·3	56·0	32·6	45·2	35th	49th	47th	23rd	40th	52nd	57th	20th	40th
Nerol (P & S)	45·5	48·8	45·6	42·3	48·0	45·3	39·6	53·3	45·6	45th	44th	42nd	39th	42nd	42nd	38th	55th	41st
Lemongrass oil (WHH)	38·1	25·5	54·3	50·8	55·5	33·8	45·9	46·6	46·2	33rd	17th	53rd	52nd	51st	27th	44th	42nd	42nd
Isoeugenol (GIV)	50·6	62·5	44·5	38·8	47·5	53·5	50·0	44·4	47·6	51st	69th	38th	36th	41st	55th	51st	38th	43rd
Friar's Balsam (local pharmacy)	43·8	45·3	53·9	42·3	58·3	43·7	62·8	30·9	48·8	39th	37th	52nd	39th	55th	38th	64th	18th	44th

Eugenol (P & S)	41·8	62·8	56·6	20·8	63·5	53·8	50·6	47·4	49·2	36th	70th	59th	16th	69th	57th	52nd	45th	45th	45th
Parsley, garden fresh	50·1	51·0	48·8	49·3	43·8	55·2	34·1	69·1	49·4	50th	50th	48th	50th	35th	60th	25th	82nd	46th
Terpineol (DIS)	45·1	58·5	54·4	31·8	64·3	47·2	53·9	44·4	49·8	44th	58th	54th	27th	72nd	45th	54th	38th	47th
Phenylethyl dimethyl carbinol (FLD)	56·0	66·3	44·5	45·8	48·5	54·5	57·0	41·1	50·1	58th	74th	38th	47th	43rd	58th	59th	34th	48th
Cananga oil (WHH)	52·1	48·0	48·0	56·3	46·3	49·7	48·9	51·6	50·1	54th	42nd	45th	59th	38th	48th	49th	51st	48th
Amyl butyrate ex tech. amyl alcohol (BDH)	32·5	47·5	68·6	17·5	64·0	59·2	58·8	40·0	50·6	26th	40th	78th	13th	71st	67th	60th	31st	50th
Coconut flavouring essence (ABR)	43·1	60·0	59·9	26·3	61·5	58·0	63·5	36·6	50·9	38th	63rd	66th	21st	68th	63rd	67th	28th	51st
Chives, garden fresh	55·3	66·8	47·5	43·8	31·0	76·8	39·0	67·3	51·4	57th	75th	44th	44th	20th	86th	37th	76th	52nd
Butyl acetate (TSH)	47·6	61·0	55·4	34·3	54·3	60·3	46·2	58·3	51·5	49th	64th	58th	30th	50th	70th	45th	61st	53rd
Onion, raw, cut	62·6	82·3	40·9	43·0	32·0	77·3	43·7	62·1	51·8	66th	94th	35th	42nd	22nd	87th	43rd	69th	54th
Terpinolene (DIS)	44·5	50·3	59·3	38·8	60·8	51·7	46·9	58·3	51·9	40th	48th	65th	36th	67th	53rd	46th	61st	55th
Tonka beans, tincture in benzyl alcohol (FLD)	61·3	59·5	44·0	63·0	42·5	55·8	56·0	48·3	52·6	64th	61st	37th	68th	34th	62nd	57th	47th	56th
Amyl acetate (M & B)	47·3	61·5	58·1	33·3	52·7	65·8	47·7	59·1	52·7	48th	67th	62nd	29th	48th	75th	47th	63rd	57th
Heliotropin or piperonal cryst (GIV)	61·1	72·0	46·1	50·3	60·5	49·0	49·6	58·9	53·6	63rd	79th	43rd	51st	65th	47th	50th	64th	58th
Musk natural, 2 per cent tincture in alcohol (FLD)	53·8	59·3	54·8	48·3	58·8	53·7	60·0	46·9	54·3	55th	60th	57th	49th	59th	56th	61st	43rd	59th
Benzyl acetate (BDH)	44·8	51·3	66·4	37·5	59·3	62·8	55·3	54·0	54·7	41st	51st	76th	33rd	61st	72nd	55th	56th	60th
Ethyl alcohol 99–100 per cent, duty paid (BDH)	69·9	59·8	39·0	80·0	39·2	55·4	55·9	55·0	55·5	77th	62nd	33rd	93rd	30th	61st	56th	59th	61st
Rose 2321 perfume concentrate (FLD)	64·4	55·5	48·0	73·3	55·8	45·2	38·9	78·4	56·2	70th	56th	45th	84th	52nd	41st	36th	94th	62nd
Alpine Violet, perfume concentrate (FLD)	77·0	75·5	36·4	78·5	40·7	58·2	73·9	34·6	56·7	85th	84th	27th	90th	31st	64th	86th	25th	63rd
Oil of geranium, Bourbon (WHH)	56·3	36·5	60·0	76·0	56·3	45·6	67·3	44·0	58·0	59th	31st	67th	88th	54th	43rd	74th	36th	64th
α-Ionone (P & S)	63·6	64·5	54·4	62·8	60·7	54·8	65·0	51·3	59·0	69th	71st	54th	67th	66th	59th	69th	49th	65th
Camphor (CCC)	63·0	72·8	58·0	53·3	67·7	58·2	47·7	77·0	60·5	68th	81st	61st	56th	80th	64th	47th	92nd	66th
α-Ionone (ABR)	54·6	47·8	66·6	61·5	70·1	50·5	65·7	54·1	60·6	56th	41st	77th	65th	84th	50th	73rd	58th	67th
α-n-Methylionone (P & S)	58·9	59·0	64·9	58·8	60·0	65·8	69·1	52·6	61·9	61st	59th	73rd	63rd	63rd	75th	76th	54th	68th

TABLE 3—contd.

Odour preferences (Table 1) analysed according to sex, age and temperament—*continued*

Odorant	AVERAGE PLACING									PREFERENCE RANKING (Rank of Average Placing)								
	Sex			Age			Temperament		Whole Group	Sex			Age			Temperament		Whole Group
	M	M Excluding those under 15 years	F None were under 15 years	Under 15	15–25 years	Over 25	Intro-vert	Extro-vert		M	M Excluding those under 15 years	F None were under 15 years	Under 15	15–25 years	Over 25	Intro-vert	Extro-vert	
β-Ionone (ABR)	62·9	52·3	61·8	73·5	73·0	44·2	61·6	63·3	62·3	67th	52nd	68th	85th	86th	39th	62nd	72nd	69th
Citronella oil, Ceylon (WHH)	70·8	61·3	57·1	80·3	66·5	50·5	65·3	62·1	63·9	80th	65th	60th	94th	75th	50th	70th	69th	70th
Patchouli, clear resin (FLD)	68·3	52·5	62·1	84·0	58·5	59·3	69·2	60·0	65·2	75th	53rd	69th	102nd	57th	69th	77th	65th	71st
β-Ionone (P & S)	77·1	70·5	53·6	83·8	53·2	65·3	68·7	61·1	65·4	86th	77th	51st	101st	49th	73rd	75th	67th	72nd
Hydroxycitronellal (GIV)	62·5	65·5	68·9	59·5	69·0	66·5	62·7	69·6	65·7	65th	72nd	80th	64th	82nd	77th	63rd	83rd	73rd
Allyl caproate (ABR)	46·0	54·3	87·5	37·8	84·5	68·3	63·6	70·8	66·8	46th	55th	102nd	34th	98th	78th	68th	88th	74th
Kewda (screw-pine) otto of Pandanus odoratissimus, India	59·6	48·8	74·1	70·5	78·8	52·5	65·6	68·6	66·9	62nd	44th	90th	76th	94th	54th	71st	80th	75th
Ethylene glycol (G & T)	77·5	83·8	58·1	71·3	51·2	82·2	65·6	70·7	67·8	87th	97th	62nd	79th	45th	95th	71st	87th	76th
Ionone, Indian mixed isomers (HFC)	65·8	45·3	73·5	86·3	69·0	59·2	70·9	68·0	69·6	71st	37th	89th	105th	82nd	67th	80th	79th	77th
α-Amyl cinnamic aldehyde (GIV)	69·4	68·0	70·6	70·8	67·5	72·0	71·7	67·9	70·0	76th	76th	86th	77th	79th	83rd	82nd	78th	78th
Naphthalene (G & T)	70·6	103·0	69·6	38·3	58·7	102·8	71·0	69·0	70·1	79th	113th	84th	35th	58th	117th	81st	81st	79th
Tonkin musk, natural (FLD)	74·3	52·8	66·3	95·8	74·3	49·2	63·2	79·3	70·3	83rd	54th	75th	114th	91st	46th	66th	95th	80th

Anisaldehyde ex anethole (ABR)	67·0	61·3	75·0	72·8	82·3	58·5	74·3	66·7	71·0	73rd	65th	92nd	83rd	96th	66th	87th	75th	81st
Methyl salicylate (ABR)	72·8	84·0	69·3	61·5	66·0	81·8	62·8	80·7	71·1	81st	98th	82nd	65th	73rd	94th	64th	98th	82nd
Patchouli oil, Singapore (WHH)	78·3	65·5	64·1	91·0	67·0	62·2	86·3	51·7	71·2	92nd	72nd	72nd	109th	77th	71st	101st	52nd	83rd
Veratrol (P & S)	80·1	86·3	63·4	72·0	59·8	82·2	71·9	70·2	71·2	95th	99th	71st	81st	62nd	95th	83rd	86th	83rd
γ-Benzene hexachloride (BDH)	74·1	77·0	70·5	71·3	74·0	71·3	80·2	62·1	72·3	82nd	86th	85th	79th	88th	81st	92nd	69th	85th
Nitrobenzene (TSH)	81·5	90·8	63·1	72·3	66·7	78·0	77·6	65·6	72·3	99th	102nd	70th	82nd	76th	88th	88th	74th	85th
Peach synthetic concentrate (Pêche pur) (GIV)	68·0	78·5	77·4	57·5	74·0	81·0	71·9	73·2	72·4	74th	90th	94th	62nd	88th	91st	83rd	90th	87th
Acetone (BDH)	83·0	83·0	65·5	83·0	58·3	84·3	77·8	69·7	74·3	102nd	95th	74th	99th	55th	99th	90th	84th	88th
Ambergris, best grey natural (FLD)	81·0	93·3	69·1	68·8	71·0	83·3	73·6	77·0	75·1	98th	105th	81st	74th	85th	98th	85th	92nd	89th
Amyl cinnamic aldehyde (ABR)	77·5	73·0	72·9	82·0	74·2	71·7	81·1	67·6	75·2	87th	82nd	87th	97th	90th	82nd	93rd	77th	90th
Anisaldehyde ex cresol (RAN)	81·8	81·8	68·7	81·8	67·2	81·0	93·1	49·5	75·7	100th	93rd	79th	95th	78th	91st	112th	48th	91st
Anisaldehyde ex cresol (ABR)	78·1	76·8	74·4	79·5	75·7	74·8	87·3	60·0	76·4	91st	85th	91st	91st	92nd	85th	105th	65th	92nd
Cigarette ash	65·9	77·0	92·0	51·0	76·4	96·5	69·3	91·8	76·8	72nd	86th	106th	53rd	93rd	108th	78th	105th	93rd
Ethyl lactate (TSH)	79·8	80·0	74·5	79·5	83·0	68·8	87·0	64·4	77·1	94th	91st	91st	91st	97th	79th	104th	73rd	94th
Methyl anthranilate (GIV)	70·0	75·0	85·1	65·0	85·3	78·2	83·3	70·1	77·6	78th	83rd	98th	70th	100th	89th	95th	85th	95th
Phenyl acetaldehyde (ABR)	84·6	102·8	75·1	66·5	89·7	79·0	70·4	92·0	79·9	105th	112th	93rd	73rd	103rd	90th	79th	106th	96th
Benzaldehyde, redistilled (BDH)	87·3	91·3	73·4	83·3	67·8	91·2	77·7	83·7	80·3	107th	103rd	88th	100th	81st	104th	89th	101st	97th
Styralyl acetate (methyl phenyl carbinyl acetate) (ABR)	77·5	72·5	84·4	82·5	89·8	71·0	87·9	72·0	80·9	87th	80th	97th	98th	104th	80th	107th	89th	98th
Undecalactone (ABR)	76·9	99·8	85·6	54·0	87·8	92·8	82·6	79·6	81·3	84th	109th	99th	57th	102nd	105th	94th	96th	99th
Toluene, BS 805A (G & T)	95·4	105·3	69·3	85·5	66·0	96·5	89·1	73·6	82·3	114th	116th	82nd	103rd	73rd	108th	109th	91st	100th
p-Methylacetophenone (WJB)	78·6	71·3	87·1	86·0	90·2	73·5	84·9	80·3	82·9	93rd	78th	100th	104th	105th	84th	98th	97th	101st
Skatole (BDH)	80·1	107·8	87·1	52·5	84·5	107·0	79·5	87·9	83·4	95th	118th	100th	54th	98th	120th	91st	102nd	102nd
Diacetone alcohol (G & T)	83·8	78·0	83·3	89·5	73·3	89·9	84·3	82·4	83·5	103rd	88th	96th	107th	87th	103rd	96th	99th	103rd
Ethyl acetate (TSH)	81·8	87·8	88·1	75·8	90·3	85·7	86·6	82·9	84·9	100th	101st	103rd	87th	106th	100th	102nd	100th	104th

TABLE 3—contd.

Odour preferences (Table 1) analysed according to sex, age and temperament—continued

Odorant	AVERAGE PLACING									PREFERENCE RANKING (Rank of Average Placing)								
	Sex			Age			Temperament		Whole Group	Sex			Age			Temperament		Whole Group
	M	M Excluding those under 15 years	F None were under 15 years	Under 15	15–25 years	Over 25	Intro-vert	Extro-vert		M	M Excluding those under 15 years	F None were under 15 years	Under 15	15–25 years	Over 25	Intro-vert	Extro-vert	
Methyl alcohol, acetone-free (TSH)	85·5	80·5	89·8	90·5	91·7	81·7	85·1	90·9	87·6	106th	92nd	105th	108th	107th	93rd	99th	103rd	105th
Cade oil	77·5	62·3	99·8	92·8	108·8	65·7	84·7	93·7	88·6	87th	68th	115th	110th	120th	74th	97th	108th	106th
Dimethyl sulfoxide (STP)	80·8	86·5	99·6	75·0	108·2	82·3	85·4	96·3	90·2	97th	100th	113th	86th	118th	97th	100th	111th	107th
Paradichlorbenzene (BTS)	84·0	97·3	97·3	70·8	99·7	94·4	89·3	91·3	90·2	104th	108th	108th	77th	110th	107th	110th	104th	107th
Cellosolve (G & T)	87·6	93·5	97·3	81·8	99·0	93·0	91·2	94·0	92·4	108th	106th	108th	95th	109th	106th	111th	109th	109th
Sour (not bad) milk	98·5	103·7	88·3	93·3	85·6	98·2	87·3	99·8	92·6	115th	114th	104th	111th	101st	112th	105th	115th	110th
Carbon tetrachloride (R & B)	92·3	78·0	97·4	106·5	80·8	101·0	89·0	102·3	94·8	110th	88th	110th	122nd	95th	116th	108th	118th	111th
Rape oil (BTS)	90·8	83·3	101·1	98·3	101·0	89·3	86·7	107·9	95·9	109th	96th	116th	117th	111th	102nd	103rd	120th	112th
Civet, 5 per cent tincture in alcohol (FLD)	92·8	107·3	104·3	78·3	109·8	100·7	103·3	92·3	98·5	111th	117th	118th	89th	123rd	114th	119th	107th	113th
Benzylamine (M & B)	101·0	92·8	97·4	109·3	105·3	86·3	98·9	99·6	99·2	118th	104th	110th	123rd	116th	101st	113th	113th	114th
Acetic acid, glacial (BDH)	93·8	99·8	107·0	87·8	109·2	100·0	105·3	94·0	100·4	113th	109th	120th	106th	121st	113th	121st	109th	115th
Chlorophyll, water-soluble (sodium copper chlorophyllin) (RAN)	93·4	93·5	110·7	93·3	108·2	97·3	101·1	100·3	100·8	112th	106th	125th	111th	118th	110th	117th	116th	116th

Substance	I	II	III	IV	V	VI	VII	VIII	IX	rank I	rank II	rank III	rank IV	rank V	rank VI	rank VII	rank VIII (total)
Hair waving lotion, thiovanate type, Pyridine (R & B)	100·9	104·8	102·0	97·0	101·0	104·8	99·6	103·9	101·4	119th	114th	119th	115th	117th	115th	117th	117th
Hydrazine hydrate, 60 per cent (GEN)	108·6	112·5	97·4	104·8	96·7	108·2	104·1	101·6	103·0	117th	120th	121st	121st	110th	122nd	122nd	118th
Castor oil, medicinal (local pharmacy)	110·8	109·5	96·6	112·0	103·8	98·0	108·4	108·4	103·7	122nd	115th	111th	125th	107th	120th	123rd	119th
Herring oil (HBP)	98·5	102·0	109·8	95·0	104·3	110·0	101·2	107·9	104·1	120th	118th	123rd	113th	124th	111th	115th	120th
n-Butyric acid 50 per cent (TSH)	104·0	108·7	107·0	100·5	115·6	100·7	100·9	111·0	105·6	123rd	116th	114th	118th	120th	119th	119th	121st
Chlorophyll, oil-soluble FCAS (SCB)	106·3	111·8	106·4	100·8	106·3	110·0	111·7	99·4	106·3	112th	124th	123rd	120th	119th	121st	120th	122nd
Formaldehyde, 40 per cent (R & B)	106·3	114·5	109·5	98·0	118·7	103·7	114·3	99·6	107·9	113th	125th	118th	116th	122nd	123rd	120th	123rd
Phenyl acetylene (LLT)	116·4	116·3	99·6	116·5	101·5	108·8	105·4	111·3	108·0	124th	122nd	122nd	126th	113th	124th	126th	124th
Civet, Abyssinian (FLD)	113·5	117·3	113·6	109·8	116·2	113·5	111·2	116·6	113·6	126th	123rd	126th	124th	126th	125th	125th	125th
Ethyl mercaptan 0·5 per cent in water (LLT)	111·3	122·0	121·6	100·5	119·8	123·7	116·1	116·9	116·4	127th	126th	132nd	118th	132nd	129th	124th	126th
Piperidine (BDH)	124·0	124·8	109·7	123·0	109·5	122·0	121·0	111·3	116·9	124th	130th	131st	127th	123rd	132nd	132nd	127th
Triethylamine (BDH)	117·6	117·5	117·9	117·8	121·8	113·7	117·7	117·9	117·8	128th	128th	127th	129th	128th	126th	127th	128th
p-Chlorothiophenol (EVN)	120·1	120·5	116·5	119·8	123·7	112·0	117·1	119·9	118·3	130th	127th	125th	132nd	127th	127th	129th	129th
Carbon disulphide (G & T)	121·1	123·5	119·3	118·8	122·5	118·8	121·3	118·7	120·2	129th	132nd	128th	130th	129th	130th	130th	130th
Thiomalic acid (EVN)	119·6	120·5	121·1	118·8	120·8	121·0	119·2	121·9	120·4	132nd	129th	130th	128th	131st	127th	128th	131st
(EVN)	122·0	123·8	120·6	120·3	122·7	120·7	121·2	121·4	121·3	131st	131st	129th	131st	130th	131st	131st	132nd

NOTE: The initials in brackets are indicative of the source of supply. See notes to Table 1.

rank—the ranking—is shown for each group on the right-hand side of Table 3.

The unpleasant smells: uniformity of reaction by groups

The very first glance through Table 3 shows that there is a large measure of uniformity between the olfactory reactions of the difference groups of observers. Especially marked is this uniformity in respect of the unpleasant smells, those towards the end of Table 3. For those odours that we dislike, our reactions are very much the same irrespective of sex, age or temperament. Those six odorants that as a group of people we have put at the unpleasant end of Table 3 so that they occupy the last six places, are all to be found in the last eleven of any single group's arrangement. Every one of the eight groups says unmistakably that these six are all very unpleasant. The worst mark that any group could have given them would have been to place them all in ranking orders 127–132; they did not quite do this, but they did all put them (the worst six) within the range 122–132. Such uniformity is almost perfect. The observers include children, young adults and older people of both sexes, but irrespective of their age or sex, they all say unmistakably —these smells are very unpleasant, they are those that I dislike most of all offered to me. The six (most unpleasant last) are

Ethyl mercaptan with a sulphidy, garlicky, faecal odour
Piperidine with a biting offensive odour
Triethylamine with a powerful fishy ammoniacal odour
Chlorothiophenol with a pungent and burnt sweatish odour
Carbon disulphide with a high spirituous and nauseating odour
Thiomalic acid with a smoky smell a little reminiscent of burning rubber.

Ethyl mercaptan and carbon disulphide are well known to be very unpleasant odoriferously. Triethylamine and piperidine we had not thought to have quite such an unpleasant reputation as their position justifies, but the finding is clear enough: people of all kinds find them very unpleasant. The other two, thiomalic acid (supremely unpleasant) and chlorothiophenol are less well known and have yet to make a name for themselves olfactorily, but they have made a good start in claiming high places among the unliked odours. Whether we consider the reactions of individuals (p. 30) or of groups the dislike is manifest. Uniformity is almost perfect amongst us in respect of the smells we really dislike. The physical reactions are well defined, clear cut and characteristic: the bottle containing the test sample is hastily removed from the nose and the observer makes a facial expression of disgust.

Reactions of the several groups to the pleasant odours

At the other end of the scale, the odours that we really like, those that we place at the top of our list of 132, there is a large measure of uniformity, too, but it is not quite so marked as is the uniformity of reaction to unpleasant odours. There is, too, one factor that takes away from the high degree of uniformity of liking of these pleasant odours and that factor is that the odours children (under 15) like best are very different from those preferred by older people. If we leave out this group (the children) then we find that the six smells that are most liked (red rose—stock) are all to be found in the first eight rankings of any of the other groups' arrangements. To illustrate this point, the double ten-week stock has a rich and popular odour and is grown as much for its smell as its appearance; it is ranked 6th by the whole group, and by young adults and ex-troverts, 7th by women, older adults and men and 8th by introverts. There is a high degree of uniformity; all groups, except children, rank it high (males *including* the children rank it 10th). But children rank it 24th; the smell of stock makes no compelling appeal to them. Again, red rose is ranked 1st by the whole group and by extroverts, 2nd by women, young adults and introverts and 3rd by men and older adults, but 11th by children. Sweet peas are ranked 10th by children, but no worse than 7th by any other group; rose New Dawn is ranked 12th by the children, but no poorer than 5th by any other group. Children's preferences certainly do not fit at all well into the uniform preferences of the other groups.

If we leave out the children then the degree of uniformity of liking increases at once. Let us consider the five odours that are placed first, that is are ranked 1st, 2nd, 3rd, 4th and 5th by the whole group. They are: red rose, fresh strawberries, sweet peas, rose New Dawn and rose Emily Gray. Apart from the children and of course the males including the children, there are six groups, so that in all there are thirty rankings of these five most preferred odours and we find that twenty-four of these thirty rankings occur in the first five of all the groups; only six times does one of the five odours have a ranking poorer than five. These six instances are fresh strawberries rated 7th by the 15–25 years group, sweet peas rated 7th by the males and rose Emily Gray rated 6th by males and by females and 7th by the over 25's and 6th by introverts.

For these five preferred odours there is no ranking (excluding the children's) worse than 7th.

There is therefore a very large measure of agreement amongst all groups except the children about the most-liked odours. There was a still larger measure of agreement amongst all groups even including the children, about the most disliked odours. How about those that are intermediate, neither greatly liked nor disliked?

Reactions of the several groups to the intermediate odours

There are 132 odours that were used for the test; detailed consideration has been given to the placing by the different groups of the six most disliked (127th–132nd) and of the five most liked (1st–5th) and it has been seen that there is a great deal of uniformity in the reactions of the different groups.

Arithmetic mean. The arithmetic mean of the range will comprise the five odours 64th–68th. These are geranium oil, α-ionone (P & S), camphor, α-ionone (ABR) and α-n-methylionone. Two things are immediately apparent: the first is that the uniformity of ranking is certainly not good; of the forty rankings (eight groups of people, five odorants numbered 64th, 65th, 66th, 67th, 68th) only six are filled by one of the numbers 64th–68th and five of the rankings are 80th or worse and seven are 50th or better, i.e. much worse or much better. The second thing that is so apparent is the dominance of the ionones which occupy three (65th, 67th, 68th) out of the five middle places (64th–68th); at first this seems to be unfortunate because if there was any group of people that was particularly sensitive, either in the way of liking or of disliking, to the violet smell, this would vitiate the result so far as the more general question of uniformity over the middle range was concerned. In fact, the extrovert group does show more liking for the ionones (average rankings of 49th, 58th and 54th) than does the whole group (average rankings of 65th, 67th and 68th). But despite the similarity in odour of three of the five component members of those odorants in the mean position, there is still a wide scatter of the rankings accorded by the several groups. It would seem that there is a good deal of variation here, half-way down the hedonic scale.

In order to extend this finding, let us take the five odorants that are one-third of the way down the hedonic scale and also the five that are two-thirds of the way down the scale. This gives us Tables 4 and 5.

TABLE 4

Preference rankings by groups of observers of odorants one-third down the hedonic scale

Odorants	Males (excl. children)	Females	Under 15's	15–25 years	Over 25's	Intro- verts	Extro- verts	Whole group
Lemongrass oil	17th	53rd	52nd	51st	27th	44th	42nd	42nd
Isoeugenol	69th	38th	36th	41st	55th	51st	38th	43rd
Friar's Balsam	37th	52nd	39th	55th	38th	64th	18th	44th
Eugenol	70th	59th	16th	69th	57th	52nd	45th	45th
Parsley	50th	48th	50th	35th	60th	25th	82nd	46th

There is not very much uniformity here; only three out of the thirty-five rankings in the first seven columns fall within the range of the whole group rankings 42nd–46th, shown in the last column.

TABLE 5

Preference rankings by groups of observers of odorants two-thirds down the hedonic scale

Odorants	Males (excl. children)	Females	Under 15's	15–25 years	Over 25's	Intro- verts	Extro- verts	Whole group
Benzene hexachloride	86th	85th	79th	88th	81st	92nd	69th	85th
Nitrobenzene	102nd	70th	82nd	76th	88th	88th	74th	85th
Peach synthetic concentrate	90th	94th	62nd	88th	91st	83rd	90th	87th
Acetone	95th	74th	99th	55th	99th	90th	84th	88th
Ambergris	105th	81st	74th	85th	98th	85th	92nd	89th
Amyl cinnamic aldehyde	82nd	87th	97th	90th	82nd	93rd	77th	90th

This time, thirteen out of forty-two rankings in the first seven columns of numbers fall within the range of the whole group rankings 85th–90th shown in the last column. There is a good deal of spread of the rankings; certainly there is no close uniformity. There is, however, some measure of restriction on the spread and with the exception of the remarkable tolerance of the middle age group for acetone (55th) and the liking of the children for peach concentrate (62nd), all of the rankings in the seven columns fall within about ±20 per cent of the mean for the group, i.e. between 69th and 105th (inclusive).

If the same test is applied to the group one-third of the way down the scale, the group shown in Table 4, it does not do so well, for here the mean ranking is 44th and if we admit that 35th to 53rd (inclusive) falls within the ± 20 per cent range, only twenty out of a possible thirty-five rankings do so, whereas in the group (Table 5) two-thirds of the way down the table forty out of a possible forty-two rankings fall within the ± 20 per cent range.

If the same test is applied to the five odours (64th–68th) in the middle of the scale, it is found that twenty-three out of thirty-five lie within 20 per cent of the median value of 66th i.e. between 53rd and 79th (inclusive). These findings are expressed succinctly in Table 6.

TABLE 6

Variation of uniformity with position in hedonic scale

Position in hedonic scale	Rankings of odorants	20 per cent plus or minus range of mean	Percentage of all rankings falling within the ± 20 per cent range
One-third down	42nd–46th	35th–53rd	57
Middle	64th–68th	53rd–79th	66
Two-thirds down	85th–90th	69th–105th	95

Perhaps, though, it is unfair to use a *percentage* range, because this gives a wider arithmetic range, e.g. the range of 69th–105th is much wider than that of 35th–53rd. Accordingly, we can restrict the ranges to plus or minus nine rankings either side of the mean value, the same as in the first row in Table 6, and then we have Table 7.

TABLE 7

Another expression of variation of uniformity with position in the hedonic scale

Position in hedonic scale	Rankings of odorants	Plus or minus 9 rankings range	Percentage of all rankings falling within the ± 9 range
One-third down	42nd–46th	35th–53rd	57 (20 of 35)
Middle	64th–68th	57th–75th	49 (17 of 35)
Two-thirds down	85th–90th	78th–96th	64 (27 of 42)

This time, although the test is unfairly loaded against the two-thirds down position, it is this position that still does the best.

So that what we find is excellent agreement amongst all the observers about the worst smells, very good agreement except for the children about the best-liked odours, and very poor agreement in detail about the ranking of the large middle group of odours. In the middle region the position is much more confused that at either end of the table and it is clear that we need much more information about this crowded middle. An investigation of the extent and location of the crowding may perhaps throw some light on the subject. But in Tables 6 and 7 there is already some indication to be seen that the confusion is noticeably less marked when we get well down the hedonic scale; as unpleasantness supervenes there is more agreement amongst the observers.

Distribution of average placings

Whilst the odorants in Table 1 were being arranged in order of preference, it was strikingly clear that the average placings were

TABLE 8

Distribution of odour preference placings illustrating particularly the crowding in the middle ranges

Range of placings	Number of odours placed in specified range by:							
	SEX		AGE			TEMPERA-MENT		WHOLE GROUP
	M (excluding children)	F (no children in this group)	Under 15	15–25 years	Over 25	Introvert	Extrovert	
0–5	4	3	1	3	4	2	0	0
5·1–10	4	4	7	3	5	4	5	5
10·1–15	3	0	2	1	2	2	2	2
15·1–20	4	1	5	2	2	3	4	1
20·1–25	1	6	4	4	5	3	1	2
25·1–30	10	2	6	6	3	6	4	8
30·1–35	3	9	6	8	8	9	9	7
35·1–40	3	8	6	3	6	11	6	7
40·1–45	4	8	8	7	5	3	8	7
45·1–50	11	8	5	7	8	8	9	8
50·1–55	8	8	7	6	11	3	11	13
55·1–60	8	10	7	13	10	7	7	5
60·1–65	8	6	6	9	3	8	7	5
65·1–70	5	11	4	11	7	9	11	8
70·1–75	7	9	12	8	6	9	7	10
75·1–80	8	2	7	3	5	4	5	8
80·1–85	7	2	9	5	9	7	5	8
85·1–90	3	8	5	5	4	12	1	2
90·1–95	5	1	6	3	4	2	8	5
95·1–100	4	9	4	3	6	3	5	3
100·1–105	5	3	4	5	6	5	4	6
105·1–110	5	6	3	8	5	2	3	4
110·1–115	3	2	1	0	3	3	3	1
115·1–120	3	3	5	4	1	4	5	4
120·1–125	6	3	2	5	4	3	2	3
125·1–132	0	0	0	0	0	0	0	0

very numerous, that is very close together, in the middle range: there would, for example, be many more odorants that had average placings between fifty and sixty than between nought and ten or between ten and twenty. This can be seen from Table 8 in which the distribution of the odour preference placings is shown within each range of five, e.g. 0–5, 5–10, 10–15 and so on. By way of clarification the method of derivation of two of the figures in it may be given: reference to Table 3 shows that for the females there are *three* odorants which have average placings between nought and five; they are red rose 4·5, sweet pea 3·4, and honeysuckle 4·5, and no others so that in Table 6 in the females column, we find the figure 3 for the range 0–5: similarly, the extroverts in the range 20·1–25 are given the figure of 1 in Table 8 and this is because in Table 3 they have given an average placing of 23·2 to meadowsweet. To no other odorant have they allocated a value between 20·1 and 25. In similar fashion all the other distribution figures in Table 8 were derived from Table 3.

Crowding in middle ranges. The crowding in the middle ranges is easy to see in Table 8. For example, the whole group of observers assigns average placings of between fifty and fifty-five to so many as thirteen different odorants and the children (under 15 years) assign average placings of between seventy and seventy-five to no fewer than twelve different odorants.

The crowding is significant in two respects, the first being more obvious than the second, but this latter being equally real. The more obvious significance of the crowding is that the preferences in the middle ranges of one odorant over another are only very slight in contrast to the well-marked preferences at the top and the bottom of Table 3; there are only marginal differences between the degrees of liking shown by the observers when they are comparing those odorants which occupy the body or the middle ranges of Table 3. The second inference to be drawn from the incidence of crowding is that there is a considerable lack of uniformity between the opinions of the different observers in the middle ranges of Table 3; they all agree about the smells they really dislike, and they agree quite well about those that they really like, but they disagree and contradict each other about the relatively greater number of odorants to which they are more or less indifferent in the crowded middle ranges.

This disagreement can be illustrated clearly by the preparation of histograms from the information in Table 8.

Histogram for whole group. In such histograms each range of

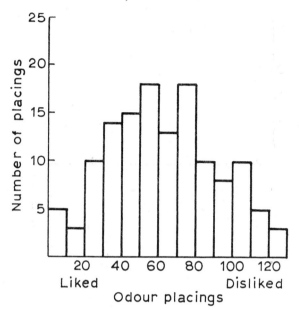

FIG. 1.—Histogram showing distribution of odour preferences by the whole group of people. The crowding together of many odours in the middle ranges is noteworthy.

odorant placings e.g. 0–10, 10–20, 20–30 and so on is represented by a column and the height of the column is proportional to the number of odorants that *on average* have been placed in that group. Fig. 1 is the histogram for the whole group of observers; it is easy to see from it that in the ranges at either end, namely 0–10, 10–20, 110–120, and 120–130, the columns are short and the frequency of placings in those ranges is correspondingly small, whereas in the centre the histogram rises, the columns are high and the number of placings correspondingly high. In order to appreciate the significance with respect to our odour placings of these properties of the histogram, it will be well to examine the histograms which would obtain in two extreme cases (1) perfect agreement of odour preferences, (2) complete disagreement of the same.

Histogram for perfect agreement. If we had a histogram for just one person's odour preference placings, it would be as shown in Fig. 2; there would be ten placings in the range 0–10, ten again in the range 10–20, ten again in the range 20–30 and so on so that the histogram would simply consist of a series of columns of uniform height. If, next, we were to make a histogram of the odour

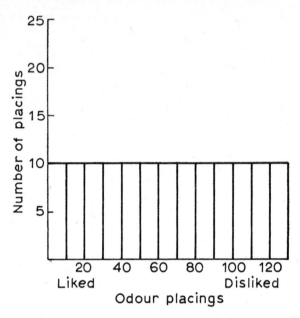

F<small>IG.</small> 2.—Histogram for one person's distribution of odours or alternatively for a group of people who agree exactly in their preference placings.

preferences of two people and their preferences were exactly the same, so that each placed red rose 1st, fresh strawberries 2nd, sweet peas 3rd and so on, then the relative numbers in the different ranges would be unaltered and so the corresponding histogram (Fig. 2) which was designed to express the arrangement of just the first observer, would equally represent the arrangements of the second observer and indeed of any number of observers provided that they made exactly the same preference arrangements as the first had done. Accordingly Fig. 2 is characteristic of perfect agreement of preferences between a number of observers. Departure from agreement is measured by the departure of the histogram column tops (Fig. 2) from the straight line. But in comparing the uniformity of preference of two groups of observers by departure from the straight horizontal line of the column tops of their two histograms, it is necessary that the two groups be roughly of equal size, because except in the ideal and unlikely case of complete agreement between observers, the greater the number of observers in the group the greater will be the deviation from the straight horizontal line.

Histogram for complete disagreement. Let us now consider the hypothetical case of two observers who did not agree at all in their odour preferences, two who disagreed so completely that the odour that one of them, A, liked most and placed first, the other, B, disliked most and placed 132nd, what A placed 2nd, B placed 131st, what A placed 3rd, B placed 130th, and so on so that finally what A placed 132nd, B placed 1st. The average placing of these

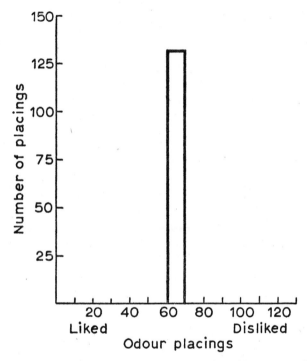

FIG. 3.—Histogram for a "group" of two people who disagree completely in their odour preference placings.

two observers will be $\frac{1}{2}(132+1)$ or $\frac{1}{2}(131+2)$ or $\frac{1}{2}(130+3)$ or 66·5 for every one of the odorants, and if we plot their histogram, we shall get a single vertical column as shown in Fig. 3. Perfect uniformity of preference gives column tops in a horizontal line (Fig. 2); complete lack of uniformity gives one tall column, in effect a vertical line (Fig. 3) when the distribution of the average placings are plotted in histogram fashion. Armed with this knowledge, we can now take a look at the corresponding histograms for the other groups of observers. These will all show crowding in the middle ranges, but

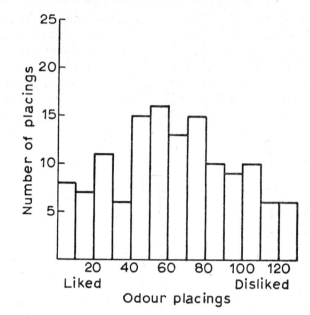

FIG. 4.—Histogram for adult males. It is flatter resembles Fig. 2 more than does Fig. 1 for the whole group of people.

there are differences between them and these differences may be informative if they can be interpreted.

Histograms for males and females. Fig. 4 is the histogram for the males (excluding children) and Fig. 5 that for the females (there were no children in this group). First, we may compare them with Fig. 1, the histogram for the whole group of subjects: it is evident enough that Fig. 4 is much flatter than Fig. 1 and this is an indication that there is greater uniformity of odour preferences within the group of males than within the whole group of people; still, the middle columns of the males' histogram (Fig. 4) are higher than those at either side, but not nearly so much higher as in Fig. 1 (the histogram for all the people). Amongst the males there is both uncertainty and disagreement in the middle ranges of the odour preference scale, but they are not so great as they are in the whole group of people.

The histogram for the females (Fig. 5) is more similar to Fig. 1 than is that for the males (Fig. 4): most of the uncertainty that is evident in the middle ranges of Fig. 1 can be seen, too, in Fig. 5; for example, the peaks are equally high, but there is a little more uniformity in Fig. 5 especially within the range 70–110 than there is

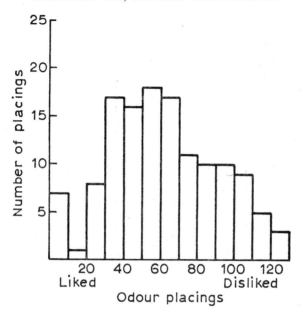

FIG. 5.—Histogram for adult females; it is intermediate in flatness between Fig. 1 and Fig. 4. The females are less sure of their olfactory preferences than the males.

in Fig. 1 in the same range. Another observation that should not pass unremarked is that the highest parts of the histogram for the females (Fig. 5) is shifted a little to the left compared with those for all the people (Fig. 1) and for the males (Fig. 4). The interpretation of these observations would seem to be that the females are unsure of their preferences amongst the fairly pleasant odours which the men sort out more certainly, but that the females have surer responses amongst the fairly unpleasant odours within the range of placings from 70–110.

Histograms for different age groups. Corresponding histograms for the three age groups are shown in Fig. 6 (under 15's), Fig. 7 (15–25 years) and Fig. 8 (over 25's). It is clear that the peaks, the regions of maximum uncertainty, move towards the left with increasing age; the children place a greater proportion of their reactions in the range 70–100, a little unpleasant, than do the other age groups. The crowding of the middle ranges is clearly shown in all the histograms, but this crowding is more noticeable in Fig. 1 for the whole group than it is in Fig. 6 for the children. Perhaps, too, the histogram for the children (Fig. 6) approaches more closely

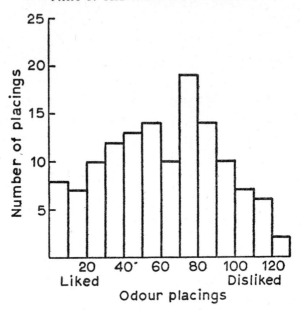

FIG. 6.—Histogram for children under 15. It shows better agreement of olfactory preferences than does Fig. 1 for the whole group.

in its column tops to a horizontal line than does that for the whole group (Fig. 1), but it must not be forgotten that they constitute a smaller group.

Histograms for different temperaments. Fig. 9 represents the distribution of the odour placings of the introverts and Fig. 10 those of the extroverts, and they show very considerable differences. The greater concentration of placings by the extroverts within the fairly pleasant range 30–70 seems to indicate a lower degree of discrimination and greater disagreement amongst themselves so far as the fairly pleasant odours are concerned and this is reminiscent of the behaviour of the females (Fig. 5).

Significance of the distribution of average placings

Broadly the histograms illustrate two separate measures: those of middle indifference and of uniformity of liking or lack of it.

Middle indifference. That there are more average placings of odours in the range of scores of 30–40 and similar ranges than in the end ranges of 0–10 and 110–120 shows that the differences in liking or disliking (of the particular group of observers to which the histogram refers) are smaller between the odorants in the middle

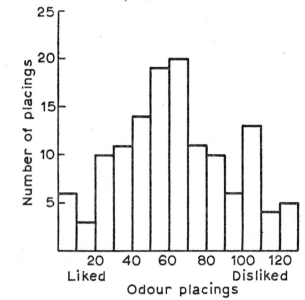

FIG. 7.—Histogram for young adults, the 15–20's.

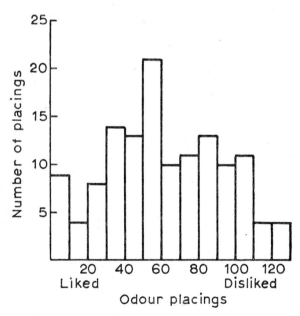

FIG. 8.—Histogram for people over 25.

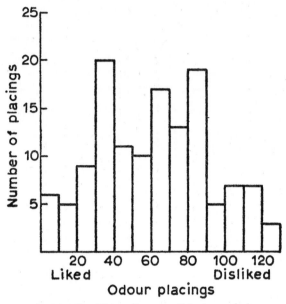

FIG. 9.—The preferences of the introverts.

of the like–dislike scale than between those at either end. The observers do not find it so easy to express their preferences. It is as if there are a few fairly big intervals of measure of liking or disliking at either end of the scale, but that a large intermediate class of odours evokes responses that are not very different one from another. This middle indifference occurs in all of our seven groups of observers and of course in the whole group, too. But it does seem to be less noticeable in the children; they apparently have a brighter panel of likes and dislikes than do the adults; their responses are simpler and more definite. But there is no doubt that middle indifference does exist in their group as in the others, although it is rather less noticeable. Examination of Figs. 4 and 5 shows that the middle indifference is more pronounced in the females than in the males; the likes and dislikes of the males as a group, although they are less evenly distributed than those of the children, are more so than those of the females.

Uniformity. The histograms for the different groups of people all show peaks and do so especially near the middle of the range, that are indicative of middle indifference. But these peaks vary a good deal from one group to another; the shapes of the histograms for the different groups are themselves different and these

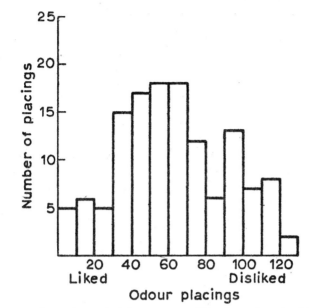

Fig. 10.—The preferences of the extroverts. This picture is noticeably different from Fig. 9 for the introverts.

differences are a measure of the departure from uniformity of the groups. The introverts have a more uniform spread of likes and dislikes in the middle ranges than the extroverts. So far as concerns age, the peaks move in the direction of liking and away from disliking with increase of age; in Figs. 6, 7 and 8, the peaks move progressively to the left, to the liking end of the scale.

Rules

Those general rules that can be discerned in the subject matter of this chapter would seem to be:

Rule 5. There is excellent agreement between people of all kinds about really bad smells; they agree unanimously in their dislikes.

Rule 6. There is very good agreement between most people about the odours they like best, but the agreement is not nearly so perfect as is that about their pronounced dislikes.

Rule 7. The uniformity of liking of pleasant smells in a group of people becomes still better if children are excluded from the group, but still not so good as the uniformity of disliking of unpleasant smells.

Rule 8. In the intermediate range of odours, those that are neither greatly liked nor disliked, the preferences shown are confused and there is much disagreement. This applies to all groups of observers.

Rule 9. As odours become unpleasant, even only slightly so, two-thirds of the way down the hedonic scale, agreement of preferences between observers becomes much better. The confusion gradually lessens.

Rule 10. There are many more odours to which people are more or less indifferent than there are of well-liked or greatly disliked odours. The crowd of odours in the middle of the hedonic scale, evoke marginal and often uncertain and contradictory preference responses.

CHAPTER 3

VARIATION OF ODOUR PREFERENCES WITH SEX

WE HAVE already seen (p. 50) that women are less sure of their preferences amongst those odours that are fairly pleasant than men are and that they become more confused when they try to arrange them in order of preference than men do. On the other hand, the women have surer responses than the men amongst the fairly unpleasant odours, those ranked 70th–110th. The two histograms Fig. 4 for males and Fig. 5 for females are significantly different, and the interpretation put upon the differences leads to those conclusions that have just been expressed.

Exclusion of children from male group

A first comparison of the average placings (Table 3) of the 132 odorants by the male and female groups suggested that two of the attributes that we shall find belong to the children (Chapter 4) were also to be found in the records of the males, these two being:

(1) a relative lack of appreciation of some fine flower smells,

(2) a marked liking for fruity odours and flavours.

But in considering these trends it had to be remembered that only three of the twelve observers were under 15 and that all three of them were males; consequently the male likes and dislikes were heavily loaded by the likes and dislikes of the children in the group. It is for this reason that the placings are shown in Table 3 not only for the whole group of males (1st Column) but also separately for the adult males (2nd Column) omitting the results from the under 15's. When this exclusion is made we get a straight comparison between mature people of the two sexes.

Flower smells

This straight comparison between adult members of the two sexes is shown for flower likings in Table 9.

57

TABLE 9

**Comparison of odour preferences of adult males
and females for flower scents**

Odorant	Average placing by	
	Males	Females
Red rose	2·7	4·5
Sweet pea	9·3	3·4
Rose, New Dawn	4·0	6·4
Rose, Emily Gray	8·5	9·0
Stock, double	9·3	9·1
Honeysuckle	1·3	4·5
Wild rose	7·5	22·2
Meadowsweet	14·3	20·3
Heliotrope	16·0	29·4
Mock orange	11·0	45·0

There is good reason to believe in a large measure of uniformity of sensation of all kinds between different individuals. It seems very likely that one person's sensation of red colour or of rose smell is much the same as another's but it is impossible to be certain about it. There may be minor differences of sensation and undoubtedly there are differences of liking. Amongst groups of people there are certainly differences in reactions to the same stimuli, whether or not the primary sensations are different or the same. In our present considerations, the author as one of the male observers can never know exactly how the females react to the different smells. To him the two "purest", simplest, and most delightful of the flower smells are wild rose and honeysuckle. Neither of them makes the slightest appeal to the children and they seem, too, to make less appeal to women than to men. Heliotrope and mock orange are also clearly much more appreciated by men than by women; probably they are absolutely appreciated more but certainly they are so, relative to the other odours that were used in these tests. But both of these are sophisticated and by no means typical flower scents.

Flavour smells. The reactions of adult members of the two sexes to the odours of flavouring are shown in Table 10.

TABLE 10

**Comparison of odour preferences of adult males
and females to flavour odours**

Odours	Average placing by	
	Males	Females
Fresh strawberries	2·0	7·6
Raspberry flavouring essence	28·3	24·8
Lemon flavouring essence (BTS)	27·5	33·5
Peppermint flavouring essence	26·3	36·9
Strawberry flavouring	41·8	31·3
Lemon flavouring essence (ABR)	30·5	35·3
Banana flavouring essence	41·0	34·6
Vanilla flavouring essence	49·0	28·1
Almond flavouring essence	50·8	48·6
Coconut flavouring essence	60·0	59·9

When the contents of Tables 9 and 10 are examined it is clear enough that the two apparent differences which we had thought to see at first between male and female preferences, viz. relative lack of appreciation of males for flower smells and their marked liking for fruity flavours are not real; they were due only to the influence of the children in the small group of males and these two trends which are real enough in the children projected themselves through the male/female comparison. Examination of Table 9 shows that the likings for roses and stocks of the adult males are not very different from those of the females; for some of the more complex flower smells such as meadowsweet, heliotrope and mock orange the men find more liking than either the females or the children. Examination of Table 10 shows also that the apparent liking for fruity flavours on the part of the males was due to the children in the group and that when they have been eliminated as they have in Table 10, the males are not so very different from the females; the males like peppermint a little better and the females like vanilla better. But there are no generalizations that can be drawn about the comparative likings of the two sexes for flower smells and fruit flavours, other than that there are no very great differences between them.

Essential oil odours. The reactions of adult members of the two sexes to some essential oil odours are to be seen in Table 11. The essential oils are the oily parts of the flowers or leaves, or bark, or twigs or roots that have been extracted from the natural odorous materials, the vegetation; they include nearly all of the odorous constituents and, olfactorily at least, they contain the essential parts of the natural growth, be it flowers or leaves or bark or roots. For the most part the essential oils have odours that are pleasant; it is true that they are concentrated but they are nearly always complex mixtures of many odorous chemicals which blend perfectly to smell pleasantly.

TABLE 11

Comparison of odour preferences of adult males and females to essential oil odours

Odours	Average placing by	
	Males	Females
Sweet orange	26·8	22·1
Spearmint	49·0	30·4
English lavender	21·8	19·3
French lavender	19·5	20·8
Ylang-ylang	14·8	34·4
Cinnamon leaf	28·3	43·8
Rose attar	27·8	32·6
Cinnamon bark	30·8	49·9
Neroli	39·5	34·6
Lemongrass	25·5	54·3
Cananga	48·0	48·0
Geranium	36·5	60·0
Citronella	61·3	57·1

It is evident that most of the essential oils are placed fairly equally by the two sexes, but there are a few that show significant differences. Women place spearmint higher up the scale than do men; they like it better and yet it is mostly the men who indulge in gum chewing. Even in America it is rare to see women chewing, although it is a habit with some of their men, and even although from what we can now see, the women probably like the odour and flavour of spearmint better than do the men. There are, of course, considerations of dignity, repose, and beauty to be taken into account. Cinnamon leaf and bark oils are both rated better by men than by women and one is reminded of the biblical story of the woman, "subtil of heart", who perfumed her bed with myrrh, aloes, and cinnamon.[12] Why is lemongrass placed so much better by males (25·5) than by females (54·3)? Some of our most popular home disinfectants for direct application to the body smell strongly of lemongrass; perhaps women use them more than men and have come to associate their use with unpleasant conditions. Their dislike is real enough because citral, which is the essential constituent of lemongrass oil, although placed as favourably as 26·3 by men, is placed as poorly as 52·0 by women. At first we thought that lavender oils both English and French were much preferred by females to males, but when the children were excluded from the male group, the differences in odour preference between the sexes disappeared as can be seen from Table 12.

TABLE 12
Reactions to lavender oils

| Type of Lavender oil | Average placing by | | | |
	Males (all)	Females (all 15 or over)	Children under 15 (all male)	Males of 15 or over
English	39·5	19·3	57·3	21·8
French	44·9	20·8	70·3	19·5

The dislike that the children have for lavender is evident enough, but take out the children and there is no great difference between females and males.

The musks. Natural musk is the prerogative of the male musk deer; its scent carried by the wind draws to him the females from miles away. And yet, amongst humans (who only very exceptionally have a natural musky smell) it is the women who wear it, inasmuch as it is usually the women who wear scent, perhaps partly for the gratification of their male companions. Is it the case that men like musk better than women do? A comparison of the olfactory rankings of the musky compounds that occurred in our range of odorants is shown in Table 13.

TABLE 13
Reaction of men and women to musky compounds

| Musky compound | Ranked by | |
	Men 15 years and over	Women
Musk lactone 10 per cent solution	26th	28th
Musk ambrette (a synthetic)	14th	64th
Musk, natural, 2 per cent tincture in alcohol	60th	57th
Tonkin musk grains, natural	54th	75th

It is odd that men should rank the relatively cheap and synthetic musk ambrette so very favourably. Musk lactone is ranked favourably by both men and women and has a lovely smell; it probably approaches very closely to natural muscone, the essential odorant of natural musk. Ambergris is often considered as an odorant of the same class as musk; it also is one of the few animal products that are extensively used by the perfumer in compounding his scents. Whereas men rank ambergris poorly at 105th, women tolerate it better and rank it 81st. Civet, another animal perfume material is ranked almost equally badly by men (117th as a tincture, 129th pure) and women (118th as tincture, 132nd pure), it is only when it is dilute that it becomes really tolerable. So, too, musk and ambergris become delightful and attractive when highly diluted.

Alcohol. Strangest of all the findings in this chapter is that women rank pure alcohol 33rd, but men rank it 62nd. Women (at least those who took part in our tests) like its smell much better than men do. Most of our drinks, beer, wine, whisky, rum and so on, contain powerful odorants in their own right which hide the smell of the alcohol; vodka does not and any chemist on first encountering vodka is likely to think rather poorly of it, as it smells just like dilute ethyl alcohol. Is vodka liked better by women than by men? It ought to be but social and economic considerations may hide the true answer. But the liking of women for the smell of ethyl

TABLE 14

Comparison of men's and women's best-liked odours

| Odour | Ranked by | |
	Men 15 years and over	Women
Honeysuckle	1st	2nd
Fresh strawberries	2nd	5th
Red rose	3rd	2nd
Rose, New Dawn	4th	4th
Wild rose	5th	12th
Rose, Emily Gray	6th	6th
Sweet pea	7th	1st
Red rose	3rd	2nd } joint
Honeysuckle	1st	3rd }
Rose, New Dawn	4th	4th
Fresh strawberries	2nd	5th
Rose, Emily Gray	6th	6th

alcohol is quite specific; the chemical near-relative wood spirit or methyl alcohol, they rank as badly as 105th, whilst men rank it 92nd. Methyl alcohol is disliked by both sexes; ethyl alcohol is liked by both sexes, but liked very much more by women. **The smells that are ranked highest.** The smells ranked highest of the 132 that were used are shown in Table 14.

Table 14 tells its own tale; those odours that are most liked by the men are also quite nearly those that are most liked by the women. All of the observers are human beings first in their olfactory reactions, and only sexed secondly. So it is, too, at the end of Table 3; the really disliked odours are disliked equally by men and women. But in between, where there is room for opinion, where odours are neither delightful nor disgusting, there are some significant differences between the olfactory reactions of men and women.

TABLE 15

Odorants to which the reactions of men and women were considerably different

| Odorant material | Placing of odorant by | | Odour preferred by | Ratio of placings of men and women |
	Men 15 years and over	Women		
Honeysuckle flower	1·3	4·5	Men	1 : 3·5
Wild rose	7·5	22·2	Men	1 : 3·0
Heliotrope	16·0	29·4	Men	1 : 1·8
Mock orange	11·0	45·0	Men	1 : 4·1
Mint	19·0	34·5	Men	1 : 1·8
Vanilla essence	49·0	28·1	Women	1·7 : 1
Ylang-ylang	14·8	34·4	Men	1 : 2·3
Cinnamon leaf oil	28·3	43·8	Men	1 : 1·5
Citral	26·3	52·0	Men	1 : 2·0
Cinnamon bark oil	30·8	49·9	Men	1 : 1·6
Bay leaf	48·3	24·6	Women	2·0 : 1
Musk ambrette	19·5	58·8	Men	1 : 3·0
Geraniol ex Palma Rosa	27·0	54·6	Men	1 : 2·0
Lemongrass oil	25·5	54·3	Men	1 : 2·1
Onion, Raw	82·3	40·9	Women	2·0 : 1
Heliotropin	72·0	46·1	Women	1·6 : 1
Ethyl alcohol	59·8	39·0	Women	1·5 : 1
Alpine violet perfume	75·5	36·4	Women	2·1 : 1
Allyl caproate	54·3	87·5	Men	1 : 1·6
Naphthalene	103·0	69·6	Women	1·5 : 1
Toluene	105·3	69·3	Women	1·5 : 1
Skatole	107·8	87·1	Women	1·2 : 1
Cade oil	62·3	99·8	Men	1 : 1·6

The biggest differences. The biggest differences in the olfactory preferences that were encountered in these trials are collected together in Table 15.

Those odorants that the men like much more than the women do, are: mock orange, honeysuckle, wild rose, musk ambrette, ylang-ylang, and lemongrass; those that the women like much better than the men are: Alpine violet perfume, bay leaf, and onions. The men like some flowers much the more, the women like perfume and culinary associations.

Rules

Those general rules that we can derive from the contents of this chapter are:

Rule 11. In accordance with Rules 5 and 6, men and women agree well about the smells that are very bad and those that are very good, but in the intermediate ranges there are significant differences between the olfactory preferences of the two sexes.

Rule 12. Amongst the fairly pleasant odours men's preferences are surer than those of women (cf. Rule 19 relating to children).

Rule 13. Amongst the slightly unpleasant odours, the women's preferences are surer than the men's.

Rule 14. The simple flower scents are liked equally by men and women, but some flower scents that are more complex (less typically floral) such as mock orange and heliotrope are ranked much higher by men than by women. Women like their flowers straight, but men can tolerate sophistication.

Rule 15. The odours of many flavour essences appeal nearly equally to men and women, notably raspberry, strawberry, lemon and coconut.

Rule 16. Many essential oils are ranked nearly equally by the two sexes, notably: orange, lavender, rose, orange-blossom (neroli), cananga (the later and less good cuts of ylang-ylang distillate) and citronella. Men show more appreciation than women for ylang-ylang, cinnamon, lemongrass, and geranium.

Rule 17. Musks are generally ranked better by men than by women; ambretta musk, a fairly cheap synthetic musk is ranked surprisingly high by men (cf. Rule 46).

Rule 18. Culinary odours, for example bay leaf and raw onion are ranked more highly by women than by men.

REFERENCE

12. *Proverbs*, Chapter 7, verses 10, 17.

CHAPTER 4

VARIATION OF ODOUR PREFERENCES WITH AGE

IT WILL BE possible to see that the differences in odour preferences according to age are greater than those differences between the sexes, and furthermore that they can be much more boldly defined. In particular, children have well-marked odour preferences that differ significantly from those of their elders: they are much less favourably impressed by flower scents, much more impressed by fruity flavours, and there is some evidence that the young will tolerate without disturbance some of the animal odours that adults consider unpleasant.

Variation of most crowded regions of the hedonic scale with age

In Figs. 6, 7 and 8 the crowding of the odours in the middle ranges was shown in histogram form for the three age groups. It was evident (p. 51) that the peaks of the histograms which indicate the

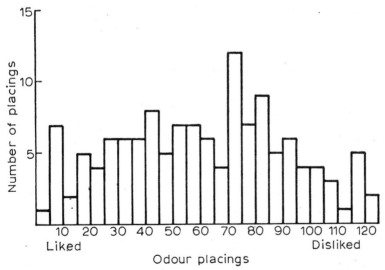

FIG. 11.—Histogram for children, similar to Fig. 6, but with groups of 5 instead of 10 placings. It shows better agreement of preferences than could have been deduced from Fig. 6.

regions of maximum uncertainty moved towards the pleasant end of
the odour scale with increasing age. These histograms (Figs. 6, 7,
8) were based on groups of ten placings; they showed the number
of odorants to which average scores of between 0 and 10, 10 and
20, 20 and 30 and so on had been given. If, instead of taking groups

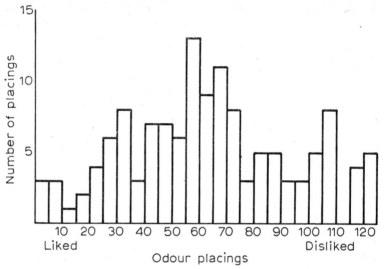

FIG. 12.—Histogram for young adults, similar to Fig. 7, but with more detail.
It does not yield any information that was not to be found in Fig. 7.

of ten as in Figs. 6, 7 and 8, we were to take groups of five we might
be able to see a little more detail. This has been done in Figs. 11,
12 and 13 which are based on the number of average scores between
0 and 5, 5 and 10, 10 and 15 and so on. The most obvious difference
is that Fig. 11 is very much flatter over the region 15–65 odour
placings than could have been deduced from a consideration of
Fig. 6. It really does seem that over a very considerable intermediate range of fairly pleasant odorants, the children's preferences
are surer than are those of older people. In the 15–25 years group a
comparison of Fig. 12 with Fig. 7 does not seem to reveal much
new information; the two histograms are very much alike indeed.
And so with the over 25's, too, there is not very much to be read
out of Fig. 13 that was not already evident from Fig. 8. But the
point just made relative to the children's behaviour in sorting out
so regularly their preferences in the fairly pleasant range is significant, and was very much less easy to see in Fig. 6 than it is in
Fig. 11. Liking and disliking, pleasantness or unpleasantness are

immediate and unanswerable sensations and call for no deep thought; it is the first impression that counts, thought and introspection only muddle the judgment. Perhaps the children with their lighter background of experience are able to give a straight answer more easily to the question "Do you like this better than that?" Their elders with much more detail and confusion of experience in their background, and with the learnt lesson that it is not always good to speak before you think may be not quite so slick at giving

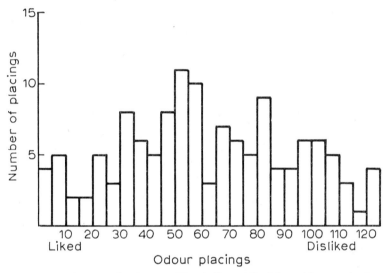

FIG, 13.—Histogram for the over-25's, similar to Fig. 8 but with more detail.

an immediate and straight answer to "Do you like this better than that?" Additionally, and perhaps even more importantly the children may have an anatomical advantage in their olfactory system, as they demonstrably have in the wider distribution of their taste-buds resulting as was found by Richter and Campbell[13] in a lower threshold concentration for the sweet taste (0·68 per cent sucrose as against 1·23 per cent for adults).

Reactions of children to flower smells. Children do not rate flower smells highly. Their rankings compared with those of the whole group for those fresh flowers that were included in the test were as shown in Table 16.

In every case except that of mock orange which has a bitter atypical floral odour, the children are much less favourably impressed by the flower smells than are their elders. Mock orange is,

TABLE 16

Children's reactions to flower smells

Flower	Average ranking of the	
	Children	Whole group
Red rose, Ena Harkness	11th	1st
Sweet pea	10th	3rd
Rose, New Dawn	12th	4th
Rose, Emily Gray	9th	5th
Stock, double ten-week	24th	6th
Honeysuckle	46th	7th
Wild rose	18th	8th
Meadowsweet	44th	12th
Heliotrope	48th	15th
Mock orange	15th	20th

oddly, more attractive to the children despite its sophisticated note. But this is exceptional, and of all the generalizations that can be drawn about olfactory preferences, this relative lack of appreciation by children for flower smells is at the root of one of the most evident of them.

The indifferent average placing of meadowsweet (43·8) by the children is inexplicable to the author, who carries a vivid childhood memory of meadowsweet growing profusely by a brook and of a hot summer morning lying on the grass, sniffing flower after flower, and revelling in the delicious smell, quite intoxicated by it. And yet today's children did not think overmuch of meadowsweet; partly perhaps because it had been picked and carried to the laboratory and thereby lost a little freshness. It may be apposite to remember that jasmine flowers grown in Provence for the perfume industry are best picked in the early morning for that is when the odour is strongest and best.

Children's reactions to fruit smells. Contrary to their relative indifference to the olfactory delights offered by flowers, children rate fruity smells much better than do adults. Their rankings compared with those of the whole group for the fruity smells (including some nutty flavouring essences) that were included in the test were as shown in Table 17.

There is really only one notable exception to the generally better rating given by children to the fruity smells and that is that some concentrates are disliked by children; sweet orange oil and synthetic vanillin they both liked less than did adults, although orange essence they rated better than adults did, and vanilla essence about

TABLE 17

Children's liking of fruity smells

Fruit or essence	Average ranking of the fruity smell by	
	Children *	Whole group
Strawberries, fresh	1st	2nd
Raspberry essence	2nd	9th
Sweet orange oil	22nd	10th
Lemon essence (BTS)	14th	11th
Lemon essence (ABR)	7th	16th
Strawberry essence	3rd	14th
Banana essence	4th	17th
Vanilla essence	20th	21st
Orange essence	8th	28th
Citral	16th	30th
Strawberry aldehyde	28th	35th
Vanillin ex eugenol	71st	37th
Almond essence	23rd	40th
Lemongrass oil	52nd	42nd
Amyl butyrate	13th	50th
Coconut essence	21st	51st
Butyl acetate	30th	53rd
Tonka beans tincture	68th	56th
Amyl acetate	29th	57th
Benzyl acetate	33rd	60th
Allyl caproate	34th	74th
Peach synthetic concentrate	62nd	87th
Ethyl acetate	87th	104th

the same as adults. Yet when the children smelled the fruity esters, they rated them better than adults; for example, allyl caproate, which to most adults is an intolerably crude pineapple and quite offensive, the children quite liked (34th against 74th for the whole group). So too with amyl acetate with its pear drops smell; the children rated it 29th compared with the group's 57th. Not all of the concentrates are disliked by the children, but some of them are. These are, however, only minor exceptions to the general rule that children like fruity smells much better than adults do. Essences, and those used were very good essences indeed that usually contained a high proportion of natural fruit extract, were well-liked: raspberry, strawberry, lemon (one but not the other), banana and orange, were all rated very favourably indeed. Simple fruit essences are the flavours to titillate the youngsters' palates.

The less simple fruits, those that are nutty rather than fruity, also fare fairly well. Coconut and almond essences, especially the former, are liked much more by children than by adults, and vanilla is at least as acceptable to children as to their elders. Oils are disliked by children: sweet orange oil does badly (22nd against 10th for the group), although orange essence does very well (8th against 28th for the group). Similarly, lemongrass oil does badly (52nd against 42nd for the group), although citral, which is its main odoriferous constituent, does very well (16th against 30th for the group).

Children's dislike of oily smells. In our discussion of children's liking of fruity smells, we have just seen that in two examples an oiliness detracted from the likeability of the fruity smell, in sweet orange oil and lemongrass oil. But oils generally fare badly with children: they do not like the oily smell and this oiliness will overcome their liking for the underlying odours. Table 18 illustrates the dislike that children have for oiliness in an odour.

TABLE 18
Children's dislike for oily smells

Oil of	Average ranking of the oily smell by	
	Children	Whole group
Sweet orange	22nd	10th
Spearmint	6th	18th
Lavender, English	60th	19th
Lavender, French	75th	23rd
Ylang-ylang	55th	25th
Cinnamon leaf	24th	27th
Rose (attar)	60th	29th
Cinnamon bark	19th	32nd
Neroli bigarade	69th	38th
Lemongrass	52nd	42nd
Cananga	59th	48th
Geranium, Bourbon	88th	64th
Citronella	94th	70th
Kewda (India)	76th	75th
Patchouli, Singapore	109th	83rd
Cade	110th	106th
Rape	117th	112th
Castor	113th	120th
Herring	118th	121st

Spearmint does amazingly well; no wonder that chewing gum has been popular amongst the young. Unexpectedly, cinnamon which is ordinarily looked on as a sophisticated odour with mild aphrodisiac tendencies does a shade better with the children than it does with the group in general. Also unexpectedly, children find nineteen smells worse than castor oil, although the whole group finds only twelve. Spearmint is outstandingly preferred by the young, but it is exceptional and most oils, even those of otherwise pleasant materials are disliked. Children's dislike of lavender is unexpected but it is real enough, and most children even dislike the smell of the flower and dislike it in clothes drawers. Inspection of Table 18 is all that is necessary to satisfy oneself that oily smells are disliked by children; there is no room for hesitation about the results. There are a few exceptions, notably cinnamon bark and spearmint; perhaps their odours are less "oily" than those of most oils.

Young adults and older people. A comparison of the age groups 15–25 and over 25 years does not show nearly such well-defined differences as distinguish the under 15's from the other groups. Indeed, one of the most striking features that is seen in comparing the odour placings of the 15–25 group with the over 25's is their remarkable agreement about many of the smells.

Flower smells. Their liking for flower smells is a case in point; although these odours made little impression on the children they are highly esteemed, and nearly equally so, by the two higher age groups. The equality of liking of flower smells by the two groups may be seen from the examples in Table 19.

TABLE 19

Likeness of flower smell preferences by the middle and high age groups

Odorant	Average placing by	
	15–25 years group	Over 25 group
Red rose, Ena Harkness	4·0	4·0
Sweet pea	4·7	6·0
Rose, New Dawn	8·0	3·5
Rose, Emily Gray	8·5	9·3
Stock, double ten-week	9·2	9·3
Honeysuckle	3·2	4·0
Wild rose	25·5	8·0
Heliotrope	32·4	11·0
Mock orange	63·8	9·6

Amongst those flowers that are most generally liked there is excellent agreement between the two age groups, but the last three odorants in Table 19 show that there are some flower smells towards which there are considerable differences of degrees of liking by the two groups.

Outstanding differences. Such considerations are just as true amongst odours other than those of flowers; in the main, there is a large measure of agreement between the 15–25's and the over 25's but there are nevertheless, many instances where there is considerable disagreement; some of the most striking of these are shown in Table 20.

TABLE 20

Differences in degrees of liking of some odours by the middle and high age groups

Odorant	Average placing by	
	15–25 years group	Over 25 group
Fresh strawberries	10·2	1·6
Lemon flavouring essence (BTS)	37·3	21·7
Lemon flavouring essence (ABR)	44·3	23·0
Musk lactone, 10 per cent	52·3	15·5
Orange flavouring essence	49·0	22·0
Cinnamon bark oil	56·0	31·0
Musk ambrette	60·2	31·2
Geraniol ex Palma Rosa	59·0	31·8
Chives	31·0	76·8
Onion	32·0	77·3
Naphthalene	58·7	102·8
Tonkin musk	74·3	49·2
Cade oil	108·8	65·7

The three musks are all thought more highly of by the over 25's than by the 15–25 group; the real musk, the Tonkin, is rated poorer than the musk lactone and the musk ambrette which are both synthetic; the former, the musk lactone is chemically similar to natural musk in that it is a macrocyclic compound. Four fruity smells: two lemon and one orange flavours and the fresh strawberries are more highly appreciated by the over 25's than by the 15–25 group; conversely the chives and onions are much less favoured by them. There seems to be no doubt about the preferences expressed for these three small groups: the musks, the fruit flavours, and the alliaceous smells; they are all three well marked: the over 25's are more appreciative of the musks and the fruit flavours, the 15–25's are more appreciative of the alliaceous smells. The young adults also tolerate naphthalene surprisingly well.

Men and boys. Amongst the odours at the pleasant end of the scale there are big differences between the preferences of men and boys, but at the unpleasant end such differences are not apparent: piperidine is placed at 117·5 by the men and at 117·8 by the boys; ethyl mercaptan is placed 124·8 by the men and 123·0 by the boys. At the pleasant end of Table 3 the biggest differences are amongst the flower smells, but there is another observation that may be significant and that is that the best average placings by the men are lower than the boys' best placings. For example the men give an average placing of 1·3 to honeysuckle, one of 2·0 to strawberries, and one of 2·7 to red rose, but the best average placings given by the boys are strawberries 4·0, raspberry flavouring 5·5 and strawberry flavouring 6·3. Presumably this means that there is less unanimity amongst the boys about what is best; the men are more certain.

The biggest differences. In Chapter 3 the biggest differences in odour preferences between men and women were noted and were included in Table 15. Not very many odorants exhibited a great deal of difference; such as did had rather to be searched for. In coming, as we now do, to assemble a list of those odorants which affect differently the three different age groups, it is only too clear that there are a great many of the odorants which qualify for inclusion in the list. Those with the strongest claims have been selected to build up Table 21.

Children's tolerance for skatole. The odorants in Table 21 have been selected so that there is a ratio of at least 1:2 between two of the age groups and most of them are in the flowery or fruity classes. There are however one or two smells usually considered unpleasant that have found their way in. Of these, skatole with a faecal odour (compare the word skatological) is the most significant; the children tolerate it very much better than do their elders and they rank it (54th) better than ylang-ylang oil (55th) and camphor (56th). The tolerance, indeed the liking of children for naphthalene is also noteworthy, although perhaps of less significance. Civet which like skatole has a strong faecal note is tolerated better by the children with an average placing of 100·5 than by the other age groups who place it 119·8 and 123·7.

Validity of inferences. Only twelve people took part in the tests on which Tables 1 and 3 have been built: only three of them were

TABLE 21

Odorants to which the reactions of the different age groups were considerably different

Odorant	Placing of odorant by			Odour liked best by	Ratio of placings by		
	Under 15's	15– 25's	Over 25's		Under 15's	15– 25's	Over 25's
Red rose	17·0	4·0	4·0	15–25's and over 25's	4·3 : 1		: 1
Fresh strawberries	4·0	10·2	1·6	over 25's	2·5 :	6·4 :	1
Sweet pea	14·3	4·7	6·0	15–25's	3·0 :	1 :	1·3
Rose, New Dawn	17·3	8·0	3·5	over 25's	4·9 :	2·3 :	1
Stock, double ten-week	29·0	9·2	9·3	15–25's	3·2 :	1 :	1·0
Honeysuckle	45·5	3·2	4·0	15–25's	14·3 :	1 :	1·3
Wild rose	21·0	25·5	8·0	over 25's	2·6 :	3·2 :	1
Raspberry flavouring essence	5·5	24·7	27·2	under 15's	1 :	4·5 :	4·9
Meadowsweet	22·0	12·3	27·1	15–25's	1·8 :	1 :	2·2
Peppermint flavouring essence	7·8	28·8	37·8	under 15's	1 :	3·7 :	4·8
Strawberry flavouring essence	6·3	33·3	36·2	under 15's	1 :	5·3 :	5·7
Heliotrope	46·0	32·4	11·0	over 25's	4·2 :	2·9 :	1
Lemon flavouring essence (ABR)	9·7	44·3	23·0	under 15's	1 :	4·6 :	2·4
Banana flavouring essence	7·3	34·8	38·7	under 15's	1 :	4·8 :	5·3
Spearmint oil	9·5	28·5	44·7	under 15's	1 :	3·0 :	4·7
English lavender oil	57·3	19·7	21·0	15–25's	2·9 :	1 :	1·1
Mock orange	20·0	63·8	9·6	over 25's	2·1 :	6·6 :	1
French lavender oil	70·3	18·7	22·0	15–25's	3·8 :	1 :	1·2
Ylang-ylang oil	53·0	22·2	33·3	15–25's	2·4 :	1 :	1·5
Musk lactone 10 per cent	40·3	52·3	15·5	over 25's	2·6 :	3·4 :	1
Orange flavouring essence	10·0	49·0	22·0	under 15's	1 :	4·9 :	2·2
Rose attar	57·3	26·0	36·0	15–25's	2·2 :	1 :	1·4
Citral	20·8	52·2	34·7	under 15's	1 :	2·5 :	1·7
Cinnamon bark oil	25·0	56·0	31·0	under 15's	1 :	2·2 :	1·2
Bay leaf	66·3	23·2	40·2	15–25's	2·9 :	1 :	1·7
Vanillin	66·0	46·8	30·0	over 25's	2·2 :	1·6 :	1
Eugenol	20·8	63·5	53·8	under 15's	1 :	3·1 :	2·6
Terpineol	31·8	64·3	47·2	under 15's	1 :	2·0 :	1·5
Amyl butyrate	17·5	64·0	52·9	under 15's	1 :	3·7 :	3·0
Coconut flavouring essence	26·3	61·5	58·0	under 15's	1 :	2·3 :	2·2
Chives	43·8	31·0	76·8	15–25's	1·4 :	1 :	2·5
Onion	43·0	32·0	77·3	15–25's	1·3 :	1 :	2·4
Ethyl alcohol	80·0	39·2	55·4	15–25's	2·0 :	1 :	1·4
Allyl caproate	37·8	84·5	68·3	under 15's	1 :	2·2 :	1·8
Naphthalene	38·3	58·7	102·8	under 15's	1 :	1·5 :	2·7
Skatole	52·5	84·5	107·0	under 15's	1 :	1·6 :	2·0

children, i.e. under 15 years. Is it justifiable to draw such general conclusions as have been incorporated in Rules 19–23 (p. 79) from such a small number of subjects? Is it not possible, even probable, that another small group of children might think very differently about the odours? Are the general rules that have been deduced dependent on the particular likes and dislikes, on the idiosyncrasies, of a few people, and liable to vary from one group of subjects to another? Or are they soundly based, so that the inferences that have been drawn will be equally applicable to other groups of people?

The children constitute the smallest group, so it will be appropriate to take one of the general rules that relate to their behaviour, and examine its validity. Rule 20 states categorically that children do not appreciate sweet flower smells nearly so much as adults.

Is this statement dependable, or is it suspect because it was derived from the behaviour of a small group of twelve people of whom only three were children? Before a detailed analysis is attempted it is well to note that although only three children took part in the tests, the number of typical flower smells, i.e. sweet smells of fresh flowers, was nine. Two fresh flowers that are omitted from this group but that were members of the 130 or so odorants are mock· orange and privet flower; the reason they are omitted is that neither has a sweet typical flower scent; mock orange is described in Table 1 as "floral but bitter and astringent" and privet flower as "bitter, floral" and they are both quite atypical flower smells. If we confine our attention to the nine typical fresh flower smells and to the three children who made the tests, we have available the information shown in Table 22.

TABLE 22
Children's placings of sweet flower smells

	Average placing by					
			WG (14 yr.)		Whole group	Whole group
Fresh flower	MH (12 yr.)	ARL (10 yr.)	1st run	2nd run	(from Table 1)	excldg. children
Red rose, Ena Harkness	—	17	—	—	5·1	4·0
Sweet pea	8	18	20	11	7·6	5·3
Rose, New Dawn	22	16	19	12	8·7	5·5
Rose, Emily Gray	—	14	—	—	9·4	8·9
Stock, double ten-week	28	22	—	37	13·8	9·2
Honeysuckle	55	24	57	46	14·8	3·6
Wild rose	—	21	—	—	18·4	18·0
Meadowsweet	56	19	55	45	25·4	18·1
Heliotrope	54	—	—	38	28·7	24·4

If we knew nothing about the relative liking or disliking for sweet flower smells of children and adults we could say that there was an equal chance of any child's placing of any particular flower smell being better or worse than that of the adults. This neglects the chance that the two placings would be the same, but in a group of about 130 odorants the chance of exactly similar placings by the two groups of people is unlikely. It would not invalidate the argument if this coincidental possibility was neglected; it could make only a very slight difference to the inferences to be drawn and it would considerably facilitate the quantitative argument, so it is better neglected. This leaves the position that there is half a chance that child MH will place the sweet pea perfume better and half a chance that he will place it worse than the average of the group of adults who give an average placing of 5·3 to it; in fact MH places it at 8, i.e. worse. There is similarly half a chance that MH will place rose New Dawn better and half a chance that he will place it worse than the adult average of 5·5; in fact he places it at 22 i.e. much worse. Similarly he places the ten-week stock perfume at 28, whereas the adult group gives it an average placing of 9·2. The chance that he (MH) would place sweet pea *and* rose New Dawn *and* stock worse than the adult group (if it was chance alone that was the determinant) is 0·5×0·5×0·5 or 0·125, i.e. there are seven chances against him giving such placings to one chance that he will. In fact, MH also gives poorer placings to the three other sweet flower smells that are included in his test, namely honeysuckle (55th against an adult average of 3·6), meadowsweet (56th against 18·1) and heliotrope (54th against 24·4). The chance, if it was chance and not a systematic preference that was the determinant, that he would have placed all six odorants worse than the adult average is 1 in 64, or 1 in 2^6 or 63 to 1 against. Similarly the child ARL places each of the eight flowers that he smells worse than the adult average, and the chance, if it were only chance of him doing this would be only 1 in 2^8 or 255 to 1 against. The chance of both MH and ARL doing as they did, if it had been only chance, is 1 in 2^{14} or 16383 to 1 against. The child WG in his first run smells four of the flowers and places each one of them worse than the adult average, and in his second run does the same with six flowers; the two runs were made with a longish interval between them so that he could not have remembered in his second run what he had done in the first, and furthermore the nine sweet flowers were interspersed in more than 100 other odorants so that no effort to memorize could have been successful. The chance that all ten smells would have been placed worse than the adult average, as in fact they were, is 1 in 2^{10}. Therefore the chance, if chance had been the determinant, of the three children placing their sweet flower smells as they did was 1 in 2^{24} or more than 16 million to 1 against. Clearly chance was not the determinant. The real determinant was the fact that the children did not like the flower smells so much, or place them so favourably, as did the adults. It is noteworthy, too, that as a rule (Table 22) the placing assigned by a child to a sweet flower smell was not just marginally worse than the adult average, but very much worse e.g. 55, 24, 57 and 46 for honeysuckle against an adult average of 3·6. How, wonders the author, who has smelled honeysuckle this same afternoon whilst cutting a hedge, can children be so indifferent to its heavenly perfume? That question cannot be answered yet. But Rule 20 which asserts that children do not appreciate sweet flower smells nearly so much as do adults is true enough.

The next rule, 21, which has also been derived from the evidence in Table 1 states that children are much more appreciative of fruity smells, for example flavouring essences, than are adults. Can a justification for this be similarly provided and found to be similarly overwhelming?

If we confine our attention to fruit and fruit essences we can extract from Table 1 the relevant information shown in Table 23.

TABLE 23

Children's placings of fruity smells

| Fruity material | MH (12 yr.) | ARL (10 yr.) | Average placing by | | Whole group (from Table 1) | Whole group excldg. children |
| | | | WG (14 yr.) | | | |
			1st run	2nd run		
Strawberries	—	2	4	6	5·5	5·9
Raspberry flavouring essence (ABR)	12	1	6	3	20·8	25·9
Sweet orange oil	3	87	1	18	24·6	23·7
Lemon flavouring essence (BTS)	25	8	11	32	25·3	29·5
Strawberry flavouring essence 1512	13	4	3	5	27·6	34·8
Lemon flavouring essence (ABR)	17	3	9	—	28·9	32·8
Banana flavouring essence (ABR)	11	5	5	8	29·4	36·8
Orange flavouring essence (ABR)	10	—	—	—	37·4	41·3

From this table the unlikelihood of the preferences of the children relative to the adults for fruity smells being due to chance can be calculated and when this is done it transpires that the odds of such placings being arrived at by chance are more than a million to one against.

The method by which this figure is derived is as follows:

MH gives a better placing to each of the seven fruity odours that he smells than the adult average. The chance that he will do this by chance is only 1 in 2^7 i.e. 127 to 1 against.

ARL gives a better (much better) placing to six out of seven of the fruity smells than do the adults on average, but he gives a much less favourable placing to sweet orange oil, probably mainly because children dislike oily smells (Rule 23). The likelihood that by chance a child will place six of the seven more favourably than the adult average is 1 in $2^7/7$ or about 17 to 1 against.

WG in his first run places all seven of the fruity smells more favourably than the adult and the likelihood that he will do this, by chance, is 1 in 2^7 or 127 to 1 against. In his second run WG places two of the fruity smells less favourably than the adult average. He places fresh strawberries 6 against an adult average of 5·9, poorer if only marginally poorer, and he assigns a placing of 32, against an adult average of 29·5 to lemon flavouring essence (BTS). The chances that a child will place two out of six of the smells less favourably and the other four more favourably by chance are 1 in $2^6/15$ i.e. about 3 to 1 against.

The chances that the children would assign the placings that they do to the fruity smells (in relation to the adults' placings) if actuated only by chance are therefore 1 in $(2^7 \times 2^7/7 \times 2^7 \times 2^6/15)$ or 1 in $2^{27}/105$ or 1 in 1,278,264 i.e. odds of well over a million to 1 against.

Rule 20 relating to children's lack of appreciation of flower smells was shown to be supported by odds of 16 million to 1 in its favour. Rule 21 relating to the children's extra liking for fruity smells is shown to be supported by odds of about $1\frac{1}{4}$ million to 1 in its favour. Both are moral certainties. Both, too, are supported by considerable additional proximate evidence; it could easily be shown from Table 1 that there is abundant proof that children rate fruity smelling chemicals, esters such as allyl caproate, better than adults do.

Similar analyses and proofs could be derived for the other rules that have been arrived at in Part I of this book. It has to be remembered that as much information is gained from a dozen people testing 130 odorants as would be gained from 130 people testing twelve odorants.

How true Rule 21 relating to children's appreciation of fruity smells really is can be seen by looking at Fig. 19 which is based on the reactions of 550 people of ages from five years upwards to the smell of strawberry flavour. The information that was obtained from the responses of a few (12) people to many (130) smells is amply confirmed by the information gained from the responses of many (550) people to a few (10) smells. Whichever way one looks, by comparison of the two approaches described in Parts I and II of the book, or by quantitative analysis, the rules are found to be soundly based.

Rules

The general rules that we can derive from the contents of this chapter are:

Rule 19. Children are able to sort out their preferences amongst intermediate but fairly pleasant odours better and more uniformly and surely than men (cf. Rule 12).

Rule 20. Children do not appreciate sweet flower smells nearly so much as do adults.

Rule 21. Children are much more appreciative of fruity smells, for example flavouring essences, than are adults (cf. Rule 52).

Rule 22. Children are generally more appreciative of nutty smells than adults; much more so of coconut and definitely more so of almond, but vanilla they like about as well as adults.

Rule 23. Children dislike oily smells; they are more sensitive to them than are adults. Spearmint affords an important exception (cf. Rule 53).

Rule 24. Simple flower smells are greatly liked by the 15–25's and the over 25's, and the two groups rank them very similarly.

Rule 25. Sophisticated flower smells, for example, heliotrope and mock orange are rated much more highly by the over 25's than by the young adults.

Rule 26. Musky smells are thought more highly of by the over 25's than by the young adults. A synthetic macrocyclic musk, chemically not very different from natural muscone, is particularly well liked by the over 25's.

Rule 27. Fruity flavours are rated better by the over 25's than by the young adults, although not nearly so highly as they are by the children.

Rule 28. Chives and onions, alliaceous smells with culinary associations are much more appreciated by the 15–25's than by the over 25's.

Rule 29. Olfactory preferences vary much more between different age groups than they do between the two sexes. Age is a more powerful determinant than is sex of what odours are liked best (cf. Rule 50).

Rule 30. Some synthetic fruit flavours, e.g. pear drops, thought to be crude and unpleasant by adults, are considered at least passable by the children.

Rule 31. Alcohol is not rated highly by any of the age groups, but the 15–25's give it relatively the best placing and the children give it the worst.

Rule 32. Children exhibit a remarkable tolerance for substances with a faecal note in their odour; they do not like these substances but they are more or less indifferent to them whereas the adults actively dislike them (cf. Rule 57).

REFERENCE

13. C. P. Richter & K. H. Campbell, Sucrose taste thresholds of rats and humans, *Amer J. Physiol.*, 1940, **128**, 291–297.

CHAPTER 5

VARIATION OF ODOUR PREFERENCES WITH TEMPERAMENT

DOES temperament have much effect on olfactory preferences? Do the gay carefree extroverts have different preferences from the thoughtful and introspective introverts?

Large measure of agreement

When we come to analyse the results that have been assembled in Table 3 our first observation is that a large number of the odorants are scored not very differently by the two temperament groups of people; some illustrative examples are shown in Table 24.

TABLE 24

Many odorants are scored similarly by introverts and extroverts

Odorant	Average placing by	
	Introverts	Extroverts
Sweet pea	7·8	7·3
Honeysuckle	15·6	13·6
Peppermint flavouring	24·8	29·7
Cinnamon leaf oil	34·4	38·4
Eugenol	50·6	47·4
Amyl acetate	47·7	59·1
β-Ionone (P & S)	68·7	61·1
Methyl anthranilate	83·3	70·1
Paradichlorbenzene	89·3	91·3
Castor oil	101·2	107·9

These examples are typical; they are not picked out as being those showing the very best agreement: there are, in fact, examples which show closer agreement, but such may be partly adventitious, whereas the less exact measure of agreement that is illustrated in Table 24 is fairly general.

Extroverts' preferences similar to children's

When comparing the preferences of introverts and extroverts and noting the differences between them one is struck by the similarity that is often evident in the preferences of the extroverts to those of the children. Some examples in which there are considerable differences between the odour placings by introverts and extroverts have been assembled in Table 25, and alongside for comparison the placings of the same odours by the children are given.

TABLE 25

**The odour preferences of extroverts are often similar
to those of children**

Odorant	Average placing by		
	Introverts	Extroverts	Children
Fresh strawberries	3·3	9·0	4·0
Wild rose	5·8	31·0	21·0
Sweet orange oil	15·7	36·0	27·3
Strawberry flavouring	36·0	16·9	6·3
Heliotrope	17·9	54·0	46·0
Banana flavouring essence	36·9	19·7	7·3
Mock orange	12·4	52·2	20·0
Mint	26·0	41·0	42·3
French Lavender oil	28·0	39·0	70·3
Musk lactone (10 per cent)	41·2	28·1	40·3
Privet flower	28·8	45·9	30·7
Strawberry aldehyde	51·8	30·7	32·5
Vanillin	34·2	61·7	66·0
Neroli oil	34·8	56·8	63·5
Almond essence	56·0	32·6	28·7
Friar's balsam	62·8	30·9	42·3
Parsley	34·1	69·1	49·3
Coconut flavouring essence	63·5	36·6	26·3
Chives	39·0	67·3	43·8
Rose 2321 perfume concentrate	38·9	78·4	73·3
Camphor	47·7	77·0	53·3
Patchouli oil	86·3	51·7	91·0
Anisaldehyde, ex cresol (RAN)	93·1	49·5	81·8
Cigarette ash	69·3	91·8	51·0
Rape oil	86·7	107·9	98·3
Chlorophyll, oil-soluble	114·3	99·6	98·0

In these examples which have been selected primarily to show considerable differences between the two temperament groups, it is the introverts who greatly prefer the flower smells, and the mint and the parsley and the chives. It is the extroverts who prefer the strawberry and banana and coconut flavourings, the strawberry aldehyde, and the almond essence, and who tolerate better the rather unpleasant oil-soluble chlorophyll. There is a pattern running through these results that shows the extroverts' scoring as being more like the children's than is the introverts'. Extrovert likings are often childish likings. Often, but not always: the extroverts' liking for musk lactone is not shared by the children. Of the twenty-six odorants shown in Table 23 the extroverts' score is nearer to that of the under 15's in sixteen cases; of the ten odorants in which the introverts' score is nearer to the children's than is the extroverts', six occur in the last ten examples in Table 23. Amongst the pleasant odours the extroverts' preferences run similar to those of the children; amongst the less-liked odours it is the introverts' preferences that approach those of the children. If one dare draw any inference from this, it is that in their likings children are extrovert, in their dislikes they are introvert. Perhaps it is true; children accept thoughtlessly what is happy and pleasant, but they do give a good deal of thought to what is unhappy and unpleasant: they brood and worry with an intensity which as adults we are only too ready to forget.

Another observation that may be significant is that some of the synthetic esters which have coarse, fruity odours, not really closely similar to natural fruits, are more liked by the extroverts than by the introverts. Examples of such preferences are amyl butyrate and ethyl lactate, although it must be added that this tendency is reversed in amyl and butyl acetates.

The odours most liked by the two temperament groups. It is interesting to see the similarities and differences between the odours that the two temperament groups rank the best. These are shown in Table 26.

TABLE 26

The best liked odours: the two temperaments compared

Odorant ranked	Introverts	Extroverts
1st	Fresh strawberries	Red rose
2nd	Red rose	Sweet pea
3rd	Wild rose	Fresh strawberries
4th	Rose, New Dawn	Rose, Emily Gray
5th	Sweet pea	Rose, New Dawn
6th	Rose, Emily Gray	Stock
7th	Mock orange	Honeysuckle
8th	Stock	Raspberry flavouring

The beauty of the wild rose and the mock orange eludes the extroverts, but otherwise there is a large measure of correspondence. On the best liked odours there is a very good agreement indeed between the two temperament groups. And so, of course, there is about the most disliked odours, as a glance at the end of Table 3 will show.

The biggest differences

Which are those odorants which produce the biggest differences in response between the two temperaments? Those which show the greatest discrepancies in placings are assembled in Table 27.

TABLE 27

Those odorants appealing most differently to the two temperament groups

Odorant	Average placing by		Preferred by	Ratio of placings by introverts: extroverts
	Introverts	Extroverts		
Fresh strawberries	3·3	9·0	Introverts	1 : 2·7
Wild rose	5·8	31·0	Introverts	1 : 5·3
Sweet orange oil	15·7	36·0	Introverts	1 : 2·3
Strawberry flavouring	36·0	16·9	Extroverts	2·1 : 1
Heliotrope	17·9	54·0	Introverts	1 : 3·0
Mock orange	12·4	52·2	Introverts	1 : 4·2
Friar's Balsam	62·8	30·9	Extroverts	2·0 : 1
Rose 2321 perfume concentrate	38·9	78·4	Introverts	1 : 2·0
Alpine violet perfume concentrate	73·9	34·6	Extroverts	2·1 : 1

Whichever temperament the reader may possess it will doubtless seem clear enough that that temperament group shows a better sense of values.

Ease of discrimination

As we saw when we considered the histograms in Figs. 9 and 10, the extroverts were inclined to concentrate more of their average placings than the introverts within the fairly pleasant range of 30–70 on the hedonic scale. This seems to point to a lower degree of discrimination and agreement amongst themselves so far as concerns the odours in this range. The thoughtful introverts spread out their preferences more certainly and more regularly. If histograms are drawn with intervals of 5 instead of 10, so that there are twice as many columns over the range 0–132 (Figs. 14, 15) and compared with Figs. 9 and 10 (similar to the way in which this was done for age groups in Figs. 11, 12 and 13) the pictures, although showing more detail than Figs. 9 and 10 are unchanged in general outline. There is once again a higher concentration of placings by the

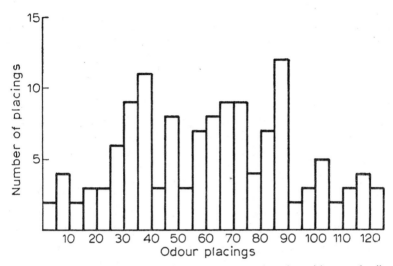

FIG. 14.—A histogram for the introverts similar to Fig. 9 but with more detail. There is less crowding in the range of placings 30–80 evident than in Fig. 15.

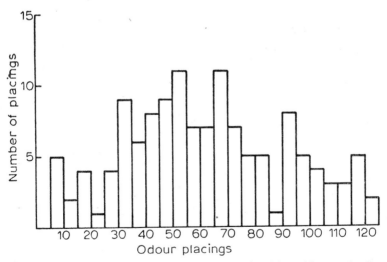

FIG. 15.—A histogram for the extroverts similar to Fig. 10 but with more detail. There is a little more crowding of preferences evident than in Fig. 14.

extroverts in the fairly pleasant range and no such high concentration anywhere in the scale by the introverts. The conclusion that the introverts exercise a greater degree of discrimination in their olfactory preferences is indicated.

Rules

Those general rules that can be derived from the subject matter of this chapter would appear to be as follows:

Rule 33. A large proportion of odorants are rated very equally by introverts and extroverts; temperament has little effect on the assessment of many of them. But the introverts spread out their placings more uniformly than do the extroverts.

Rule 34. Amongst the pleasant odours, the extroverts' preferences, when they do differ significantly from those of the introverts, are more like the children's preferences.

Rule 35. Amongst the unpleasant odours, in those cases where the two temperament groups show significant differences, it is the introverts whose preferences are the more similar to the children's.

Rule 36. A hint of the unusual, an odour component not frequently encountered, is less acceptable to extroverts than it is to introverts. Examples are afforded by wild rose (slightly astringent note), heliotrope and mock orange.

CHAPTER 6

ODOURS WITH MARKEDLY DIVERSE EFFECTS

THE WORK already outlined had shown that there was very good agreement amongst all the observers about what were very bad smells; almost complete unanimity had prevailed and bad smells were regarded with unerring and unvarying dislike. About the very pleasant smells there was often excellent agreement, but there was this salient difference, that the children reacted differently from the adults; the most inspiring of flower smells left them more or less unmoved and they found their own peculiar delights in the fruity smells, which they liked much more than did the adults. With the exception of the children the observers agreed very well amongst themselves about what smells they really liked, those that they placed above the hundred odd others that they were confronted with. For very bad smells, almost perfect agreement; for very good smells, very good agreement but not quite so perfect as for the bad smells, and with the children living in a different world from their elders as far as preferences of pleasant odours were concerned.

In the middle ranges, where the smells were neither liked nor disliked with any great intensity, there was a good deal of overlap, and a tendency to crowd a large number of odorants close together so far as concerned the liking or disliking of these smells. But even here there was usually a considerable measure of agreement between the different groups of observers. For example anisaldehyde (ex cresol) has a hawthorn smell, warm but not fine and a little coarse perhaps because of its origin, and one might have thought it unlikely to be uniformly regarded because some people profess to find the smell of "may" unpleasant, although most of us find it tolerable and even in a country lane on an early summer evening, enchanting. And yet the seven different groups rank it: 85th (male), 91st (female), 91st (children), 92nd (15–25 years), 85th (over 25), 105th (introverts), and 65th (extroverts): there are differences and they are not to be minimized, but there is a surprisingly large measure of agreement. And most of the odorants that were used did in fact give results which added up to a somewhat similar sum of partial agreements.

Some significant differences

But there were, nevertheless, many of the odorants which did show remarkable differences in the degree of liking or disliking evoked from the different groups. For example, cinnamon bark oil was liked much more by males (ranked 28th if the children are excluded, 19th if they are included) than by females (ranked 49th); Friar's balsam was ranked 64th by introverts but as pleasant as 18th by extroverts, whereas parsley was ranked 25th by introverts but as poor as 82nd by extroverts. It seemed to be of special interest to see which of the 132 odorants we had used showed the most diverse reactions from the several groups of observers; this information was furthermore required in order that the next stage of the research, the presentation of a small number of odorants to a large number of people would give the most informative results.

TABLE 28
Those odorants showing the very greatest differences

Odorant	Groups that place it very differently	Preferred by	Ratio of placings
Sex			
Mock orange	Males (excluding under 15's) and Females	Males	1 : 4·1
Honeysuckle	Males (excluding under 15's) and Females	Males	1 : 3·0
Wild Rose	Males (excluding under 15's) and Females	Males	1 : 3·0
Musk ambrette	Males (excluding under 15's) and Females	Males	1 : 3·0
Age			
Honeysuckle	Under 15's and 15–25's	15–25's	14·3 : 1
Mock orange	15–25's and over 25's	over 25's	6·6 : 1
Fresh strawberries	15–25's and over 25's	over 25's	6·4 : 1
Strawberry flavouring essence	Under 15's and over 25's	under 15's	1 : 5·7
Temperament			
Wild rose	Introverts and extroverts	Introverts	1 : 5·3
Mock orange	Introverts and extroverts	Introverts	1 : 4·2
Heliotrope	Introverts and extroverts	Introverts	1 : 3·0
Fresh strawberries	Introverts and extroverts	Introverts	1 : 2·7

Those odorants exhibiting the greatest differences of liking

Those odorants that showed the biggest differences in placings by the several groups can be picked out easily from Tables. 15 (sex), 21 (age) and 27 (temperament). The four most notable from each of these Tables are collected together in Table 28.

It is remarkable that the twelve odorants in the first column embrace only seven different odorants. Mock orange occurs in all three groups, and honeysuckle, wild rose, and fresh strawberries each occur in two of the groups. It is also remarkable that in these selections of greatest differences it is always the males who show the preference and so it is with the introverts. If there is a very big difference in liking of an odour between the two sexes it is probable that it will be the males who like it the better. If there is a very big difference in liking of an odour between the two temperaments it is probable that it will be the introverts who like it the better.

Effect of similarity of odour

The likeness of odours is easy enough to assess in the sense that all fruity smells have something in common, but in a finer discrimination the odours of raspberry and strawberry are quite different so that there could be no possibility of confusing one with the other.

A method of estimating the degree of likeness of any two odours was worked out some time ago by the author[14]. It depended on a correlation between odour likeness and olfactory adaptation; whereas odour similarity is impossible to measure directly, the olfactory adaptation which is caused by an odorant is easy to measure. If a sniff is taken at one odorant, then the sensitivity of the nose is much reduced for the next sniff of the same odorant, i.e. adaptation has ensued. But if a sniff is taken of the first odorant, and then a sniff of a second dissimilar odorant, the sensitivity of the nose will not have been so greatly reduced for the second and dissimilar odorant. The reduction of sensitivity can be assessed by measuring the increase in the threshold concentration for that odorant. By way of example, the olfactory threshold concentration of acetone in water (the lowest concentration in which the smell of acetone can be recognized) is 0·03 per cent, but if one previous sniff (a normal but positive inspiration of breath) is taken of pure acetone, then with the next breath nothing less than 5·0 per cent acetone can be recognized; the olfactory adaptation has increased the threshold concentration from 0·03 to 5·0 per cent, i.e. some 170 times. If now, similar experiments are made with n-butyl alcohol it can be smelled in 0·005 per cent concentration but after one prior inspiration of pure butyl alcohol nothing less than 1·0 per cent butyl alcohol can be recognized, i.e. self-adaptation has raised the threshold about 200 times. If now cross-adaptation is used, i.e. after smelling pure acetone, the next inspiration is of butyl alcohol, it (butyl alcohol) can be recognized in a concentration as low as 0·06 per cent so that its threshold concentration has been raised only twelve times. Conversely, if butyl alcohol is smelled, a subsequent inspiration of acetone is detectable in 0·2 per cent so that its (acetone's) threshold has been raised only seven times. As a continuation of these experiments it was found that very similar odorants raise the threshold concentration of each other very considerably; very dissimilar odorants raise them only slightly. The two most similar odorants found were amyl and butyl acetates which had a coefficient of likeness (unity represents complete

TABLE 29

Comparison of closeness of preference rankings with coefficients of likeness found by self- and cross-adaptation

Odorant pair	Coefficient of likeness (from previous work)[14]	Placings by whole group	Rankings assigned by whole group	Differences in ranking
Amyl acetate	0·89	52·7	57th	4
Butyl acetate		51·5	53rd	
α-Ionone (ABR)	0·45	60·6	67th	2
β-Ionone (ABR)		62·3	69th	
α-Ionone (P & S)	Not measured but probably close to 0·45	59·0	65th	7
β-Ionone (P & S)		65·4	72nd	
Nitrobenzene	0·40	72·3	85th	12
Benzaldehyde		80·3	97th	
Cellosolve	0·29	92·4	109th	5
Benzylamine		99·2	114th	
Methanol	0·20	87·6	105th	4
Cellosolve		92·4	109th	
Acetone	0·12	74·3	88th	17
Methanol		87·6	105th	
Diacetone alcohol	0·12	83·5	103rd	6
Cellosolve		92·4	109th	
Methanol	0·09	87·6	105th	2
Diacetone alcohol		83·5	103rd	
Acetone	0·08	74·3	88th	21
Cellosolve		92·4	109th	
Acetone	0·04	74·3	88th	15
Diacetone alcohol		83·5	103rd	

likeness) of 0·89, whilst acetone and butyl alcohol which have quite dissimilar smells were found to have a coefficient of likeness as low as 0·05. The components of some of the odour pairs that were used in this earlier investigation had been included in the 132 odorants used for determining preferences. Were the placings by the whole group of those pairs that had been found previously to have fairly high coefficients of likeness close together? The answer is to be seen in Table 29.

There are some anomalies to be seen, but there is no doubt that the figure in the last column, which represents the difference in pleasantness ranking, between the two of a pair, increases as the table is descended. It has to be remembered that two odorants might be quite dissimilar and yet equally liked. On the other hand, no pair of odorants that has been found to have a high coefficient of likeness is likely to have very different pleasantness rankings. In Table 29 there are three odorants; methanol, Cellosolve, and diacetone alcohol which have very indifferent odours, hardly pleasant or unpleasant, and although they are dissimilar their lack of individuality has brought them closer together in the ranking list than one could have foretold from a knowledge of their coefficients of likeness.

Neutrality on the hedonic scale

Those odorants high up in Table 3, the roses and the strawberries, are undoubtedly very pleasant without a trace of unpleasantness; those near to the bottom, the castor oil, the herring oil and the civet are decidedly unpleasant without much evidence of having any trace of pleasantness. Where does pleasantness change to unpleasantness? Could one say that acetone is neither pleasant nor unpleasant, that it is ranked 88th (two-thirds of the way down the hedonic scale), that those odours ranked higher are pleasant, that those ranked lower are unpleasant; that in fact two-thirds of the hedonic scale comprises pleasantness and only one-third unpleasantness? There is, in reality, such a wide range of indifference (neither marked pleasantness nor unpleasantness) that any such sharp division would seem to be impossible. Rather is it easier to think of all these indifferent odorants as containing elements of both pleasantness and unpleasantness, so that there is considerable overlap, and so that the balance between the two is finely held over a wide range. There are many pleasant odorants that have a trace of unpleasantness; some very fine roses have a trace of mawkishness in their beautiful perfumes; pineapple with its lovely smell has a just detectable hint of unpleasantness and on the other hand civet, with its foul fæcal smell is used in perfumes; and even butyric acid in high dilution has a pleasant sourness of odour. Pleasantness and unpleasantness of odour are separate attributes, not one the negation of the other, but separate and additive so that the affective reaction that they induce depends on the balance of the two attributes. Only exceptionally is one of the two almost absent; most odorants arouse mixed feelings but their pleasantness and unpleasantness are experienced separately as interest shifts. (cf. Rule 75). It may be that if most groups of observers agree fairly well with each other about the ranking of an odour, but that one group disagrees with all the others, the underlying reason is that it finds some emotional response in that odour.

The chosen ten

The first stage of the work which the foregoing chapters have described was designed to examine the olfactory preferences of a few people towards a large number of odorants. One of the purposes of this investigation had been to find some odorants to which different kinds of people had different reactions of liking or disliking. This has been done and those odorants which evoke the biggest differences in liking are shown in Tables 15, 21 and 27, and those that showed the biggest differences of all are assembled in Table 28.

The next stage in the investigation was to select a small number of odorants which could be expected to show considerable differences in liking with different kinds of people, and then to offer them to a large number of people, so that a more exact estimate could be made of the differences among the people in their olfactory preferences. It was considered that ten would be a suitable number of odorants, small enough to be dealt with quickly and easily by observer and subject, not big enough to create confusion, and yet big enough to include a wide range of odour qualities. In considering the selection of the ten it would of course have been very satisfying to have been able to take as a start the seven odorants in Table 28, the seven that included the four that showed the biggest difference between the sexes, the similar four for the age groups and four for the two temperaments. But this was not practicable for several reasons. The first is that the tests were expected to continue over several months (actually they continued over several years) and it was necessary to use odorants that would be available at any season and this consideration cut out the strawberries and the flowers which accounted for nearly all of the odorants in Table 28. Secondly, it was clearly desirable to cover a fairly wide range of qualities of odour; it would have reduced the usefulness of the work to have included, for example, several of one type such as flower smells; what was required was a spread. A third condition which it was thought necessary to observe was that the ten chosen smells should not include anything toxic, nauseating, disgusting or even very unpleasant. The few people who had arranged the 132 odorants had known what to expect and had been prepared for some unpleasant olfactory experiences. One could not, however, contemplate the inclusion of a mercaptan, or civet, or pyridine or anything similarly objectionable or toxic in a set of samples that were to be used on large numbers of lay subjects, including very young schoolchildren. Still another consideration was that the odours should be easily noticeable and salient so that observers would have an immediate and bright perception of pleasure or displeasure. Stability of the odorant material was also desirable. Compromise was necessary and after careful consideration, the ten odorants shown in Table 30 were chosen. The placings that the various groups had assigned to them are also shown to illustrate the degrees of difference of liking already manifest.

TABLE 30

The chosen ten

Odorant	Average placing						
	SEX		AGE			TEMPERAMENT	
	Males (15 and over)	Females	Under 15 years	15–25 years	Over 25 years	Introvert	Extrovert
Strawberry flavouring	41·8	31·3	6·3	33·3	36·2	36·0	16·9
Spearmint oil	49·0	30·4	9·5	28·5	44·7	33·4	25·1
Lavender oil (French)	19·5	20·8	70·3	18·7	22·0	28·0	39·0
Musk lactone (100 per cent)	28·5	36·6	40·3	52·3	15·5	41·2	28·1
Vanillin	45·7	37·4	66·0	46·8	30·0	34·2	61·7
Neroli oil	39·5	34·6	63·5	34·0	39·2	34·8	56·8
Almond flavouring essence	50·8	48·6	28·7	47·3	51·3	56·0	32·6
Naphthalene	103·0	69·6	38·3	58·7	102·8	71·0	69·0
Rape oil	83·3	101·1	98·3	101·0	89·3	86·7	107·9
Chlorophyll, oil-soluble	114·5	109·5	98·0	118·7	103·7	114·3	99·6

One difference that must be mentioned is that in the placings of the 132 odorants, a 10 per cent solution of musk lactone had been used. For the ten, 100 per cent musk lactone was used instead so that there would be no change of odour due to loss of solvent during use over lengthy periods; the placings given in Table 30 are for 10 per cent musk lactone, but it was 100 per cent that was used in the "ten"; actually there is very little difference in odour between the 10 per cent solution and the pure.

All of the ten are harmless; none is nauseous or too unpleasant and all showed considerable differences in the placings that had been assigned by the different groups. Looking back on the choice, the only one about which regret is felt is that of the chlorophyll; the differences in response to it are not very great between the groups and nearly everybody disliked it. In one sense it served a useful purpose in showing whether an odorant that had been uniformly disliked by a small group of people would be similarly uniformly disliked by a much larger group. However, those were the ten that were chosen and were used for the large scale tests to be described in the ensuing chapters.

Rules

Two general rules can be derived from the contents of this chapter. They are:

Rule 37. If there is a very big difference between the two sexes in their ranking of an odour, it is probable that it will be the males who like it the better.

Rule 38. If there is a very big difference between the two temperaments in their ranking of an odour, it is probable that it will be the introverts who like it the better.

REFERENCE

14. R. W. Moncrieff, Olfactory adaptation and odour likeness, *J. Physiol.*, 1956, **133**, 301–316.

PART II

Development of the Trends into General Findings

**A study of the preferences of many people towards ten
dissimilar odours**

CHAPTER 7

ARRANGEMENT OF TEN ODOURS BY MANY PEOPLE ACCORDING TO THEIR PREFERENCES

IN THIS second stage of the investigation into the dependence of olfactory preferences on sex, age and temperament, ten odorant materials were offered to a large number of people who were asked to arrange them in order of preference; a note was taken of their arrangements and when some 500 people had made the test their results were analysed.

The ten odorant materials (about 20 grams of each) were placed in 6 oz. glass bottles with wide necks and ground glass stoppers. The bottles were numbered 1–10 and the numbers were assigned as shown below.

1. Strawberry flavouring essence (ABR No. 1512); an excellent essence that contained a very high proportion of natural material.
2. Spearmint oil (RAN), an excellent oil with a fine characteristic note.
3. French lavender oil (WHH Exquisia); a fine oil with a high ester content which makes its odour a little more fruity than that of English lavender.
4. Musk lactone (100 per cent), a synthetic macrocyclic musk with a powerful sweet smell, probably closely related in structure to muscone, the essential odorant of natural musk, the sex attractant of the musk-deer.
5. Vanillin (GIV), a synthetic made from eugenol but identical chemically with the essential odorant of the vanilla pod.
6. Neroli oil (WHH). The natural oil, now so highly priced that it is only little used in perfumery, was used for the tests; it had a high bright note, almost a "dazzling" smell.
7. Almond flavouring essence (ABR No. 1327); a very fine flavour.
8. Naphthalene (G & T), the pure chemical, with its familiar smell reminiscent of moth-balls and fire-lighters.
9. Rape oil (BTS) with a nutty and oily odour.

10. Oil-soluble chlorophyll (SCB quality FCAS); a strong and unpleasant odour, although not nauseating or irritant.

The bottles, labelled with these numbers, were placed on a bench or table and grouped together in random order. The subject was asked if he or she would arrange them in order of liking, the one most liked on the extreme left, the one liked least or disliked most on the extreme right. He was shown how to sniff them: a bottle was picked up, the stopper removed and the subject smelled for a couple of seconds or so at the contents, and he was told that all that was required was whether he liked the smell or not. Each bottle was sniffed and the subject was advised to place those bottles that he liked in one group, those that he disliked in another; usually this resulted in a 5–5 or a 6–4 or 4–6 division. Then he was advised to smell again those in his "liked" group and put the one he liked most of all on the extreme left, the one he liked second next to it and so on, and then to treat the disliked similarly, putting the bottle most disliked on the extreme right. This resulted in the ten bottles arranged in a line according to the subject's preferences and at this stage he was asked to run through the bottles quickly, to make sure that he had arranged them in the proper order; he would smell the most liked first and then see that there was a progressive decrease in liking as he went down the line; often this resulted in reversing the positions of two of the bottles, usually 2nd and 3rd, or 3rd and 4th. At this stage a note was made of the subject's arrangement, e.g. 4, 3, 6, 1, 2, 5, 9, 7, 8, 10, which would indicate that he liked No. 4 (musk lactone) best, No. 3 (lavender) next best and so on until No. 10 (chlorophyll) which he liked least or disliked most. When we started this work the bottles were re-grouped at this stage again in random order and the subject was asked if he would do it again; usually a little conversation had ensued after his first arrangement, the request to do a repeat was unexpected, and the subject had forgotten what his first arrangement had been. Sometimes, if it was known that the subject would be available, the request for the second arrangement was not made until the following day, but whenever it was done the second arrangement nearly always corresponded fairly well with the first. The quality of this agreement is discussed in Chapter 8. At one stage we wondered if there might be a predisposition on the part of the subjects to arrange the bottles in numerical order: 1, 2, 3, 4 and so on; accordingly the bottles were subsequently labelled on their bottoms instead of on their sides, so that the labels were not ordinarily seen by the subject, but this made no difference. Probably most of the subjects gave no thought to the numbering and those who did suspected an intention to mislead or confuse them. It apparently made no difference at all to the results whether the sample numbers were visible or not.

At first, tests were made on people who happened to come into the laboratory: visitors, representatives, carriers and so on, as well as on friends and relatives of the laboratory personnel. Almost without exception, the subjects were interested and willing to make the test, and almost without exception they declared that they were not very good at smelling. When they got down to the task, they did it easily and carefully. The time for an arrangement was usually about ten minutes; professional people were much slower and more careful and took much longer than the average, but judging by a comparison of their two arrangements they were no more reliable than anybody else. The occasional self-confident subject who said at the beginning "Ah, yes, I've got an excellent nose" did just about as well as the average.

Whilst the tests were being made it was emphasized that all that mattered was pleasantness or unpleasantness; did the subject like or dislike the first sniff? It was the immediate reaction that was wanted. Attempts on the part of the subjects to identify the odorants by the smell were discouraged, and no indication of the identity of the odorants was ever given until the test arrangements had been completed. Occasionally a subject attempted to associate an odour with some past experience and this too was discouraged. Very occasionally a subject said he could not smell one of the odorants (it was usually No. 5, vanillin) and when this happened he was advised to place it between his "liked" and "disliked" groups. The first 120–130 people who were tested were all given two runs, but as it was then contemplated carrying out tests in other people's time, e.g. at schools, and as it was desirable to do this with the least inconvenience to them, and least possible disturbance of their routine, it was decided to make only one instead of two test runs on each individual. We had no misgivings about this change of procedure because the tests on the first 120–130 subjects had always shown such good agreement between their two runs. This subject is discussed in more detail in Chapter 8.

In order to obtain enough subjects, it soon became necessary to take the samples out for people to test, for example in two schools, a training college, a Women's Institute, an old people's home, an hotel bar (not too many here; only fifteen subjects) and in the homes of the laboratory personnel who enlisted the help of their neighbours. About 90 per cent of all the tests were made by four testers who became practised in the art, dealt competently with the task and took care that the subjects gave full attention to their arrangements. The other 10 per cent of the tests were carried out by three other testers, who obviously had had less practice, but who were first given some coaching in the laboratory before being commissioned with outside testing. This coaching included the handling of difficult subjects, by preferring (for their practice) such comments as "I can't smell this one", "Is this one camphor?", "I love this one, what is it?", "How terrible", "I don't know which I like the best of these". Then, if they subsequently encountered such comments in their field work, they could deal with them adequately. But the difficulties were exceptional; nearly everybody made their arrangements carefully and gracefully. Care was also taken to ensure that these occasional testers knew what was meant by "introvert" and "extrovert" and could classify correctly. Apart from three of the children (two of African descent, one of Asiatic) all the subjects were Western European and, as all the tests were carried out in England, nearly all were British. In every case a note was taken of the subject's name, sex, age and temperament and all this information, except for the names (replaced by numbers) of the subjects is given in Tables 31–50. As in the first part (Chapters 1–6) of the investigation, the results for the two sexes and the two temperaments were separated; but this time, because of the much greater number of people tested, the number of age groups was increased. Instead of classifying the results in three groups of under 15, 15–25 years and over 25, as had been done in the first part of the investigation, five age groups were considered; these were: under 8, 8–14 years, 15–19 years, 20–40 years, and over 40 years. This enabled more information to be extracted, especially concerning children and young people. Primary records are given in full in Tables 31–50, not only to provide a justification for the inferences drawn from them in the succeeding four chapters, but also as it is likely that there is considerably more information in the Tables than the author has extracted from them. Given the primary results, other workers who have interest in the subject may well be able to glean still more information from them. With two sexes, two temperaments, and five age groups, there are twenty different classes of subjects and their arrangements are shown in Tables 31–50. In Tables 31–50 only the first run is given in those cases where a subject was given two runs, and in the subsequent treatment of the primary results, only the figures given in Tables 31–50 were used, so that the second run figures were not included. However, in Table 51 (Chapter 8), there are shown separately the two runs for all the subjects who made them, so that an adequate estimate can be made of the reproducibility. But in Tables 31–50 only the first run is given; most of the subjects made only one run.

TABLE 31

Preferences shown by 22 introvert males under 8 years

Subject no.	Age (years)	Primary arrangement of bottles										Placings assigned to odorants nos.									
												1	2	3	4	5	6	7	8	9	10
1	5	1	5	9	8	6	3	10	4	2	7	4	9	6	8	2	5	10	4	3	7
2	5	5	9	3	1	6	10	4	7	8	2	1	10	3	7	1	5	8	9	2	6
3	5	1	5	8	9	4	2	10	3	6	7	1	6	8	5	2	9	10	3	4	7
4	5	1	4	8	5	3	6	10	3	7	2	1	10	5	2	4	6	9	3	7	8
5	5	1	2	7	3	5	8	9	10	5	6	2	2	4	8	5	10	3	6	7	9
6	5	3	1	8	2	6	7	4	9	6	10	1	4	1	7	9	5	6	3	8	10
7	6	1	5	8	2	2	8	3	9	6	10	1	5	7	3	2	9	4	6	8	10
8	6	1	9	4	7	7	8	3	5	6	4	1	3	7	10	8	9	5	6	2	4
9	6	1	5	2	10	8	9	3	4	6	10	1	3	7	8	2	9	4	5	6	10
10	6	1	10	2	7	8	4	6	9	7	8	1	7	5	6	4	7	9	10	8	2
11	7	1	5	4	5	10	8	2	7	3	6	4	5	9	3	2	10	8	6	4	5
12	7	1	5	9	9	2	8	3	10	7	10	2	3	7	4	1	10	9	6	3	8
13	7	5	4	2	4	3	9	6	7	8	10	1	4	5	2	1	7	8	9	6	10
14	7	5	1	4	1	9	7	6	8	3	10	1	2	9	3	6	7	6	8	5	10
15	7	1	2	4	2	7	5	6	3	8	10	1	6	8	5	2	7	5	9	4	10
16	7	1	5	8	9	4	2	6	9	3	10	1	9	9	4	2	7	4	4	8	10
17	7	1	3	5	7	8	9	6	7	3	10	1	8	2	4	3	7	8	3	6	10
18	7	1	6	8	4	8	9	3	2	2	10	1	5	7	4	3	2	9	5	6	6
19	7	1	5	8	10	2	10	7	6	7	3	1	3	10	7	2	8	7	5	9	8
20	7	1	5	9	8	2	6	4	10	9	3	1	5	10	6	2	6	9	3	4	10
21	7	1	5	9	2	4	4	8	7	6	10	1	3	5	6	2	9	8	7	4	10
22	7	1	3	5	9	8	4	6	2	7	10	1	8	2	6	4	7	9	5	3	10
Average		1	5	9	2	8	3	7	6		10	1·36	5·45	6·18	5·23	3·14	7·32	7·18	5·64	5·32	8·18

TABLE 32

Preferences shown by 27 extrovert males under 8 years

Subject no.	Age (years)	Primary arrangement of bottles										Placings assigned to odorants nos.									
												1	2	3	4	5	6	7	8	9	10
23	4	5	3	4	2	1	6	8	7	9	10	5	4	2	3	1	6	8	7	9	10
24	5	1	2	7	3	8	4	5	6	9	10	1	2	4	6	7	8	3	5	9	10
25	5	1	5	8	7	2	10	6	4	9	3	1	5	10	8	2	7	4	3	9	6
26	5	1	9	2	6	3	8	5	7	4	10	1	3	5	9	7	4	8	6	2	10
27	5	5	4	2	1	3	8	7	6	9	10	4	3	5	2	1	8	7	6	9	10
28	5	3	1	7	2	4	8	5	9	6	10	2	4	1	5	7	9	3	6	8	10
29	5	1	5	9	2	8	4	3	7	6	10	1	4	7	6	2	9	8	5	3	10
30	6	1	8	4	5	10	9	3	2	6	7	1	8	7	3	4	9	10	2	6	5
31	6	3	5	9	2	4	1	7	8	6	10	6	4	1	5	2	8	7	9	3	10
32	6	7	1	8	9	6	5	3	4	2	10	4	9	7	8	6	5	1	3	2	10
33	6	1	7	2	9	8	5	3	4	6	10	1	3	8	7	6	9	2	5	4	10
34	6	1	10	9	5	2	4	7	8	6	3	1	5	10	6	4	9	7	8	3	2
35	6	1	9	5	8	10	7	6	4	2	3	1	9	10	8	3	7	6	4	2	5

TABLE 32—continued

Preferences shown by 27 extrovert males under 8 years

Subject no.	Age (years)	Primary arrangement of bottles										Placings assigned to odorants nos.									
		1	2	3	4	5	6	7	8	9	10	1	2	3	4	5	6	7	8	9	10
36	6	1	2	7	3	9	5	4	8	6	10	1	2	4	7	6	9	3	8	5	10
37	6	1	3	5	8	10	9	4	7	2	6	1	9	2	7	3	10	8	4	6	5
38	7	1	9	5	6	4	7	8	2	10	3	1	8	10	5	3	4	6	7	2	9
39	7	1	5	7	2	4	8	9	3	6	10	1	4	8	5	2	9	3	6	7	10
40	7	1	5	4	9	7	8	2	6	3	10	1	7	9	3	2	8	5	6	4	10
41	7	5	1	3	2	6	8	4	7	10	9	2	4	3	7	1	5	8	6	10	9
42	7	5	1	8	4	2	6	7	9	3	10	2	5	9	4	1	6	7	3	8	10
43	7	5	1	4	8	9	7	3	6	10	2	2	10	7	3	1	8	6	8	5	9
44	7	1	7	3	5	2	9	6	8	4	10	1	5	3	9	4	7	2	8	6	10
45	7	1	5	6	4	8	7	2	3	9	10	1	7	8	4	2	3	6	5	9	10
46	7	1	3	4	2	9	6	7	4	8	10	1	4	2	8	3	6	7	9	5	10
47	7	1	3	2	2	5	8	6	7	9	10	1	4	2	3	5	7	8	6	9	10
48	7	1	2	8	5	3	4	6	7	9	10	1	2	5	6	3	7	8	4	9	10
49	7	1	2	7	6	3	4	8	9	10	5	1	2	5	6	10	4	3	7	8	9
Average		1	5	2	8	4	3	7	9	6	10	1·70	5·04	5·70	5·66	3·63	7·07	5·70	5·63	6·00	8·85

TABLE 33

Preferences shown by 38 introvert females under 8 years

Subject no.	Age (years)	Primary arrangement of bottles										Placings assigned to odorants nos.									
												1	2	3	4	5	6	7	8	9	10
50	5	5	2	1	8	9	4	10	7	6	3	3	2	10	6	1	9	8	4	5	7
51	5	1	5	8	9	4	3	6	2	7	10	1	8	6	5	2	7	9	3	4	10
52	5	1	5	8	7	3	6	4	9	2	10	1	9	5	7	2	6	4	3	8	10
53	5	1	10	3	8	4	2	6	5	7	9	1	6	3	5	8	7	9	4	10	9
54	5	1	3	8	9	4	2	—	10	5	6	1	6	2	5	9	10	—	3	4	2
55	5	1	2	9	7	4	8	3	5	6	10	6	2	7	5	8	9	4	6	3	8
56	5	5	8	10	9	7	1	3	2	4	6	5	8	7	9	1	10	5	2	4	10
57	5	8	2	5	3	1	7	9	6	4	10	1	2	4	9	3	8	6	1	7	3
58	6	1	2	2	5	8	7	4	6	3	10	6	3	9	7	4	8	6	5	2	10
59	6	3	9	9	4	8	7	10	1	7	6	1	2	1	4	8	10	9	5	3	7
60	6	1	2	7	3	8	2	4	2	6	10	1	6	4	7	2	9	3	5	8	10
61	6	1	5	2	7	2	4	3	4	6	6	2	5	7	6	2	9	4	8	3	8
62	6	4	1	3	5	3	8	7	8	9	6	2	3	5	1	4	10	7	6	9	10
63	6	2	1	2	7	9	8	5	10	4	10	1	1	3	9	7	8	4	6	5	10
64	6	1	3	4	8	8	9	6	6	8	10	2	3	2	9	4	7	8	5	6	10
65	6	7	2	10	9	3	9	7	7	6	9	1	8	5	3	7	4	1	9	6	3
66	6	1	8	3	8	2	7	2	4	3	6	1	5	8	7	4	9	6	2	6	5
67	6	1	9	2	5	4	6	4	7	10	5	1	4	9	8	3	10	7	6	10	9
68	6	1	8	2	2	7	3	9	5	10	6	1	4	3	7	6	10	5	2	2	9
69	6	1	7	8	9	3	2	6	2	5	7	1	6	5	7	10	8	2	4	8	7
70	6	1	3	9	3	2	4	7	4	6	6	1	5	2	6	9	10	8	3	3	9
71	6	1	8	3	3	9	4	6	2	10	10	1	7	4	6	3	8	10	2	4	7
72	7	1	7	9	9	5	2	4	10	8	6	1	6	3	8	5	10	2	9	4	7

TABLE 33—*continued*

Preferences shown by 38 introvert females under 8 years

Subject no.	Age (years)	Primary arrangement of bottles										Placings assigned to odorants nos.									
												1	2	3	4	5	6	7	8	9	10
73	7	1	2	7	5	9	3	4	8	10	6	1	2	6	7	4	10	3	8	5	9
74	7	1	2	9	4	8	7	5	6	3	10	1	2	9	4	7	8	6	5	3	10
75	7	5	2	4	5	9	8	3	6	7	10	2	8	7	3	4	8	9	6	5	10
76	7	1	1	7	6	8	3	7	2	4	10	2	4	9	9	1	4	3	5	7	10
77	7	1	8	5	2	4	6	7	9	3	10	1	6	4	5	3	6	7	2	8	10
78	7	1	5	9	3	4	6	6	7	8	10	1	4	7	5	2	7	8	9	3	10
79	7	1	5	9	2	7	3	3	6	8	10	1	4	2	6	2	8	5	9	3	10
80	7	1	3	9	2	5	8	4	7	8	10	1	3	7	7	5	9	8	6	3	10
81	7	1	5	2	7	5	8	3	4	6	10	1	5	6	8	2	9	4	6	5	10
82	7	5	4	7	9	2	3	8	7	10	6	3	8	9	2	1	10	8	7	4	9
83	7	1	7	5	4	8	9	6	2	3	10	1	2	9	4	3	7	2	5	6	10
84	7	1	2	2	8	4	3	7	6	5	10	1	3	6	5	3	8	7	4	6	10
85	7	1	7	9	2	9	3	4	8	4	5	1	4	2	7	8	9	2	5	4	10
86	7	1	3	6	7	9	9	8	4	10	6	1	4	3	8	10	3	5	7	6	9
87	7	1	4	3	5	9	9	7	8	10	10	1	4	3	2	5	10	7	8	6	9
Average	1	2	5 ⎱	8	9	3	7	4	6	10		1·58	4·53	5·42	6·00	4·53	8·21	5·70	5·13	5·18	8·69

TABLE 34

Preferences shown by 11 extrovert females under 8 years

Subject no.	Age (years)	Primary arrangement of bottles										Placings assigned to odorants nos.									
												1	2	3	4	5	6	7	8	9	10
88	4	1	10	5	4	7	8	9	2	3	6	1	8	9	4	3	10	5	6	7	2
89	4	1	5	3	4	2	6	9	8	7	10	1	5	3	4	2	6	9	8	7	10
90	5	1	2	9	10	4	8	5	6	3	7	1	2	9	5	7	8	10	6	3	4
91	6	1	7	2	8	4	6	5	9	3	10	1	3	9	5	7	6	2	4	8	10
92	6	1	2	8	7	3	5	4	9	6	10	1	2	5	7	6	9	4	3	8	10
93	6	1	7	9	3	5	6	8	4	10	2	1	10	4	8	5	6	2	7	3	9
94	6	1	2	3	8	5	6	7	4	9	10	1	2	3	8	5	6	7	4	9	10
95	7	7	8	4	1	6	5	2	9	10	3	4	7	10	3	6	5	1	2	8	9
96	7	1	5	2	7	8	4	3	9	6	10	1	4	7	6	2	9	3	5	8	10
97	7	7	1	9	6	2	5	8	10	4	3	2	5	10	3	6	8	1	7	4	9
98	7	1	5	8	2	3	4	7	9	6	10	1	4	5	6	2	9	7	3	8	10
Average		1	5 }									1·36	4·73	6·73	5·36	4·64	7·45	4·64	5·00	6·64	8·45

TABLE 35

Preferences shown by 46 introvert males aged 8–14

Subject no.	Age (years)	Primary arrangement of bottles										Placings assigned to odorants nos.									
												1	2	3	4	5	6	7	8	9	10
99	9	4	1	8	9	7	6	2	5	3	10	2	7	9	1	8	6	5	3	4	10
100	11	8	1	5	6	7	9	4	3	2	10	2	9	8	7	3	4	5	1	6	10
101	11	4	2	1	6	5	8	7	3	9	10	3	2	8	1	5	4	7	6	9	10
102	11	1	5	8	4	9	7	3	2	6	10	1	8	7	4	2	9	6	3	5	10
103	11	1	3	6	9	2	4	5	8	7	10	1	5	2	6	7	3	9	8	4	10
104	11	4	1	3	2	7	5	5	8	9	3	2	4	3	1	6	7	5	4	9	10
105	11	1	4	5	8	6	9	6	9	7	10	1	7	10	2	3	5	9	4	6	8
106	11	1	4	5	8	2	7	2	4	3	10	1	5	9	2	3	7	6	2	8	10
107	11	4	8	7	2	6	5	6	7	10	10	4	4	7	8	6	5	3	3	10	9
108	12	5	5	8	1	2	9	3	9	6	10	2	5	7	1	2	9	8	3	6	10
109	12	4	1	4	8	3	6	3	5	7	10	3	7	5	3	1	6	9	4	8	10
110	12	1	8	1	2	9	7	2	8	6	10	1	4	7	1	8	6	9	2	5	10
111	12	4	2	9	4	5	7	3	6	8	10	1	2	7	4	5	9	6	8	3	10
112	12	1	4	3	5	5	6	2	8	9	10	2	7	3	2	4	8	6	9	5	10
113	12	4	1	2	3	6	3	7	2	6	10	1	3	4	1	5	6	7	8	9	10
114	12	1	8	7	4	8	2	9	9	8	10	2	8	6	4	5	9	3	2	7	10
115	12	1	1	5	3	7	2	7	9	3	10	1	6	4	3	3	5	7	5	8	10
116	12	1	5	4	7	7	3	6	6	9	10	1	6	9	4	2	7	4	7	9	10
117	12	1	5	2	4	8	3	8	6	9	10	1	3	6	4	2	8	5	3	9	10
118	12	5	1	8	4	7	6	2	3	9	10	2	7	8	4	1	6	5	3	9	10

No.											n											Average
119	2	10	6	3	9	5	7	4	8	1	12	9	6	2	4	8	5	3	7	10	1	
120	10	9	6	8	3	5	4	7	2	1	13	10	9	7	3	8	5	4	6	2	1	
121	5	9	8	10	7	4	3	6	2	1	13	7	9	8	6	3	10	5	4	2	1	
122	10	8	3	2	9	1	10	7	6	4	13	10	6	9	3	2	4	1	8	7	5	
123	9	8	2	6	7	4	4	5	1	3	13	4	10	9	6	7	3	5	1	8	2	
124	9	8	5	2	10	7	7	6	3	1	13	6	10	9	5	3	8	4	2	7	1	
125	10	8	5	2	4	1	1	9	6	3	13	10	3	9	4	2	8	6	1	7	5	
126	10	8	9	7	5	3	5	6	4	2	13	10	8	9	7	3	6	2	5	1	4	
127	9	6	4	7	10	2	3	8	3	1	13	6	10	3	7	9	4	8	2	5	1	
128	10	8	5	7	4	1	2	6	9	1	13	10	2	9	7	3	8	6	4	5	1	
129	10	7	5	3	8	1	10	9	6	4	13	10	3	6	9	2	8	1	7	4	5	
130	8	6	5	7	3	2	3	9	4	2	13	4	3	10	7	9	8	2	6	1	5	
131	10	8	5	9	4	3	1	6	7	1	13	10	7	9	2	3	8	6	4	5	1	
132	10	9	4	6	7	3	2	8	5	2	13	10	9	3	6	7	2	8	5	1	4	
133	10	5	6	7	8	3	2	4	9	1	14	10	2	6	7	8	9	3	5	4	1	
134	10	6	4	9	5	3	5	8	7	1	14	10	7	3	2	9	6	8	5	4	1	
135	2	7	4	8	6	9	6	9	5	1	14	8	3	7	9	6	2	8	5	4	1	
136	2	7	10	4	9	2	3	8	6	3	14	7	6	3	9	2	4	7	1	10	3	
137	10	8	7	10	5	8	3	1	4	1	14	10	5	9	8	4	6	2	4	10	1	
138	9	8	6	5	4	2	1	7	9	1	14	8	2	9	3	8	7	6	4	5	1	
139	10	6	10	7	5	3	2	2	4	4	14	10	10	5	7	9	6	2	7	3	4	
140	9	6	5	3	9	10	8	8	7	1	14	7	6	3	2	9	8	1	5	5	2	
141	4	6	5	10	7	3	2	5	8	2	14	5	10	2	6	9	3	8	3	4	1	
142	10	7	4	5	6	2	6	3	1	1	14	10	8	4	9	6	7	10	5	4	2	
143	10	7	9	6	8	3	2	9	4	4	14	10	3	6	9	7	8	2	8	5		
144	10	5	3	7	9	2	6	8	1		14	10	6	3	7	4	9	1				
Average	9·02	7·13	5·30	6·17	6·52	3·76	3·63	6·46	5·22	1·78		10	9	6	3	7	8	2	5	4	1	

TABLE 36

Preferences shown by 45 extrovert males aged 8–14

Subject no.	Age (years)	Primary arrangement of bottles										Placings assigned to odorants nos.									
												1	2	3	4	5	6	7	8	9	10
145	8	6	2	9	3	10	7	4	8	5	1	1	9	7	4	2	10	5	3	8	6
146	11	10	7	8	3	9	6	2	5	4	1	1	4	7	2	3	5	9	8	6	10
147	11	10	8	8	6	7	5	2	4	3	1	1	4	2	3	5	7	6	9	8	10
148	11	10	8	3	6	9	5	4	7	2	1	1	2	8	4	5	7	3	9	6	10
149	12	10	8	9	—	3	5	7	1	6	2	3	1	6	—	5	2	4	9	8	10
150	12	10	2	9	6	3	7	8	4	5	1	1	9	6	3	2	4	5	4	8	10
151	12	3	7	10	9	1	5	6	2	7	8	6	3	10	2	5	9	9	1	7	8
152	12	10	6	3	7	9	8	2	4	5	1	1	4	8	3	2	9	7	5	6	10
153	12	10	9	8	7	2	4	3	6	1	5	2	6	4	5	1	3	7	8	9	10
154	12	10	7	3	6	9	5	8	4	2	1	1	2	8	3	5	7	9	4	6	10
155	12	10	7	8	2	6	9	3	5	4	1	1	7	4	2	3	6	9	8	5	10
156	12	10	5	7	4	3	6	9	2	1	8	2	3	6	7	9	5	8	1	4	10
157	12	10	6	8	4	7	9	2	5	1	5	1	4	3	7	1	9	6	8	5	10
158	12	9	10	7	6	8	—	3	3	2	1	2	2	4	—	3	7	8	6	10	9
159	12	10	9	8	4	8	7	6	5	1	5	1	8	3	7	1	4	5	1	9	10
160	13	10	7	3	6	9	2	3	9	4	1	1	5	4	2	3	7	9	8	6	10
161	13	10	2	9	4	6	8	1	4	5	7	4	9	8	7	2	4	5	6	3	10
162	13	10	6	9	7	3	2	8	8	1	5	2	5	6	3	1	6	7	4	8	10
163	13	10	3	9	7	6	1	5	1	4	2	5	1	9	2	4	9	7	3	8	10
164	13	4	6	9	3	5	7	10	—	2	8	3	2	7	10	6	9	5	1	8	4

First set

Person	1	2	3	4	5	6	7	8	9	10
165	5	10	6	2	9	7	4	8	3	1
166	10	7	8	9	3	1	4	6	5	2
167	10	8	1	4	5	7	3	6	9	2
168	10	9	6	4	3	5	8	2	7	1
169	10	9	7	1	3	2	8	6	4	5
170	10	8	6	9	5	1	7	4	2	3
171	9	9	6	4	7	2	5	8	3	1
172	10	8	4	2	9	5	3	7	6	1
173	10	10	5	2	6	3	4	8	7	1
174	10	9	4	6	7	5	2	8	3	1
175	10	5	3	9	6	2	4	8	7	1
176	10	9	5	7	4	2	3	8	6	2
177	10	7	9	4	8	6	1	3	5	1
178	10	7	9	8	6	3	5	4	2	1
179	1	9	6	3	9	4	2	8	5	6
180	10	9	2	6	5	4	1	8	7	1
181	5	9	8	8	4	2	5	7	3	4
182	10	9	10	3	3	6	7	5	2	1
183	10	10	3	9	7	2	4	6	8	1
184	10	4	5	7	7	2	4	8	6	1
185	10	5	5	9	6	2	3	8	9	1
186	10	3	3	8	7	2	1	8	6	4
187	10	4	6	5	4	7	2	8	5	1
188	10	4	3	6	8	7	2	9	6	1
189	10	9	3	6	5	1	4	7	8	2
Average	9·27	7·36	5·40	5·93	6·11	3·51	4·00	6·42	1·93	4·98

Second set

Person	1	2	3	4	5	6	7	8	9	10
165	9	6	3	5	8	10	4	2	7	1
166	10	7	8	9	3	2	4	6	1	5
167	10	2	9	5	8	6	7	4	1	8
168	10	9	4	2	3	5	7	6	3	1
169	10	9	4	8	8	1	2	6	5	7
170	10	7	9	4	3	6	3	1	2	5
171	9	9	3	6	8	4	7	2	5	1
172	10	6	9	3	2	5	8	4	7	1
173	10	10	3	2	6	8	4	5	7	1
174	10	9	3	6	7	5	8	2	4	1
175	10	7	3	2	6	9	4	8	5	1
176	10	9	6	7	2	8	6	4	1	1
177	10	8	7	9	5	2	7	3	2	4
178	10	8	3	9	5	4	3	5	4	1
179	8	6	3	9	6	2	5	7	8	1
180	10	9	8	2	8	6	5	7	5	1
181	9	9	7	3	1	4	6	2	2	4
182	10	9	2	4	7	3	1	6	5	10
183	10	9	3	6	5	8	4	7	5	1
184	10	7	3	6	3	10	4	8	5	1
185	10	2	7	7	2	8	9	4	5	1
186	10	7	6	6	6	9	1	8	4	4
187	10	3	2	5	2	2	6	9	4	1
188	10	3	7	5	8	7	9	8	1	1
189	10	9	2	3	2	6	4	8	7	5
Average	10	9	3	6	7	8	2	4	5	1

TABLE 37

Preferences shown by 32 introvert females aged 8–14

Subject no.	Age (years)	Primary arrangement of bottles										Placings assigned to odorants nos.									
												1	2	3	4	5	6	7	8	9	10
190	12	1	7	2	5	4	6	3	8	9	10	1	3	7	5	4	6	2	8	9	10
191	12	1	4	8	7	5	2	6	9	3	10	1	6	9	2	5	7	4	3	8	10
192	12	1	8	5	7	4	9	6	2	3	10	1	8	9	5	3	7	4	2	6	10
193	12	1	5	8	4	2	6	9	7	3	10	1	5	9	4	2	6	8	3	7	10
194	12	1	2	3	8	6	7	5	9	4	10	1	2	3	9	7	5	6	4	8	10
195	13	1	5	2	4	3	7	8	10	6	9	1	3	5	4	2	9	6	7	10	8
196	13	7	1	4	8	5	2	9	3	10	6	2	6	8	3	5	10	1	4	7	9
197	13	1	5	2	4	8	6	9	7	3	10	1	3	9	4	2	6	8	5	7	10
198	13	1	2	5	4	6	8	3	10	9	7	1	2	7	4	3	5	10	6	9	8
199	13	1	4	5	8	7	2	6	9	3	10	1	6	9	2	3	7	5	4	8	10
200	13	1	5	8	2	10	4	9	7	3	6	1	4	9	6	2	10	8	3	7	5
201	13	1	5	8	4	3	7	9	10	2	6	1	9	5	4	2	10	6	3	7	8
202	13	1	8	7	3	5	6	4	2	9	10	1	8	4	7	5	6	3	2	9	10
203	13	1	8	2	3	4	7	5	6	9	10	1	3	4	5	7	8	6	2	9	10

Subj.											n										
204	9	6	3	8	10	7	4	5	2	1	13	6	10	7	5	9	3	4	8	2	1
205	7	4	6	2	10	3	5	9	8	1	13	6	3	2	10	8	4	9	5	7	1
206	7	6	9	3	8	2	5	10	4	1	13	3	8	6	10	9	4	2	7	5	1
207	7	6	3	4	9	2	5	8	7	1	13	10	6	3	2	9	4	7	8	5	1
208	10	4	5	7	9	1	3	8	6	2	13	10	6	3	7	2	8	9	4	1	5
209	10	8	3	6	7	2	9	4	5	1	13	10	4	9	6	7	2	3	8	5	1
210	10	7	5	1	10	3	6	8	4	2	13	6	10	3	9	4	8	2	5	1	7
211	9	9	5	7	4	6	1	8	4	3	14	10	9	3	7	5	8	6	1	2	4
212	10	7	5	4	10	2	9	6	2	1	14	6	4	10	9	3	8	7	2	5	1
213	8	8	3	7	9	4	5	6	3	1	14	10	6	9	7	3	4	5	8	2	1
214	10	6	3	5	9	2	4	7	2	1	14	10	6	2	3	9	7	4	8	5	1
215	10	6	4	10	7	2	8	5	8	1	14	7	10	4	6	7	3	8	2	5	1
216	9	6	4	3	10	5	2	9	3	1	14	6	3	10	2	9	5	8	7	4	1
217	8	10	4	2	8	3	9	7	7	1	14	9	4	6	3	10	2	8	5	7	1
218	6	9	2	3	8	4	5	10	6	1	14	3	9	6	10	2	4	5	7	8	1
219	7	3	8	2	4	9	10	7	5	1	14	4	5	8	3	10	2	6	9	7	1
220	6	5	6	4	9	3	7	8	2	1	14	10	6	3	4	8	9	7	5	2	1
221	8	7	5	4	9	3	2	10	6	1	14	3	6	10	9	2	8	7	5	4	1
Average	8·81	7·13	4·34	4·97	7·88	3·59	5·09	7·25	4·78	1·16		10	6	3	9	7	2	5	8	5	1

TABLE 38

Preferences shown by 39 extrovert females aged 8–14

Subject no.	Age (years)	Primary arrangement of bottles										Placings assigned to odorants nos.									
												1	2	3	4	5	6	7	8	9	10
222	11	8	1	4	5	3	6	9	7	2	10	2	9	5	3	4	6	8	1	7	10
223	12	1	5	4	3	9	10	7	6	8	2	1	10	4	3	2	8	7	9	5	6
224	12	1	5	8	2	4	6	10	7	9	3	1	4	10	5	2	6	8	3	9	7
225	12	1	8	4	5	7	2	3	6	9	10	1	6	7	3	4	8	5	2	9	10
226	12	1	5	4	2	8	7	3	6	9	10	1	4	7	3	2	8	6	5	9	10
227	12	8	1	7	3	5	4	9	10	2	6	2	9	4	6	5	10	3	1	7	8
228	12	2	1	8	7	3	6	4	5	10	9	2	1	4	7	8	6	5	3	10	9
229	13	1	8	5	4	6	2	7	3	9	10	1	6	8	5	3	4	7	2	9	10
230	13	1	8	5	2	4	7	9	3	10	6	1	5	8	6	3	10	4	2	7	9
231	13	8	1	3	4	2	6	7	9	5	10	2	9	5	4	3	6	7	1	8	10
232	13	1	8	4	2	7	5	3	6	9	10	1	4	3	5	7	8	6	2	9	10
233	13	1	5	8	7	4	9	2	3	6	10	1	4	8	7	2	10	5	3	6	9
234	13	1	5	8	4	7	2	3	6	9	10	1	6	7	5	2	8	4	3	9	10
235	13	1	7	8	4	2	5	3	9	10	6	1	5	7	4	6	10	2	3	9	8
236	13	8	1	6	4	2	10	9	3	5	7	2	5	8	4	9	3	10	1	7	6
237	13	1	7	5	4	8	2	3	6	9	10	1	6	7	4	3	8	2	5	9	10
238	13	1	5	4	2	3	7	8	6	9	10	1	4	5	3	2	9	6	7	8	10

	1	2	3	4	5	6	7	8	9	10	n	1	2	3	4	5	6	7	8	9	10
239	8	6	3	2	10	4	5	9	7	1	13	6	3	10	2	9	4	5	8	7	1
240	9	7	3	5	10	4	8	6	1	2	13	6	10	4	9	3	7	5	8	1	2
241	10	8	3	2	9	5	7	4	6	1	13	10	6	9	4	2	5	3	8	7	1
242	9	7	4	8	5	2	6	3	10	1	13	2	10	7	9	4	5	8	8	5	1
243	5	9	1	10	7	3	2	8	6	4	13	7	9	3	6	2	6	1	3	4	8
244	6	10	1	7	9	5	4	8	3	2	13	9	6	3	7	10	10	4	5	1	8
245	10	9	6	7	8	5	4	2	3	1	14	10	9	6	7	8	5	4	2	3	1
246	8	10	4	9	5	3	7	2	6	1	14	9	7	10	4	2	5	8	2	3	1
247	10	9	6	7	8	2	3	4	5	1	14	10	9	6	7	8	6	3	5	5	1
248	7	10	5	3	9	4	2	8	6	1	14	9	6	3	10	2	2	5	4	4	1
249	10	9	4	3	8	2	5	6	7	1	14	10	9	6	2	3	8	8	7	5	1
250	9	5	7	3	10	2	4	6	8	5	14	6	10	2	8	3	4	4	7	5	1
251	6	8	4	1	10	2	3	9	7	1	14	6	3	9	2	10	9	8	7	5	1
252	10	7	3	4	8	5	2	9	6	1	14	10	3	6	9	2	1	7	4	4	7
253	10	8	3	4	9	5	6	7	2	1	14	10	6	9	3	4	5	7	8	2	1
254	3	5	4	2	10	7	6	8	9	1	14	6	2	3	5	4	5	8	8	7	1
255	9	10	8	6	7	2	3	5	4	1	14	9	10	8	6	7	9	2	10	5	1
256	4	10	2	6	8	3	5	9	7	1	14	9	3	6	2	7	3	10	4	8	1
257	10	8	4	6	9	2	5	7	3	1	14	10	6	9	3	7	4	8	5	5	1
258	4	5	7	8	6	3	2	10	9	1	14	3	2	7	8	6	4	10	2	4	1
259	9	8	4	7	10	2	5	3	6	1	14	6	10	9	7	2	9	8	5	5	1
260	10	9	8	2	6	3	1	5	7	4	14	10	9	8	2	6	3	1	3	7	4
Average	8·41	8·05	3·77	5·31	7·90	3·64	4·41	6·28	5·77	1·44		10	9	6	3	2	7	4	8	5	1

TABLE 39

Preferences shown by 18 introvert males aged 15–19

Subject no.	Age (years)	Primary arrangement of bottles										Placings assigned to odorants nos.									
		1	2	3	4	5	6	7	8	9	10	1	2	3	4	5	6	7	8	9	10
261	15	1	2	5	7	3	8	6	4	10	9	1	2	5	8	3	7	4	6	10	9
262	15	1	5	9	8	4	7	2	6	3	10	1	7	9	5	2	8	6	4	3	10
263	15	1	5	8	4	7	6	3	2	9	10	1	8	7	4	2	6	5	3	9	10
264	15	1	5	7	8	3	2	6	4	9	10	1	7	6	4	2	8	3	5	9	10
265	15	1	5	2	10	8	4	9	6	3	7	1	3	9	6	2	4	7	10	8	5
266	15	4	1	6	9	10	7	5	3	8	2	2	5	8	1	3	9	7	6	4	10
267	15	7	1	4	5	2	8	3	6	9	10	2	6	8	3	4	7	1	9	5	10
268	15	1	8	3	6	4	7	9	5	2	10	1	8	3	6	5	4	7	2	9	10
269	15	5	1	4	2	8	6	3	7	9	10	2	4	8	3	1	6	9	5	7	10
270	15	7	8	1	5	4	6	9	3	2	10	3	9	7	5	4	6	1	2	8	10
271	16	4	5	2	3	7	8	1	6	9	10	5	6	4	1	2	3	8	7	9	10
272	18	5	1	6	7	3	8	2	9	10	4	2	3	6	5	1	10	4	7	8	9
273	18	2	1	8	6	5	4	3	7	9	10	2	1	4	10	6	3	8	5	9	7
274	18	3	2	5	9	4	8	10	6	7	1	3	2	1	6	5	4	10	7	9	8
275	19	1	2	7	9	8	4	3	6	5	10	1	8	6	5	3	2	7	9	4	10
276	19	1	5	2	3	4	6	8	9	7	10	1	9	7	6	2	4	3	5	8	10
277	19	1	7	8	3	5	2	9	4	6	10	1	6	4	5	7	3	2	9	8	10
278	19	1	7	8	3	5	4	2	6	9	10	1	6	4	7	5	8	2	3	9	10
Average		1	5	2	4	7	8	3	6	9	10	1·72	5·00	5·89	5·00	3·28	6·45	5·22	5·78	7·33	9·33

TABLE 40

Preferences shown by 22 extrovert males aged 15–19

Subject no.	Age (years)	Primary arrangement of bottles										Placings assigned to odorants nos.									
												1	2	3	4	5	6	7	8	9	10
279	15	1	5	8	2	9	7	4	6	3	10	1	4	9	7	2	8	5	3	6	10
280	15	5	1	3	4	2	10	9	8	6	7	2	5	3	4	1	9	10	8	7	6
281	15	1	3	4	8	5	6	9	2	7	10	1	8	2	3	5	6	9	4	7	10
282	15	4	7	1	8	5	9	3	6	2	10	3	9	7	1	5	8	2	4	6	10
283	15	4	1	2	8	8	9	7	3	6	10	2	3	8	1	4	9	7	5	6	10
284	15	1	5	4	5	6	7	2	9	3	8	1	7	9	3	2	5	6	4	8	10
285	15	1	5	4	2	6	7	9	3	2	10	1	4	8	3	2	6	5	10	7	9
286	15	4	8	1	5	7	6	7	2	9	8	3	8	7	1	4	9	3	2	7	10
287	15	1	5	7	4	9	8	6	5	3	10	1	8	7	4	2	6	5	6	9	10
288	15	2	4	1	6	8	10	3	2	9	7	3	1	5	2	8	4	3	5	5	6
289	15	10	1	5	7	4	8	2	5	8	9	2	7	7	6	1	8	10	9	10	1
290	15	5	4	5	1	8	8	3	6	7	6	4	3	5	2	1	8	4	5	8	5
291	15	1	5	2	4	7	7	10	4	9	10	1	3	7	4	2	8	9	5	9	10
292	15	5	2	8	1	8	9	6	4	3	6	4	2	9	8	1	10	6	3	6	7
293	15	1	2	5	9	7	7	4	3	10	10	1	4	9	8	3	7	5	5	4	10
294	15	3	5	7	2	8	—	6	4	10	10	2	3	8	—	2	7	6	7	9	10
295	17	1	1	2	6	7	5	8	4	8	9	1	2	1	8	6	4	3	9	10	7
296	18	2	2	4	7	3	8	3	9	8	6	3	3	5	3	6	10	5	7	8	10
297	18	3	3	7	7	5	9	4	6	9	10	1	1	2	7	5	8	4	9	9	10
298	18	1	4	7	7	8	1	2	8	4	6	6	7	3	2	7	9	4	6	6	10
299	18	3	2	6	7	9	5	5	4	9	9	1	2	1	8	3	3	4	5	9	10
300	19	1	7	5	3	2	8	8	6	9	4	1	5	4	10	3	8	2	7	9	6
Average		1	5	2	4	7	8	3	6	9	10	2·05	4·45	5·82	4·52	3·59	7·32	5·41	5·72	7·59	8·46

TABLE 41

Preferences shown by 77 introvert females aged 15–19

Subject no.	Age (years)	Primary arrangement of bottles										Placings assigned to odorants nos.									
												1	2	3	4	5	6	7	8	9	10
301	15	1	4	5	3	8	7	2	10	9	6	1	7	4	2	3	10	6	5	9	8
302	15	1	5	2	7	8	4	6	3	9	10	1	3	8	6	2	7	4	5	9	10
303	15	1	5	4	7	9	3	2	10	6	8	1	7	6	3	2	9	4	10	5	8
304	15	1	7	2	5	4	8	3	6	9	10	1	3	7	5	4	8	2	6	9	10
305	15	1	4	8	7	5	3	6	2	9	10	1	8	6	2	5	7	4	3	9	10
306	15	1	5	7	2	3	8	4	10	6	9	1	4	5	7	2	9	3	6	10	8
307	15	1	7	6	5	2	3	8	4	9	10	1	5	6	7	4	3	2	8	9	10
308	15	4	1	7	5	2	3	6	10	9	8	2	3	5	1	4	6	7	8	10	9
309	15	1	7	4	5	2	8	3	6	10	9	1	5	8	3	4	9	2	6	10	7
310	18	1	5	4	3	2	8	7	9	10	6	1	5	4	3	2	10	7	6	8	9
311	18	7	5	8	1	2	3	9	4	6	10	4	5	6	8	2	9	1	3	7	10
312	18	1	8	2	3	4	9	5	7	6	10	1	3	4	5	7	9	8	2	6	10
313	18	1	5	4	3	8	2	6	7	9	10	1	6	4	3	2	7	8	5	9	10
314	18	3	1	7	4	2	8	9	6	5	10	2	5	1	4	8	7	3	6	9	10
315	18	1	2	3	8	5	9	7	6	4	10	1	3	2	9	5	8	7	4	6	10
316	18	1	2	7	3	8	4	5	6	10	9	1	2	4	6	7	10	3	5	8	9
317	18	3	1	7	8	4	5	9	6	10	2	2	10	1	5	6	8	3	4	7	9

318	319	320	321	322	323	324	325	326	327	328	329	330	331	332	333	334	335	336	337	338	339	340
10	8	10	9	10	10	9	10	10	10	7	10	9	4	10	10	10	10	9	10	10	10	10
1	5	9	5	4	8	10	3	9	3	6	8	7	1	7	7	9	9	8	4	7	6	7
8	1	4	6	8	7	5	8	6	4	2	9	6	6	5	6	1	5	3	1	1	5	4
7	9	8	2	7	1	7	4	5	6	1	4	4	9	1	3	3	6	10	8	5	4	8
9	10	5	10	6	9	8	7	8	9	10	7	10	7	9	8	6	7	7	7	9	9	9
4	6	7	4	5	4	3	5	1	8	3	1	8	3	4	4	4	1	1	6	8	8	6
5	7	6	8	9	5	6	6	3	7	4	5	1	8	2	5	8	4	4	5	4	7	3
6	3	1	3	2	2	2	1	2	2	5	3	3	5	6	2	2	3	2	3	2	3	5
3	4	3	7	3	6	4	9	7	5	9	6	5	10	8	9	7	8	6	9	6	2	2
2	2	2	1	1	3	1	2	4	1	8	2	2	2	3	1	5	2	5	2	3	1	1
10	6	10	6	10	10	9	10	10	10	6	10	6	2	10	10	10	10	7	10	10	10	10
6	7	9	10	4	6	10	2	9	6	2	8	10	7	6	2	9	9	10	2	6	6	6
8	10	7	4	8	9	6	8	6	5	1	9	5	4	2	6	4	2	9	7	5	5	7
7	4	5	2	7	8	7	6	2	4	10	6	9	6	9	9	2	6	6	6	9	4	9
3	5	4	8	6	2	4	4	8	7	9	2	8	8	3	8	6	7	2	5	2	9	5
4	9	6	9	5	4	8	5	7	2	3	4	2	3	8	4	1	8	1	4	7	8	3
5	2	8	5	9	5	2	7	1	8	4	7	7	10	5	5	5	4	4	9	4	7	8
2	3	2	3	2	1	5	9	4	9	5	3	3	5	1	7	7	3	8	3	1	3	4
1	1	1	7	3	3	3	1	3	3	8	1	1	1	4	3	3	1	3	1	3	2	2
9	8	3	1	1	7	1	3	5	1	7	5	4	9	7	1	8	5	5	8	8	1	1
18	18	18	18	18	18	18	18	18	18	18	18	18	18	18	18	19	19	19	19	19	19	19

TABLE 41—continued

Preferences shown by 77 introvert females aged 15–19

Subject no.	Age (years)	Primary arrangement of bottles										Placings assigned to odorants nos.									
		1	2	3	4	5	6	7	8	9	10	1	2	3	4	5	6	7	8	9	10
341	19	3	7	8	2	1	4	5	6	9	10	5	4	1	6	7	8	2	3	9	10
342	19	1	5	7	3	10	4	9	8	2	6	1	9	4	6	2	10	3	8	7	5
343	19	7	3	8	1	5	6	10	2	9	4	4	8	2	10	5	6	1	3	9	7
344	19	1	7	8	9	3	5	4	2	10	6	1	8	5	7	6	10	2	3	4	9
345	19	4	2	8	3	9	5	6	1	7	10	8	2	4	1	6	7	9	3	5	10
346	19	7	8	1	4	3	5	9	6	2	10	3	9	5	4	6	8	1	2	7	10
347	19	3	2	1	5	4	7	6	8	9	10	3	2	1	5	4	7	6	8	9	10
348	19	1	5	3	8	7	9	4	10	6	2	1	10	3	7	2	9	5	4	6	8
349	19	1	7	5	9	3	2	8	4	6	10	1	6	5	8	3	9	2	7	4	10
350	19	1	3	8	5	4	9	2	7	6	10	1	7	2	5	4	9	8	3	6	10
351	19	7	8	1	3	2	5	4	6	10	9	3	5	4	7	6	8	1	2	10	9
352	19	1	5	7	3	8	9	2	4	6	10	1	7	4	8	2	9	3	5	6	10
353	19	1	3	8	5	2	9	4	7	6	10	1	5	2	7	4	9	8	3	6	10
354	19	8	3	7	2	4	5	1	6	10	9	7	4	2	5	6	8	3	1	10	9
355	19	3	4	1	2	5	8	7	9	10	6	3	4	1	5	2	10	7	6	8	9
356	19	1	5	6	3	7	4	8	2	9	10	1	8	4	6	2	3	5	7	9	10
357	19	3	2	1	7	6	5	8	9	10	4	3	2	1	10	6	5	4	7	8	9

358	359	360	361	362	363	364	365	366	367	368	369	370	371	372	373	374	375	376	377	Average
10	10	10	9	10	10	10	9	9	9	9	10	9	10	10	10	10	10	10	9	9·35
9	9	8	10	2	5	6	7	7	10	10	9	8	9	6	8	9	8	8	10	7·36
8	7	6	5	9	7	9	6	3	7	7	1	3	4	2	2	5	4	4	3	4·94
7	3	7	8	8	1	4	8	6	4	3	7	5	5	9	3	4	9	2	5	4·86
3	8	9	6	6	8	8	7	10	6	5	8	10	8	3	9	7	1	9	7	7·73
5	6	3	7	4	4	5	5	5	1	2	4	6	3	4	6	6	7	6	8	4·49
6	4	5	2	3	3	2	4	4	5	8	6	7	2	5	7	8	6	7	2	5·21
1	2	1	4	5	9	7	2	2	3	1	2	4	6	7	1	1	3	5	1	3·45
2	5	2	3	1	6	1	3	8	8	4	3	1	7	8	5	3	2	3	4	5·21
4	1	4	1	7	2	3	1	1	2	6	5	2	1	1	4	2	5	1	6	2·40

358	359	360	361	362	363	364	365	366	367	368	369	370	371	372	373	374	375	376	377	Average
10	10	10	9	10	10	10	9	9	9	9	10	6	10	10	10	10	10	10	9	10
9	9	6	10	8	3	8	10	10	10	10	9	10	9	7	6	9	7	6	10	6
8	6	9	7	7	6	6	7	2	2	4	6	9	6	2	9	4	9	9	5	9
7	8	7	5	1	8	3	6	9	8	8	7	4	2	3	4	6	5	4	6	4
4	5	8	6	6	2	9	8	7	6	1	4	5	3	9	5	5	4	5	1	2
5	2	4	8	3	9	5	5	5	4	6	1	7	7	4	2	8	1	3	7	8
1	4	1	3	5	5	7	4	4	7	2	5	3	8	5	1	7	8	8	2	7
6	7	5	2	4	4	1	2	8	3	7	2	8	5	6	7	2	3	2	8	5
2	3	2	4	9	1	4	3	3	1	5	3	1	4	8	8	1	2	7	4	3
3	1	3	1	2	7	2	1	1	5	3	8	2	1	1	3	3	6	1	3	1
19	19	19	19	19	19	19	19	19	19	19	19	19	19	19	19	19	19	19	19	Average

TABLE 42

Preferences shown by 33 extrovert females aged 15–19

Subject no.	Age (years)	Primary arrangement of bottles										Placings assigned to odorants nos.									
												1	2	3	4	5	6	7	8	9	10
378	15	1	8	5	4	3	7	9	6	2	10	1	9	5	4	3	8	6	2	7	10
379	15	5	4	7	3	8	6	1	2	10	9	7	8	4	2	1	6	3	5	10	9
380	15	1	7	5	4	9	3	6	2	10	8	1	8	6	4	3	7	2	10	5	9
381	16	3	8	2	6	1	7	5	4	9	10	5	3	1	8	7	4	6	2	9	10
382	18	5	4	1	3	7	2	6	9	8	10	3	6	4	2	1	7	5	9	8	10
383	18	7	2	1	3	5	6	4	8	9	10	3	2	4	7	5	6	1	8	9	10
384	18	1	2	8	6	7	5	4	9	10	3	1	2	10	7	6	4	5	3	8	9
385	18	1	8	4	2	9	6	3	7	5	10	1	4	7	3	5	6	8	2	9	10
386	18	1	7	5	4	8	2	9	3	6	10	1	7	8	4	3	9	2	6	5	10
387	18	1	3	4	9	8	2	7	5	10	6	1	6	2	3	8	10	7	5	4	9
388	18	3	8	2	1	7	4	9	5	6	10	4	3	1	6	7	9	5	2	8	10
389	18	8	1	3	5	7	2	9	4	10	6	2	6	3	8	4	10	5	1	7	9
390	18	2	6	3	1	8	7	5	4	10	9	4	1	3	8	7	2	6	5	10	9
391	19	1	7	2	4	5	6	8	9	3	10	1	3	9	4	5	8	2	7	6	10

	392	393	394	395	396	397	398	399	400	401	402	403	404	405	406	407	408	409	410	Average
	10	9	9	10	8	10	10	10	10	9	10	10	10	10	10	10	10	10	10	9·67
	9	8	6	6	5	9	2	9	8	10	9	8	9	4	8	9	9	7	9	7·55
	6	4	3	3	2	4	1	6	2	7	4	9	6	2	2	2	5	4	2	4·27
	5	5	1	1	6	2	4	8	3	6	1	5	2	7	5	5	1	8	6	4·36
	7	6	8	9	7	8	9	7	7	4	7	7	5	3	9	8	7	9	3	6·85
	3	3	4	7	9	7	5	5	5	8	8	2	7	6	6	7	3	5	5	5·15
	4	7	5	8	10	5	7	4	9	5	6	4	8	5	7	6	2	3	4	5·43
	8	2	7	2	1	6	6	1	1	2	3	6	3	8	1	3	6	6	8	4·45
	2	10	10	5	3	3	8	3	6	3	5	3	4	9	4	1	8	1	7	4·94
	1	1	2	4	4	1	3	2	4	1	2	1	1	1	3	4	4	2	1	2·33
	10	2	2	10	4	10	10	10	10	9	10	10	10	10	9	10	10	10	10	10
	9	10	10	6	5	9	6	9	4	10	9	8	9	2	6	10	9	6	9	9
	3	9	6	4	10	6	2	7	9	5	5	9	4	3	9	6	2	7	3	6
	6	4	3	5	6	5	4	6	6	8	6	6	5	7	4	5	6	9	2	4
	8	6	9	9	7	3	3	8	2	7	4	3	8	5	5	4	3	3	7	5
	7	7	4	2	9	4	5	5	5	4	2	7	6	4	7	7	8	5	5	2
	4	8	5	1	1	8	7	4	1	6	8	4	2	9	2	1	1	8	4	3
	5	5	8	8	2	2	1	2	7	2	3	2	3	6	1	3	5	4	6	7
	2	3	1	3	8	7	9	1	8	3	1	5	7	8	8	8	4	1	8	8
	1	1	7	7	3	1	8	3	3	1	7	1	1	1	3	2	7	2	1	1

TABLE 43

Preferences shown by 22 introvert males aged 20–40

Subject no.	Age (years)	Primary arrangement of bottles										Placings assigned to odorants nos.									
												1	2	3	4	5	6	7	8	9	10
411	20	5	4	1	8	7	6	9	3	10	2	3	10	8	2	1	6	5	4	7	9
412	20	2	1	8	6	3	4	9	7	5	10	2	1	6	7	5	4	9	3	8	10
413	21	2	1	5	10	9	3	4	8	7	6	2	1	8	3	4	10	9	7	6	5
414	22	3	7	5	1	8	4	9	2	6	10	4	8	1	6	3	9	2	5	7	10
415	22	2	4	1	5	8	3	6	9	10	7	3	1	6	2	4	7	10	5	8	9
416	22	1	5	4	8	2	6	3	7	10	9	1	5	7	3	2	6	8	4	10	9
417	23	7	1	2	10	3	8	6	4	5	9	6	3	5	8	9	1	7	2	10	4
418	23	1	7	6	3	4	2	8	10	5	9	1	6	5	2	4	3	7	8	10	9
419	23	5	1	4	8	6	7	2	10	9	3	3	7	2	4	1	5	6	8	9	10
420	24	1	4	3	9	8	2	6	7	10	5	1	6	4	3	2	10	9	5	7	8
421	24	3	8	9	1	5	7	4	6	10	2	2	9	1	6	5	7	8	3	4	10
422	25	4	3	1	7	2	8	5	10	6	9	4	5	3	1	2	7	6	8	9	10
423	26	1	5	7	3	8	6	2	9	10	4	1	8	6	7	5	3	4	2	9	10
424	29	6	4	3	8	5	2	1	10	9	7	7	6	4	3	2	1	5	8	10	9
425	29	7	5	1	6	4	8	3	2	10	9	4	9	7	5	2	8	1	3	10	6
426	31	4	6	8	1	2	3	9	5	10	7	4	3	8	1	5	2	6	3	9	10
427	31	5	1	4	4	7	2	8	3	6	10	2	4	5	4	1	7	6	8	9	10
428	35	1	3	2	5	4	9	8	6	7	10	1	4	3	2	5	7	9	6	8	10
429	35	6	3	5	2	9	8	7	4	10	1	2	10	6	5	3	9	7	8	4	1
430	35	1	5	1	9	8	6	3	10	7	2	1	4	7	2	3	7	9	5	10	8
431	38	4	1	4	2	6	3	8	7	10	7	3	4	3	1	2	5	9	6	10	7
432	40	9	3	8	8	2	4	5	10	7	10	1	6	3	7	8	5	9	4	2	10
Average		1	5	4	8	3	2	6	7	9	10	2·64	5·50	4·91	3·82	3·77	6·09	6·59	5·09	7·68	8·91

TABLE 44

Preferences shown by 14 extrovert males aged 20–40

Subject no.	Age (years)	Primary arrangement of bottles										Placings assigned to odorants nos.									
												1	2	3	4	5	6	7	8	9	10
433	20	3	2	1	4	7	9	5	8	10	6	3	2	1	4	7	10	5	8	6	9
434	21	1	3	8	4	6	2	9	5	10	7	1	6	2	4	8	5	10	3	7	9
435	22	7	1	2	4	8	6	5	3	9	10	2	3	8	4	7	6	1	5	9	10
436	23	1	4	5	6	2	8	7	10	3	9	1	5	9	2	3	4	7	6	10	8
437	24	2	1	3	7	5	9	4	10	8	6	2	1	3	7	5	10	4	9	6	8
438	29	4	5	6	1	8	7	3	2	9	10	4	8	7	1	2	3	6	5	9	10
439	30	8	2	6	4	7	3	5	1	9	10	8	2	4	6	7	3	5	1	9	10
440	32	2	6	1	3	8	7	10	3	9	5	3	1	8	4	10	2	6	5	9	7
441	32	6	5	1	3	8	7	4	9	2	10	3	9	4	7	2	1	6	5	8	10
442	33	4	2	3	6	5	1	9	7	8	10	6	2	3	1	5	4	8	9	7	10
443	33	8	5	1	2	6	4	—	8	9	10	3	4	1	6	2	5	—	8	9	10
444	34	3	1	7	2	3	6	9	4	5	10	2	4	5	8	9	6	3	1	7	10
445	35	3	1	7	4	5	6	8	2	9	10	2	8	1	4	5	6	3	7	9	10
446	37	4	5	1	6	8	9	3	7	2	10	3	9	7	1	2	4	8	5	6	10
Average		1	4	3	2	6	5	8	7	9	10	3·07	4·57	4·50	4·22	5·29	4·93	5·54	5·50	7·93	9·36

TABLE 45

Preferences shown by 33 introvert females aged 20–40

Subject no.	Age (years)	Primary arrangement of bottles										Placings assigned to odorants nos.									
												1	2	3	4	5	6	7	8	9	10
447	20	7	1	5	3	9	2	8	6	4	10	2	6	4	9	3	8	1	7	5	10
448	20	7	5	6	4	3	2	1	8	9	10	7	6	5	4	2	3	1	8	9	10
449	20	6	3	1	5	4	7	8	2	9	10	3	8	2	5	4	1	6	7	9	10
450	20	8	5	7	4	9	3	2	1	6	10	8	7	6	4	2	9	3	1	5	10
451	20	7	3	1	8	4	5	2	9	6	10	3	7	2	5	6	9	1	4	8	10
452	20	1	7	9	5	4	8	3	2	6	10	1	8	7	5	4	9	2	6	3	10
453	20	5	7	8	3	4	2	9	6	10	1	10	6	4	5	1	8	2	3	7	9
454	20	3	1	4	2	8	5	9	7	6	10	2	4	1	3	6	9	8	5	7	10
455	20	1	3	7	4	2	5	8	6	9	10	1	5	2	4	6	8	3	7	9	10
456	20	3	8	5	1	7	4	2	6	9	10	4	7	1	6	3	8	5	2	9	10
457	20	5	1	4	2	3	7	8	6	10	9	2	4	5	3	1	8	6	7	10	9
458	20	3	7	8	1	5	4	6	2	10	9	4	8	1	6	5	7	2	3	10	9
459	20	3	1	5	7	6	8	2	4	9	10	2	7	1	8	3	5	4	6	9	10
460	20	3	5	8	7	2	4	6	1	9	10	8	4	1	6	2	7	5	3	9	10
461	20	1	7	8	3	2	4	5	9	6	10	1	5	4	6	7	9	2	3	8	10
462	20	3	1	7	9	5	4	2	8	6	10	2	7	1	6	5	9	3	8	4	10
463	20	3	6	4	8	1	2	5	7	9	10	5	6	1	3	7	2	8	4	9	10

Subject	N	A1	A2	A3	A4	A5	A6	A7	A8	A9	A10	B1	B2	B3	B4	B5	B6	B7	B8	B9	B10
464	20	8	5	9	3	10	4	7	1	6	2	6	8	10	4	2	9	5	7	1	3
465	20	9	10	2	1	8	3	5	7	6	4	9	10	6	3	2	4	1	5	8	7
466	20	10	8	1	5	9	4	3	6	7	2	10	6	9	2	3	7	5	4	1	8
467	20	10	7	4	8	9	3	5	1	6	2	10	6	7	9	2	4	8	5	1	3
468	21	9	5	3	4	10	2	1	8	6	7	6	10	3	1	2	9	7	8	5	4
469	21	10	8	4	3	9	2	7	5	6	1	10	6	9	4	2	3	8	7	5	1
470	22	9	10	3	1	8	4	5	6	7	2	9	10	6	2	3	4	5	8	1	7
471	27	10	9	7	6	5	4	8	2	1	3	10	9	4	8	7	6	5	1	3	2
472	27	10	9	6	7	1	3	4	2	8	5	10	9	2	7	8	1	4	5	3	6
473	28	10	8	6	4	5	7	9	2	3	1	10	4	9	5	8	6	7	2	3	1
474	30	9	8	7	3	4	1	2	10	6	5	3	10	9	8	2	1	6	7	4	5
475	30	8	9	2	3	7	6	10	1	5	4	4	9	10	6	5	2	1	7	8	3
476	35	6	7	9	10	2	4	1	5	3	8	7	8	1	9	10	3	5	2	6	4
477	35	10	9	8	3	5	6	7	4	2	1	10	9	8	4	5	6	3	7	2	1
478	36	9	10	8	5	2	7	6	3	1	4	9	10	8	5	4	7	1	3	6	2
479	39	9	10	7	5	2	3	8	1	6	4	9	10	4	8	2	7	1	5	6	3
Average		9·48	7·94	5·15	4·03	6·52	3·94	5·33	3·39	5·58	3·64	10	9	6	2	4	8	7	5	1	3

TABLE 46

Preferences shown by 33 extrovert females aged 20–40

Subject no.	Age (years)	Primary arrangement of bottles										Placings assigned to odorants nos.									
												1	2	3	4	5	6	7	8	9	10
480	20	1	2	5	8	7	4	3	10	6	9	1	2	7	6	3	9	5	4	10	8
481	20	8	7	1	3	5	4	6	2	9	10	3	8	4	6	5	7	2	1	9	10
482	20	1	3	8	2	7	4	5	6	9	10	1	4	2	6	7	8	5	3	9	10
483	20	4	3	1	8	7	6	5	9	2	10	3	7	2	1	9	6	5	4	8	10
484	20	8	2	4	3	1	5	7	9	6	10	5	2	4	3	6	9	7	1	8	10
485	20	9	1	3	5	10	7	2	8	6	4	2	8	3	10	9	4	7	6	1	5
486	20	1	4	5	7	8	3	2	9	6	10	1	7	8	2	3	9	4	5	6	10
487	20	1	2	3	7	5	10	8	4	9	6	1	2	3	7	5	10	4	6	8	9
488	20	1	3	9	5	10	8	4	7	6	2	1	10	2	8	4	9	7	6	3	5
489	20	7	5	1	8	4	3	9	2	6	10	3	9	7	5	2	8	1	4	6	10
490	22	1	5	8	3	7	4	9	6	10	2	1	10	4	6	2	8	5	3	7	9
491	22	1	3	8	7	2	5	4	9	6	10	1	5	2	7	6	9	4	3	8	10
492	27	2	3	4	6	5	8	1	7	9	10	7	1	2	3	5	4	8	6	9	10
493	27	6	1	3	8	4	2	5	7	9	10	2	6	3	5	7	1	8	4	9	10

494	495	496	497	498	499	500	501	502	503	504	505	506	507	508	509	510	511	512	Average
10	9	10	10	10	10	10	10	10	8	10	6	10	9	10	9	10	10	10	9·30
9	10	9	8	6	7	9	6	9	6	3	9	8	10	9	10	8	9	6	7·64
1	4	3	7	8	9	6	8	7	9	2	1	6	3	8	8	9	3	4	4·91
5	5	6	6	5	1	3	7	5	3	7	4	4	6	4	1	1	7	7	4·82
8	7	4	2	7	8	2	1	3	10	8	5	5	8	1	3	2	2	9	5·94
4	6	2	9	4	4	5	4	2	2	6	3	3	5	6	4	6	5	3	4·73
7	1	7	5	2	5	7	2	8	4	1	8	9	4	3	6	7	4	1	5·03
3	8	5	1	1	2	1	5	1	5	5	7	2	1	2	7	3	1	5	3·58
2	2	8	3	9	6	4	9	4	7	2	7	2	5	5	4	6	6	8	5·55
6	3	1	4	3	3	8	3	6	1	4	10	1	7	7	2	5	8	2	3·52

494	495	496	497	498	499	500	501	502	503	504	505	506	507	508	509	510	511	512	Average
10	9	10	10	10	10	10	10	6	10	1	10	9	10	9	10	10	10	10	10
9	10	9	5	2	8	9	2	9	8	2	9	4	10	9	10	8	9	6	9
6	3	2	9	8	6	1	8	4	10	6	4	9	6	8	8	9	1	2	6
4	6	4	8	6	9	4	7	8	2	7	3	2	1	1	3	4	7	7	2
1	5	7	7	9	2	8	9	1	9	5	10	8	7	5	4	5	2	9	4
7	7	3	4	7	4	5	3	7	3	3	6	6	5	2	2	1	5	3	8
5	8	6	1	5	5	2	5	2	4	1	7	7	4	7	5	2	4	8	7
3	1	8	2	1	1	7	1	6	7	9	5	5	8	4	6	3	8	5	5
2	2	5	6	4	3	6	4	5	5	8	2	3	2	1	6	6	6	1	3
8	4	1	3	3	7	3	6	3	1	4	8	1	3	6	7	7	3	4	1

E

TABLE 47

Preferences shown by 9 introvert males over 40 years

Subject no.	Age (years)	Primary arrangement of bottles										Placings assigned to odorants nos.									
												1	2	3	4	5	6	7	8	9	10
513	41	7	8	4	1	5	3	6	2	9	10	4	8	6	3	5	7	1	2	9	10
514	42	1	4	2	5	7	6	9	8	3	10	1	3	9	2	4	6	5	8	7	10
515	45	8	4	2	6	3	9	1	7	5	10	7	3	5	2	9	4	8	1	6	10
516	48	4	5	6	1	2	3	7	8	9	10	4	5	6	1	2	3	7	8	9	10
517	52	3	1	5	2	7	4	6	8	9	10	2	4	1	6	3	7	5	8	9	10
518	53	4	3	6	1	2	5	9	7	8	10	4	5	2	1	6	3	8	9	7	10
519	60	4	2	3	5	6	8	7	1	10	9	8	2	3	1	4	5	7	6	10	9
520	60	3	7	2	1	4	9	5	6	8	10	4	3	1	5	7	8	2	9	6	10
521	60	1	4	2	8	7	6	3	9	5	10	1	3	7	2	9	6	5	4	8	10
Average		4	1	2	3	7	5	6	8	9	10	3·89	4·00	4·44	2·56	5·44	5·44	5·33	6·11	7·89	9·89

TABLE 48

Preferences shown by 13 extrovert males over 40 years

Subject no.	Age (years)	Primary arrangement of bottles										Placings assigned to odorants nos.									
		1	2	3	4	5	6	7	8	9	10	1	2	3	4	5	6	7	8	9	10
522	41	3	5	4	1	2	9	8	7	6	10	4	5	1	3	2	9	8	7	6	10
523	45	4	1	2	5	3	7	6	8	9	10	2	3	5	1	4	7	6	8	9	10
524	45	7	8	3	4	6	9	2	10	5	1	10	7	3	4	9	5	1	2	6	8
525	49	10	1	2	6	4	7	8	5	3	9	2	3	9	5	8	4	6	7	10	1
526	50	5	4	1	3	6	2	7	8	9	10	3	6	4	2	1	5	7	8	9	10
527	53	5	1	8	4	7	6	3	2	9	10	2	8	7	4	1	6	5	3	9	10
528	53	4	5	6	1	2	3	7	9	8	10	4	5	6	1	2	3	7	9	8	10
529	55	6	3	1	7	2	5	8	4	9	10	3	5	2	8	6	1	4	7	9	10
530	56	7	3	5	4	2	6	8	9	1	10	9	5	2	4	3	6	1	7	8	10
531	56	5	8	1	3	2	10	7	6	4	9	3	5	4	9	1	8	7	2	10	6
532	57	8	6	5	4	10	3	2	7	9	1	10	7	6	4	3	2	8	1	9	5
533	57	4	2	3	1	5	9	7	6	8	10	4	2	3	1	5	8	7	9	6	10
534	63	1	7	8	3	5	9	2	4	6	10	1	7	4	8	5	9	2	3	6	10
Average		5	4	3	1	2	7	6	8	9	10	4·39	5·23	4·31	4·16	3·85	5·61	5·31	5·61	8·08	8·46

TABLE 49

Preferences shown by 14 introvert females over 40 years

Subject no.	Age (years)	Primary arrangement of bottles										Placings assigned to odorants nos.									
		1	2	3	4	5	6	7	8	9	10	1	2	3	4	5	6	7	8	9	10
535	42	7	8	5	1	4	3	10	9	2	6	4	9	6	5	3	10	1	2	8	7
536	44	1	3	5	6	4	2	8	7	9	10	1	6	2	5	3	4	8	7	9	10
537	46	3	6	5	4	1	7	9	2	8	10	5	8	1	4	3	2	6	9	7	10
538	48	1	5	4	8	3	9	2	6	10	7	1	7	5	3	2	8	10	4	6	9
539	49	3	6	8	4	5	1	9	2	7	10	6	8	1	4	5	2	9	3	7	10
540	49	1	2	6	4	5	3	9	7	8	10	1	2	6	4	5	3	8	9	7	10
541	51	1	3	7	8	4	5	6	9	2	10	1	9	2	5	6	7	3	4	8	10
542	52	6	2	8	7	3	5	4	9	1	10	9	2	5	7	6	1	4	3	8	10
543	54	4	6	5	1	3	2	8	10	9	7	4	6	5	1	3	2	10	7	9	8
544	54	4	1	5	8	3	7	9	6	2	10	2	9	5	1	3	8	6	4	7	10
545	57	1	7	6	4	5	2	8	9	3	10	1	6	9	4	5	3	2	7	8	10
546	58	2	8	3	5	1	4	7	9	6	10	5	1	3	6	4	9	7	2	8	10
547	62	5	1	8	4	6	9	3	2	10	7	2	8	7	4	1	5	10	3	6	9
548	80	7	2	5	6	1	3	8	4	9	10	5	2	6	8	3	4	1	7	9	10
Average		1	5	4	3	6	8	2	7	9	10	3·36	5·93	4·50	4·36	3·71	4·86	6·07	5·07	7·64	9·50

TABLE 50

Preferences shown by 11 extrovert females over 40 years

Subject no.	Age (years)	Primary arrangement of bottles										Placings assigned to odorants nos.									
												1	2	3	4	5	6	7	8	9	10
549	42	7	6	4	1	8	9	5	2	3	10	4	8	9	3	7	2	1	5	6	10
550	44	7	1	5	8	4	2	3	6	9	10	2	6	7	5	3	8	1	4	9	10
551	46	4	2	3	5	6	7	9	10	8	1	10	2	3	1	4	5	6	9	7	8
552	46	4	3	2	7	8	6	1	5	9	10	7	3	2	1	8	6	4	5	9	10
553	48	6	3	4	2	5	1	7	9	8	10	6	4	2	3	5	1	7	9	8	10
554	50	3	6	5	7	8	1	2	4	10	9	6	7	1	8	3	2	4	5	10	9
555	50	4	5	1	6	8	3	2	7	9	10	3	7	6	1	2	4	8	5	9	10
556	59	6	3	2	4	5	1	7	9	8	10	6	3	2	4	5	1	7	9	8	10
557	59	1	2	7	5	6	3	8	9	4	10	1	2	6	9	4	5	3	7	8	10
558	75	8	5	1	4	2	3	7	6	9	10	3	5	6	4	2	8	7	1	9	10
559	82	7	1	2	10	3	5	6	9	4	8	2	3	5	9	6	7	1	10	8	4
Average		4	3	5	6	7	1	2	8	9	10	4·55	4·55	4·45	4·36	4·45	4·45	4·45	6·27	8·27	9·18

CHAPTER 8

REPRODUCIBILITY OF ARRANGEMENT OF TEN
ODOURS BY MANY PEOPLE

A S HAS been described on p. 98, when this stage of the work was
started, that is when people were first asked to arrange the
ten odorant materials in order of preference, a request was usually
made soon afterwards for a second run, a repeat arrangement.
The intention was to see if the second arrangement corresponded
reasonably with the first. The subject was never advised that he
would be asked to make a second arrangement, until his first
arrangement had been made and noted down, the odorant bottles
randomly dispersed, and some conversation had ensued. At this
stage he regarded the matter as finished, and had probably dis-
missed from his mind any features of the arrangement that might
have impressed him at the time he was making it. The request for a
second arrangement was rather an imposition and obviously some
of the subjects thought that it was, but with two or three exceptions
where unwillingness was apparent and the matter was not pursued,
the subjects made the second run.

It was quite evident that nearly all the subjects viewed with some
trepidation a comparison of their first and second arrangements,
but when the two had been written down and were shown to them,
any dissatisfaction that they might have felt vanished and they
were both surprised and interested to see how well their two arrangements agreed: how well they had done the job. The diffidence
that most people feel about their sense of smell is quite unwar-
ranted; this sense is ordinarily very sensitive and discriminating
indeed, and its reliability on the odd occasions that it is measured
is usually a source of surprise and gratification to its owner.

Cases of exact correspondence

Exact agreement between two successive arrangements by a subject
was not as a rule obtained nor was it to have been expected. The
number of ways in which ten different bottles can be arranged
linearly is factorial 10 or 3,628,800, so that if a subject arranges

134

them in any one order in his first arrangement e.g. 5, 1, 3, 6, 7, 8, 4, 2, 9, 10, as subject No. 159 did, the chance that he would arrange them similarly in his second run is only 1 in 3,628,800. By chance, therefore, if there was no real liking or disliking of the smells in a preferred order, it is very unlikely indeed (odds of more than three million to one against) that any one subject would make two exactly similar arrangements. And yet as can be seen from Table 51, in which the results of the 127 subjects who each made two arrangements have been assembled, there were three subjects (425, 475, 517) whose second arrangement was identical with their first.

TABLE 51

Illustrating the measure of agreement of two successive arrangements by 127 subjects

Subject no.	Age (years)	Sex	Tempera-ment	The two arrangements of odorant bottles nos. 1–10									
48	7	M	E	1	2	5	8	3	4	6	7	9	10
				8	1	2	6	3	5	7	4	9	10
99	9	M	I	4	1	8	9	7	6	2	5	3	10
				1	4	5	9	8	2	6	3	7	10
107	11	M	I	1	8	7	2	6	5	3	4	10	9
				6	3	8	1	5	7	10	2	9	4
144	14	M	I	2	5	8	1	9	4	7	3	6	10
				2	5	8	1	9	7	4	3	6	10
145	8	M	E	1	5	8	4	7	10	3	9	2	6
				1	6	5	8	7	2	3	9	4	10
148	11	M	E	1	2	7	4	5	9	6	3	8	10
				1	7	2	4	5	8	3	6	9	10
159	12	M	E	5	1	3	6	7	8	4	2	9	10
				5	1	3	6	7	8	4	9	2	10
191	12	F	I	1	4	8	7	5	2	6	9	3	10
				1	2	7	8	5	6	4	3	9	10
192	12	F	I	1	8	5	7	4	9	6	2	3	10
				1	8	7	5	4	9	3	2	6	10
193	12	F	I	1	5	8	4	2	6	9	7	3	10
				1	5	4	2	7	8	3	9	6	10
194	12	F	I	1	2	3	8	6	7	5	9	4	10
				1	2	8	5	7	6	3	4	10	9
195	13	F	I	1	5	2	4	3	7	8	10	6	9
				1	5	4	2	8	7	3	6	9	10
196	13	F	I	7	1	4	8	5	2	9	3	10	6
				1	7	5	4	8	2	3	9	6	10
197	13	F	I	1	5	2	4	8	6	9	7	3	10
				1	8	7	5	4	2	3	6	9	10
198	13	F	I	1	2	5	4	6	8	3	10	9	7
				1	4	2	5	3	6	8	7	10	9
199	13	F	I	1	4	5	8	7	2	6	9	3	10
				1	8	2	3	4	5	7	9	10	6
201	13	F	I	1	5	8	4	3	7	9	10	2	6
				1	8	5	2	4	7	3	9	10	6
202	13	F	I	1	8	7	3	5	6	4	2	9	10
				1	4	8	7	3	5	2	6	9	10
203	13	F	I	1	8	2	3	4	7	5	6	9	10
				1	8	7	4	2	5	6	3	9	10
204	13	F	I	1	2	8	4	3	9	5	7	10	6
				1	3	8	2	10	4	9	7	5	6
205	13	F	I	1	7	5	9	4	8	10	2	3	6
				1	7	8	5	9	4	10	3	6	2
206	13	F	I	1	5	7	2	4	9	10	6	8	3
				1	5	7	4	2	3	8	6	10	9
207	13	F	I	1	5	8	7	4	9	2	3	6	10
				1	5	8	7	4	9	10	3	2	6
209	13	F	I	1	5	8	3	2	7	6	9	4	10
				1	5	3	8	2	4	7	6	9	10

TABLE 51—*continued*

Illustrating the measure of agreement of two successive arrangements by 127 subjects

Subject no.	Age (years)	Sex	Temperament	The two arrangements of odorant bottles nos. 1–10									
210	13	F	I	7	1	5	2	8	4	9	3	10	6
				7	1	8	4	9	5	6	3	2	10
212	14	F	I	1	5	2	7	8	3	9	10	4	6
				1	8	3	5	7	2	4	9	6	10
213	14	F	I	1	2	8	5	4	3	7	9	6	10
				1	2	7	5	3	4	8	6	9	10
214	14	F	I	1	5	8	4	7	9	3	2	6	10
				1	5	8	7	4	9	6	2	3	10
216	14	F	I	1	4	7	8	5	9	2	10	3	6
				7	1	5	4	8	9	10	3	6	2
218	14	F	I	1	8	7	5	4	2	10	6	9	3
				1	8	2	7	3	4	5	9	10	6
221	14	F	I	1	4	5	7	8	2	9	10	6	3
				1	7	4	5	8	2	9	3	10	6
222	11	F	E	8	1	4	5	3	6	9	7	2	10
				1	8	4	5	9	3	6	7	2	10
223	12	F	E	1	5	4	3	9	10	7	6	8	2
				1	5	4	9	3	7	8	10	2	6
224	12	F	E	1	5	8	2	4	6	10	7	9	3
				1	8	4	5	7	9	10	3	2	6
226	12	F	E	1	5	4	2	8	7	3	6	9	10
				1	5	4	7	8	9	3	6	2	10
227	12	F	E	8	1	7	3	5	4	9	10	2	6
				8	1	7	3	2	4	9	5	10	6
229	13	F	E	1	8	6	4	5	2	3	7	9	10
				1	8	5	6	4	2	7	3	9	10
230	13	F	E	1	8	5	7	2	4	9	3	10	6
				1	8	7	5	2	4	3	9	10	6
231	13	F	E	8	1	5	4	3	6	7	9	2	10
				8	1	4	5	3	6	7	2	9	10
232	13	F	E	1	8	3	2	4	7	5	6	9	10
				1	2	8	5	4	7	3	9	6	10
233	13	F	E	1	5	8	2	7	9	4	3	10	6
				2	8	5	9	1	7	3	4	6	10
234	13	F	E	1	5	8	7	4	2	3	6	9	10
				1	5	4	7	8	2	9	3	6	10
235	13	F	E	1	7	8	4	2	5	3	10	9	6
				7	1	4	8	5	3	2	9	10	6
236	13	F	E	8	1	6	4	2	10	9	3	5	7
				8	1	4	3	2	9	5	6	10	7
237	13	F	E	1	7	5	4	8	2	3	6	9	10
				1	7	5	8	4	2	3	9	6	10
238	13	F	E	1	5	4	2	3	7	8	9	6	10
				1	5	4	2	3	7	8	9	10	6
239	13	F	E	1	7	8	5	4	9	2	10	3	6
				1	7	5	8	4	9	10	3	2	6
241	13	F	E	1	7	8	3	5	2	4	9	6	10
				1	2	3	7	8	6	5	4	9	10
242	13	F	E	1	5	3	8	6	4	9	7	10	2
				1	3	5	8	6	9	4	7	10	2
243	13	F	E	8	4	5	1	10	2	6	3	9	7
				8	10	3	4	5	2	6	1	7	9
246	14	F	E	1	3	5	8	6	2	4	10	7	9
				1	8	5	7	4	2	6	3	10	9
248	14	F	E	1	4	7	5	8	2	10	3	6	9
				1	7	5	2	4	3	8	6	9	10
249	14	F	E	1	5	7	8	4	3	2	6	9	10
				1	7	5	8	4	3	6	2	9	10
250	14	F	E	1	5	7	4	9	3	8	2	10	6
				5	1	8	7	4	3	9	2	10	6
251	14	F	E	7	5	4	8	1	10	2	9	3	6
				7	5	8	4	1	9	2	10	3	6
252	14	F	E	1	4	8	7	5	2	9	6	3	10
				1	5	7	6	9	4	8	3	2	10
254	14	F	E	1	7	10	8	9	4	5	3	2	6
				1	8	7	10	5	9	4	3	2	6
255	14	F	E	1	5	4	2	3	7	6	8	10	9
				1	4	5	3	8	2	7	9	6	10
259	14	F	E	1	5	3	8	4	2	7	9	10	6
				1	3	8	5	2	4	7	9	10	6

TABLE 51—*continued*

Illustrating the measure of agreement of two successive arrangements by 127 subjects

Subject no.	Age (years)	Sex	Tempera- ment	The two arrangements of odorant bottles nos. 1–10									
271	16	M	I.	4	5	6	3	1	2	8	7	9	10
				4	5	3	1	6	2	8	7	9	10
295	17	M	E	3	1	2	6	7	5	8	4	10	9
				2	5	1	6	3	10	9	7	4	8
299	18	M	E	3	2	6	7	8	1	5	4	9	10
				2	7	3	6	1	8	4	5	9	10
301	15	F	I	1	4	5	3	8	7	2	10	9	6
				1	4	3	5	8	7	6	2	9	10
308	15	F	I	4	1	2	5	3	6	7	8	10	9
				4	1	5	2	3	6	7	8	10	9
378	15	F	E	1	8	5	4	3	7	9	6	2	10
				1	4	5	8	7	2	3	9	6	10
379	15	F	E	5	4	7	3	8	6	1	2	10	9
				1	4	7	·8	5	3	6	2	9	10
380	15	F	E	1	7	5	4	9	3	6	2	10	8
				1	7	5	4	2	6	3	9	8	10
381	16	F	E	3	8	2	6	1	7	5	4	9	10
				3	8	6	2	1	7	5	4	9	10
390	18	F	E	2	6	3	1	8	7	5	4	10	9
				2	3	6	1	7	8	5	4	10	9
421	24	M	I	3	1	8	9	5	4	6	7	2	10
				3	1	8	5	6	9	2	7	4	10
422	25	M	I	4	5	3	1	2	7	6	8	9	10
				4	5	3	1	7	2	6	8	9	10
425	29	·M	I	7	5	8	1	4	2	3	6	10	9
				7	5	8	1	4	2	3	6	10	9
427	31	M	I	5	1	2	4	3	7	6	8	9	10
				5	1	2	4	3	6	7	8	9	10
430	35	M	I	1	4	5	9	8	3	6	10	7	2
				1	4	5	9	8	7	6	3	10	2
431	38	M	I	4	5	1	2	6	8	3	10	7	9
				4	5	1	2	3	8	6	7	10	9
432	40	M	I	1	9	3	8	6	2	4	5	7	10
				9	2	7	1	5	8	4	3	10	6
437	24	M	E	2	1	3	7	5	9	4	10	8	6
				1	8	2	9	7	6	3	4	5	10
438	29	M	E	4	5	6	1	8	7	3	2	9	10
				4	5	6	1	8	3	7	2	9	10
440	32	M	E	2	6	1	4	8	7	10	3	9	5
				1	2	4	8	6	3	7	5	10	9
441	32	M	E	6	5	1	3	8	7	4	9	2	10
				3	6	1	5	7	8	2	4	9	10
470	22	F	I	7	1	8	5	4	3	2	6	10	9
				3	1	7	8	4	5	2	6	9	10
471	27	F	I	2	3	1	5	6	7	8	4	9	10
				2	3	5	1	7	6	8	4	9	10
474	30	F	I	5	4	7	6	1	2	8	9	10	3
				5	6	4	7	1	2	3	9	8	10
475	30	F	I	3	8	7	1	2	5	6	10	9	4
				3	8	7	1	2	5	6	10	9	4
476	35	F	I	4	6	2	5	3	10	9	1	8	7
				4	6	3	2	10	5	8	1	9	7
477	35	F	I	1	2	7	3	6	5	4	8	9	10
				1	5	3	6	7	2	4	8	9	10
479	39	F	I	3	6	5	1	7	2	8	4	10	9
				3	6	1	7	2	5	8	4	10	9
493	27	F	E	6	1	3	8	4	2	5	7	9	10
				6	1	8	2	3	4	7	5	9	10
505	36	F	E	8	2	5	7	6	10	3	4	9	1
				8	2	5	10	4	7	3	9	6	1
506	37	F	E	1	3	5	7	6	8	2	9	4	10
				1	3	2	5	6	7	8	4	9	10
508	38	F	E	6	3	4	7	2	5	1	8	9	10
				2	3	7	6	4	5	8	1	9	10
509	38	F	E	7	1	6	5	2	4	3	8	10	9
				6	1	2	7	4	5	9	3	8	10
510	38	F	E	7	6	3	2	1	5	4	9	8	10
				3	7	6	2	1	5	4	9	8	10
511	38	F	E	3	6	8	4	5	2	7	1	9	10
				3	4	8	7	6	5	1	2	9	10

TABLE 51—*continued*

Illustrating the measure of agreement of two successive arrangements by 127 subjects

Subject no.	Age (years)	Sex	Temperament	The two arrangements of odorant bottles nos. 1–10									
513	41	M	I	7	8	4	1	5	3	6	2	9	10
				7	8	4	1	6	3	5	2	9	10
514	42	M	I	1	4	2	5	7	6	9	8	3	10
				1	7	5	4	2	9	6	3	8	10
517	52	M	I	3	1	5	2	7	4	6	8	9	10
				3	1	5	2	7	4	6	8	9	10
518	53	M	I	4	3	6	1	2	5	9	7	8	10
				4	2	3	6	1	5	7	8	9	10
519	60	M	I	4	2	3	5	6	8	7	1	10	9
				7	8	4	3	5	2	6	9	1	10
520	60	M	I	3	7	2	1	4	9	5	6	8	10
				3	2	7	1	4	9	5	6	8	10
522	41	M	E	3	5	4	1	2	9	8	7	6	10
				3	1	5	6	4	10	8	7	9	2
523	45	M	E	4	1	2	5	3	7	6	8	9	10
				4	3	2	7	1	5	6	8	9	10
525	49	M	E	10	1	2	6	4	7	8	5	3	9
				10	1	5	8	4	3	2	6	7	9
526	50	M	E	5	4	1	3	6	2	7	8	9	10
				5	4	3	1	6	2	7	8	9	10
527	53	M	E	5	1	8	4	7	6	3	2	9	10
				5	1	4	7	8	3	6	9	2	10
529	55	M	E	6	3	1	7	2	5	8	4	9	10
				3	6	7	1	5	4	2	8	9	10
531	56	M	E	5	8	1	3	2	10	7	6	4	9
				5	8	2	10	1	7	3	6	4	9
532	57	M	E	8	6	5	4	10	3	2	7	9	1
				8	7	2	6	5	10	4	3	1	9
533	57	M	E	4	2	3	1	5	9	7	6	8	10
				4	3	2	1	5	8	6	7	9	10
534	63	M	E	1	7	8	3	5	9	2	4	6	10
				1	7	4	8	5	3	2	6	10	9
537	46	F	I	3	6	5	4	1	7	9	2	8	10
				3	6	5	1	7	9	2	4	8	10
539	49	F	I	3	6	8	4	5	1	9	2	7	10
				3	4	5	6	8	1	9	2	7	10
541	51	F	I	1	3	7	8	4	5	6	9	2	10
				1	7	9	4	5	8	6	2	3	10
543	54	F	I	4	6	5	1	3	2	8	10	9	7
				4	5	1	6	3	2	8	7	10	9
545	57	F	I	1	7	6	4	5	2	3	9	8	10
				1	5	2	7	9	3	6	4	8	10
546	58	F	I	2	8	3	5	1	4	7	9	6	10
				2	3	8	5	4	1	7	6	9	10
547	62	F	I	5	1	8	4	6	9	3	2	10	7
				5	1	4	8	7	9	2	10	6	3
548	80	F	I	7	2	5	6	1	3	8	4	9	10
				7	5	2	1	6	4	3	8	9	10
549	42	F	E	7	6	4	1	8	9	5	2	3	10
				7	6	8	3	4	2	1	9	5	10
551	46	F	E	4	2	3	5	6	7	9	10	8	1
				2	3	6	4	5	7	9	8	10	1
552	46	F	E	4	3	2	7	8	6	1	5	9	10
				4	3	7	2	1	8	9	5	6	10
553	48	F	E	6	3	4	2	5	1	7	9	8	10
				3	6	4	2	5	7	1	9	8	10
555	50	F	E	4	5	1	6	8	3	2	7	9	10
				4	6	3	2	1	8	7	5	9	10
556	59	F	E	6	3	2	4	5	1	7	9	8	10
				6	3	4	2	7	1	5	9	8	10
557	59	F	E	1	2	7	5	6	3	8	9	4	10
				1	2	7	3	6	5	8	9	4	10
558	75	F	E	8	5	1	4	2	3	7	6	9	10
				8	5	4	3	2	1	7	6	9	10
559	82	F	E	7	1	2	10	3	5	6	9	4	8
				2	1	3	5	7	6	10	9	4	8

Nearly identical repeat arrangements

Of those 127 subjects who made two arrangements, we have seen that for three of them, their second arrangement was just the same as their first and this shows that the differences in liking for the ten odorants were very definite and were progressive. If we now consider the nearly identical arrangements the best we can hope for is for one pair of odorants and no more to have been crossed. There are ten subjects (144, 159, 238, 308, 381, 422, 427, 438, 520 and 526) who have done no worse than cross two odorants in adjacent positions; for example subject 144 whose two arrangements were:

2 5 8 1 9 4 7 3 6 10 and
2 5 8 1 9 7 4 3 6 10

There were also two subjects (513 and 557) who had only one pair crossed, but the pair were separated by another number, for example the two arrangements of subject 513 were:

7 8 4 1 5 3 6 2 9 10
7 8 4 1 6 3 5 2 9 10

The agreement between the two runs is a shade less good in these two cases, but it is still very good indeed.

There are also 22 cases where the subject has the equivalent of two crosses, that is at least six of the ten numbers in the same positions in the two runs (192, 203, 214, 226, 227, 230, 231, 237, 242, 249, 251, 271, 430, 431, 471, 479, 510, 523, 539, 553, 556, 558). To what groups do these people who do so very well in repeating their arrangements belong? The distribution by sex is shown in Table 52.

TABLE 52

Distribution with sex of subjects with best agreement in two arrangements

Sex	No. of subjects in each group	No. of subjects giving			Percentage subjects included in previous three columns
		Exact repeat	Eight odorants similarly placed	Six or seven odorants similarly placed	
M	37	2	8	4	38
F	90	1	4	18	26
Both	127	3	12	22	29

It would seem that reproducibility of arrangement is rather better amongst the males than the females.

The distribution by age of the people who have provided two arrangements with excellent agreement is as shown in Table 53.

TABLE 53
Distribution with age of subjects with best agreement in two arrangements

Age group	No. of subjects in age group	No. of subjects giving			Percentage subjects included in previous three columns
		Exact repeat	Eight odorants similarly placed	Six or seven odorants similarly placed	
0–7	1	—	—	—	—
8–14	58	0	3	11	24
15–19	10	0	2	1	30
20–40	25	2	3	5	40
over 40	33	1	4	5	30
Total	127	3	12	22	29

It is fairly clear from Table 53 that the adults in their prime give better reproducibility in their two arrangements than do the children, the teenagers or the older people. It is unfortunate that only one member of the under eight class was given a repeat run; the chances are that the reliability would be poor in this age group.

The distribution between the two temperaments of these very reliable arrangers is shown in Table 54.

TABLE 54
Distribution between the temperaments of subjects with best agreement in two arrangements

Temperament group	No. of subjects in each temperament group	No. of subjects giving			Percentage subjects included in previous three columns
		Exact repeat	Eight odorants similarly placed	Six or seven odorants similarly placed	
Introvert	58	3	5	9	29
Extrovert	69	0	7	13	29
Both	127	3	12	22	29

Apparently the introverts are neither more nor less reliable than the extroverts; it may be, however, significant that all of the three people who produced second arrangements that were identical with their first were introverts: 425, a twenty-nine-year-old male; 475, a thirty-year-old female; and 517, a fifty-two-year-old male. But there is clearly not much to choose between the two temperaments in respect of reliability of arrangement.

General agreement

The excellence of agreement in the thirty-seven examples listed in Tables 52, 53 and 54 is outstanding, but it is followed by a large body of still good, if less impressive, agreement. This can be gathered by inspection of Table 51; it is perfectly clear on inspection of it that the two components of the pairs of arrangements usually agree well with each other. It is easier to assess the agreement in detail if we consider the number of placings of odorants that agree (i.e. are the same) in the pairs. We have already seen that there were three pairs of identical arrangements; there cannot be any with nine equivalent placings because if one odorant is displaced another one must be too so that from ten we drop straight to eight. But there were twelve pairs with eight similar placings, and twenty-two pairs with six or seven similar placings. We can express this in tabular form as in Table 55.

The greatest frequencies occur in the eight, six and four similar placings, corresponding to one, two and three crosses, with the odd numbers, which are indicative of more confusion, not occurring so frequently. But what is most surprising and most significant of all is that out of 1270 placings in the first arrangement, 534 or 42 per cent of the placings, are just the same in the second arrangement. If Table 51 is examined further it can be seen that of the remaining $(1270-534=736)$ places the displacement is only by one place in 373 instances. Two examples may clarify this point. Subject No. 48 made two arrangements (Table 51) of

1 2 5 8 3 4 6 7 9 10 and

8 1 2 6 3 5 7 4 9 10.

It can be seen that three of the odorants, Nos. 1, 2 and 7, are displaced by only one place. Subject 99 has displaced five odorants Nos. 1, 4, 2, 6 and 3 by only one place. For these two subjects together the total of displacements by only one place is eight. For all the subjects listed in Table 51 the total is 373. So that in only

TABLE 55

Distribution of numbers of similar placings in pairs of arrangements

No. of placings similar in the two arrangements of a pair	No. of pairs of arrangements with that number of similar placings	Equivalent to gross number of similar placings
10 (identical)	3	30
9	0 (impossible)	0
8	12	96
7	7	49
6	15	90
5	12	60
4	27	108
3	20	60
2	15	30
1	11	11
0	5	0
Total	127	534 (average 4·2 similar placings in every ten total placings)

363 cases, about 29 per cent, is the second placing of any given odorant two or more places different from the first placing. In 42 per cent of the cases of twice arranging ten odorants it is identical; in 29 per cent the second placing is only one place removed from the first; and in the remaining 29 per cent it is two or more places removed. It will be appreciated that there is a very high measure indeed of agreement between the first and second arrangements, and that for the most part the differences are only very slight. When it is remembered that these arrangements were made by unpractised subjects, by people who had no special interest in smell, and that some of the odorants were just pleasant, neither very attractive nor unattractive, the consistency is remarkable and is a sure indication of the positive nature, of the reality, of the odour preferences that the subjects were showing.

Rules

Five general rules may be derived from the contents of this chapter. They are:

Rule 39. Reproducibility of arrangement of a small number of dissimilar odours in order of preference by one subject is usually good.

Rule 40. Reliability of preference of odours, as judged by reproducibility of arrangement is better amongst adults, particularly the 20–40 age group, than amongst younger and older people.

Rule 41. Males are slightly more reliable than females in their odour preferences, that is their second arrangement of preferences is likely to agree better with their first arrangement.

Rule 42. There is no difference in reliability or reproducibility of odour preferences between people of introvert and extrovert temperaments.

Rule 43. When two preference arrangements of ten dissimilar odorants are made by a group of people, about 40 per cent of the placings will be the same in the two arrangements, about 30 per cent will only be one place removed in the two arrangements, and the other 30 per cent will be two or more places removed. This finding is based mainly on tests with people of 11 years and older and might not apply to younger children.

CHAPTER 9

ODOUR PREFERENCE VARIATIONS WITH SEX
(TEN ODORANTS, MANY PEOPLE)

THE INFORMATION on which the enquiry discussed in this chapter is based is contained in Tables 31–50. Because at the moment we are interested mainly in the effect that sex has on the individual's odour preferences, we can sum together and average the introverts' and extroverts' results in what are otherwise similar groups. An example may make this clear.

From Table 31 we have, for introvert males under eight years, average placings of:

No. 1	No. 2	No. 3	No. 4	No. 5	No. 6	No. 7	No. 8	No. 9	No. 10
1·36	5·45	6·18	5·23	3·14	7·32	7·18	5·64	5·32	8·18

From Table 32 we have, for extrovert males under eight years, average placings of:

1·70	5·04	5·70	5·66	3·63	7·07	5·70	5·63	6·00	8·85

Averaging these two lines, we get for all males under eight years:

1·53	5·25	5·94	5·45	3·39	7·20	6·44	5·64	5·66	8·52

If we do the same for the groups in Tables 33–50 we arrive at the summary shown in Table 56; all that has been condensed is the two temperament groups into one. The "average" that is used is the mean of the average introvert and extrovert group figures; the fact that there were 22 introverts (Table 31) and 27 extroverts (Table 32) is disregarded so as to avoid loading the final average either with one group or the other. The average values for introverts and extroverts separately have been found and the average for the whole age and sex group is the arithmetic mean of these two values. Similarly, the "all groups" values for each sex are the average of the age–sex groups; once again the fact that some groups contained more subjects than others has been disregarded, so that the crowding in some of the age groups does not load the "all groups" average in favour of the crowded groups.

144

TABLE 56

Placing of the ten odorants according to subject's sex

Odorant no.	Average placing by males of years:						Average placing by females of years:						Difference in average placings of males-females
	0-7	8-14	15-19	20-40	Over 40	All groups	0-7	8-14	15-19	20-40	Over 40	All groups	
1 (strawberry essence)	1·53	1·86	1·89	2·86	4·14	2·46	1·47	1·30	2·37	3·58	3·96	2·54	−0·08
2 (spearmint oil)	5·25	5·10	4·73	5·04	4·62	4·95	4·63	5·28	5·08	5·57	5·24	5·16	−0·21
3 (lavender oil)	5·94	6·44	5·86	4·71	4·38	5·47	6·08	6·76	3·95	3·49	4·48	4·95	+0·52
4 (musk lactone)	5·45	3·81	4·76	4·02	3·36	4·28	5·68	4·75	5·32	5·18	4·36	5·06	−0·78
5 (vanillin)	3·39	3·64	3·43	4·53	4·65	3·93	4·59	3·62	4·82	4·34	4·08	4·29	−0·36
6 (neroli oil)	7·20	6·31	6·89	5·51	5·52	6·29	7·83	7·89	7·29	6·23	4·66	6·78	−0·49
7 (almond essence)	6·44	6·05	5·31	6·07	5·32	5·84	5·17	5·14	4·61	4·43	5·26	4·92	+0·92
8 (naphthalene)	5·64	5·35	5·75	5·30	5·86	5·58	5·07	4·06	4·60	5·03	5·67	4·89	+0·69
9 (rape oil)	5·66	7·25	7·46	7·80	7·98	7·23	5·91	7·59	7·46	7·79	7·95	7·34	−0·11
10 (chlorophyll oil-soluble)	8·52	9·15	8·90	9·14	9·18	8·98	8·57	8·61	9·51	9·39	9·34	9·08	−0·10

If we look first at the "all groups" columns where irrespective of age or temperament all the males are grouped in one column, and all the females in another, we can see that there are some considerable differences, and in determining in which direction these lie we must remember that the lower the average placing of an odorant, the better was that odorant liked compared with the others used in the test. The biggest differences occur in 7 (almond), 4 (musk lactone), and 8 (naphthalene); females rate almond almost a whole place better than males do, and the males show nearly as great a preference for the musk smell. The females also like 8 (naphthalene) considerably better than do the males. Reference to Table 30 will show that these three preferences agree with those found in the first part of the investigation; then, as now, naphthalene was much more liked, or rather less disliked, by women than men; then, as now, the preference shown for musk lactone by the males was well marked; but the females' preference for almond essence was much less marked then than it is in the bigger group of people. The first part of the investigation showed trends and these have become sometimes better, sometimes less well defined in the second stage.

After almond essence, musk lactone and naphthalene, the biggest difference between men and women is shown in the responses to 3 (lavender) for which women show a preference over men (Table 56); this is unexpected because in the first stage of the investigation the two sexes (Table 30) had ranked it nearly equally. There is no evident explanation of this discrepancy but it must be assumed that the results in Table 56, representing as they do the experience of a much larger number of people are more reliable.

The inferences that may be drawn respecting the preference differences of the sexes, concerning the ten odorants are assembled in Table 57.

TABLE 57
Odorant preferences of the sexes

Odorants which males rank much better than females do	Odorants which females rank much better than males do	Odorants which males and females rank nearly equally
(26) Musk lactone	(40) Almond essence	(14) Strawberry essence
	(79) Naphthalene	(12) Oil-soluble chlorophyll
	(23) French lavender	(112) Rape oil
		(18) Spearmint
		(37) Vanillin
		(38) Neroli

The bracketed numbers indicate the rankings of these particular odorants that were assigned to them by the group of subjects in the first part of the investigation (Table 1). It is significant that the two most pleasant odorants and the two most unpleasant are all to be found in the third column ranked almost equally by the different sexes. This is in line with Rule 5, that people of all kinds agree unanimously (no sex differences) about their dislikes, and also in line with Rule 6 that there is very good agreement by most people about the smells that they like best. Where there are differences, these are to be expected in the intermediate range of odours, as already indicated in Rule 8. The better ranking that the females have given to almond essence is reminiscent of Rule 18 that odours with culinary associations are ranked more highly by women than men; almond essence is certainly used in the baking of cakes, but the preference is so marked that one feels that it may have a more fundamental basis.

To summarize the foregoing, out of ten selected odorants, the musky smell is much preferred by males, the almond and naphthalene smells much more by women, lavender is also preferred by women, and the other six show no great differences in the responses accorded to them by the different sexes.

Sex preferences in age groups

Comparison of the similar age groups for the two sexes can be made readily from Table 56. The most evident differences are indicated below, the point at issue at present being not the differences between the age groups, but the differences between the sexes in each of the age groups.

Under 8 years. Both boys and girls show a strong preference for (1) strawberry essence and both place (5) vanillin second, but the young girls do not like it so much as the young boys. The young girls, like all of their sex, rank almond essence better than the boys do. There are other differences but they are not so well marked. There is at this age practically no difference between the sexes in their placing of musk lactone, and both agree in their placings of the least pleasant odours. The outstanding differences are the young boys' greater liking for vanillin and the young girls' for almond essence.

8–14 years. There are bigger differences between the sexes in this group. The boys show a much better liking, or at least tolerance for (6) neroli than do the girls, and they also show a marked liking for (4) musk lactone, which has sex associations; in the under 8's there was very little difference in the responses of the two sexes to musk lactone but the boys' preference for it is very marked in the 8–14 years group. The girls' liking for (7) almond essence, evident in the youngest group, persists, and a new feature that now appears is their greater liking for naphthalene; this is unexpected because naphthalene certainly has no sweetness or fruitiness, but the preference is evident enough, and it will be seen that it persists throughout the next two age groups. It is noteworthy that although girls in the 8–14 group place (10) chlorophyll almost exactly as their 0–7 age group had done, the boys' dislike of it has grown from their younger group. Another difference between the sexes is that although the 8–14 boys show a slight falling off in their liking for (1) strawberry compared with the 0–7 boys, the 8–14 girls like this fruity smell even better than their 0–7 group, and now like it considerably more than the boys do. Musk and orange-blossom (neroli) for the boys, naphthalene and almonds for the girls; those are the outstanding features in this age group.

15–19 years. In this group the differences between the sexes in their odour preferences are even more marked; as age increases the sex differences increase too, and this supports the view that the differences that we are examining are truly associated with the subject's sex. Lavender (3) is placed by the young women at 3·95 but by the young men at 5·86, a difference of nearly two placings and indicative of a very marked preference for lavender by the women. It is difficult to suggest a reason why there should be such a preference; it is true that the lavender smell carries a hint of good housekeeping: flower sprays in the linen cupboards, and polish on the furniture, but one might just as reasonably attribute these housewifely uses to the liking that the housewife already has for the lavender smell as *vice versa*. The next biggest difference between the two sexes in this age group is in the placings given to (5) vanillin; the young men like it just as much as did the boys, but the young women are not now so fond of it. Next and still more than one whole place different comes (8) naphthalene which in fact in every age group the females find better than the men. Once again the women like (7) almonds better than the men, or at least they rank it better, and just as in the case of naphthalene they do this in every age group. One other point worthy of notice is that the oil-soluble chlorophyll which was tolerated rather better by girls in the 8–14 age group than by the boys in the same age group, has now in the young women become much less tolerable and they have assigned to it an average placing of 9·51 which is quite the poorest value that appeared in any of the age groups irrespective of sex. In this age group the main preferences are: lavender, naphthalene and almonds for the young women, vanillin for the young men, and as usual, although in this age group not quite so pronounced, a preference by the men for musk lactone.

20–40 years. The men and women are in their prime, working harder than at any other age, home-building and rearing families. For most of them life is earnest, decisions have to be made quickly, and preferences of all kinds olfactory and others are real, are accepted and worked on. Once more the biggest differences are in the preferences shown by the women for (7) almonds and (3) lavender whilst the men again prefer (4) musk lactone and (6) neroli. This time, too, there is a considerable difference in the placing of (1) the strawberry essence; neither men nor women place it nearly so high as did the children but whereas the men give it an average placing of 2·86 the women give it no better than 3·58; the mature men still like the fruity flavour (for smell is most of flavour) better than the mature women do. In this age group then, the main preferences are for almonds and lavender by the women, for musk lactone and neroli by the men.

The over 40's. Sex is becoming less important, the reproductive function has been exercised and families are grown. Will this reduce the differences in preferences for one odour or another between the sexes? Will they settle down into a uniform liking or disliking? Inspection of the relevant columns in Table 56 shows that they certainly have moved in that direction; the change is unmistakeable. The women no longer like (7) almond essence significantly better than the men and their preference for (8) naphthalene is now only marginal. There is no single odorant that women now rate one whole place better than the men; the nearest, 0·86 place, is neroli: this is an astounding change because in all the other age groups it had been preferred by the males. The men still prefer (4) musk lactone and rate it one whole place better than the women and they have developed a minor preference for spearmint. The retention of the musk preference by men in the over 40 age group is indicative of their retention of sex interest. When forty is passed the sex interest, regarded as a biological and not merely a social characteristic, is becoming unimportant to women; that part of their behaviour that was conditioned by sex fades, and included in this is a part of their olfactory preferences. With men the sex urge, regarded biologically, lives longer and they are still attracted by the sweet sexy musky smells long after they have passed forty. That some of our olfactory preferences, in the prime of life, derive from sex interest and requirements there can be no doubt.

Graphical representation of sex differences

In Figs. 16, 17 and 18 the average placing for each age group of the two sexes is plotted. The mid-age for each group is used for the plot point. In looking at the resulting curves it should be remembered

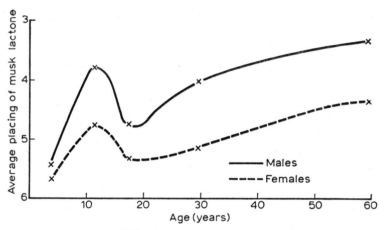

FIG. 16.—From early childhood to old age the males rate musk lactone better than the females do.

that the higher the curve (the lower the placing) the better the odour is liked. Fig. 16 is for (4) musk lactone. It can be seen that, throughout, the males (solid line) rate it better than do the females (intermittent line), and furthermore that the males' preference for it extends into old age. The musky smell is a sex-attractant to the males; they always like it better than the females do and this liking persists as long as does their sex interest.

In Fig. 17 similar curves are shown for (7) almond; this time the preference for it is shown by the females not by the males; the preference is very marked but it tapers off after age forty and later on the females then rate it about equally with the males. It has to be admitted that the males' liking for (7) almond seems to increase towards middle age, and this plays its part in bringing the two curves together. But it still remains that in childhood and in the

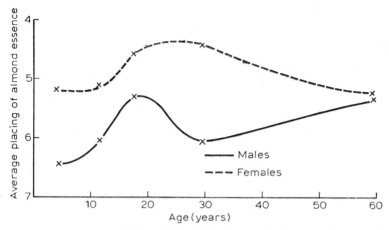

FIG. 17.—From early childhood to middle age the females rate the almond smell better than the males do.

prime of life there is a big difference between the two sexes in their liking for almond, and that this difference vanishes in middle-old age. The other odorant for which a marked difference was observed between the sexes was (8) naphthalene; curves for this are shown in Fig. 18; once again in childhood and in the prime of life the females rate the odorant much better than the males do, but this difference diminishes and has practically disappeared by middle age.

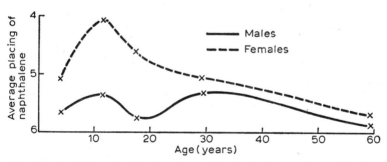

FIG. 18.—In childhood and in the prime of life the females rate the naphthalene smell better than the males, but the preference diminishes after age 30.

Arrangement of the ten odours by the sexes

It is of interest to see what differences there are between the whole sex groups in their arrangement of the ten odours. These may be seen in Table 58.

The two sexes agree on what they like best and on what they

TABLE 58

Rankings by the sexes

| Ranking | Odorant so ranked by: | |
	Males	Females
1st	Strawberry essence	Strawberry essence
2nd	Vanillin	Vanillin
3rd	Musk lactone	Naphthalene
4th	Spearmint oil	Almond essence
5th	Lavender oil	Lavender oil
6th	Naphthalene	Musk lactone
7th	Almond essence	Spearmint oil
8th	Neroli	Neroli
9th	Rape oil	Rape oil
10th	Chlorophyll	Chlorophyll

dislike most. Intermediately there are significant differences which mainly concern naphthalene and almond essence both of which the females rank better and musk lactone which the males rank better.

Rules

Those general rules that may be derived from the contents of this chapter are:

Rule 44. Some of the differences between the two sexes in respect of odour preferences are very marked (cf. Rule 11).

Rule 45. Both sexes agree on what are the best liked and also on the least liked odours; this is in accord with Rules 6 and 5. Those odours which the sexes rate differently are in the intermediate range, in line with Rules 8 and 11 and the differences are biggest between the ages of 15 and 40.

Rule 46. Males rate the musky smell of musk lactone significantly better than do females. Muskiness appears to be a sex attractant for males (cf. Rule 17).

Rule 47. Females rate the nutty smell of almond essence and the sophisticated but almost indescribable smell of naphthalene much better than males do. These preferences become less marked after age 40.

Rule 48. Odour preference differences between the sexes persist into old age if the preference is shown by males, but die away soon after 40 years of age if the preference is shown by females.

Rule 49. Sex differences in odour preferences are evident at a very early age. They are already detectable in the under 8 year olds, and some are quite well marked in the 8–14 years group. They become still more marked in the next two age groups, but mostly tend to fall away after age 40.

CHAPTER 10

ODOUR PREFERENCE VARIATIONS WITH AGE
(TEN ODORANTS, MANY PEOPLE)

THE INFORMATION on which this study is based is contained in Tables 31–50, and the average placing of the four classes (introvert male, extrovert male, introvert female, extrovert female) for each age group and for each odorant is shown in Table 59. The method of arriving at the averages may be illustrated thus: odorant No. 1 (strawberry flavour) in the 0–7 age group is given an average placing of 1·36 by the introvert males (Table 31), one of 1·70 by the extrovert males (Table 32), one of 1·58 by the introvert females (Table 33) and one of 1·36 by the extrovert females (Table 34); the average of these four placings is 1·50 which is the figure shown in Table 59. The other figures are reached in a similar way.

TABLE 59

Influence of age on olfactory preferences

Odorant		Average placing by age group				
No.	Name	0–7	8–14	15–19	20–40	Over 40
1	Strawberry flavour	1·50	1·58	2·13	3·22	4·05
2	Spearmint oil	4·94	5·19	4·90	5·30	4·93
3	Lavender oil	6·01	6·60	4·90	4·10	4·43
4	Musk lactone	5·56	4·28	5·04	4·60	3·86
5	Vanillin	3·99	3·62	4·13	4·43	4·36
6	Neroli oil	7·51	7·10	7·09	5·87	5·09
7	Almond flavour	5·81	5·59	4·96	5·25	5·29
8	Naphthalene	5·35	4·70	5·18	5·16	5·77
9	Rape oil	5·79	7·42	7·46	7·80	7·97
10	Oil-soluble chlorophyll	8·54	8·88	9·20	9·26	9·26

There are some changes in the placing of an odorant with age that are at once evident. For example, the placing assigned to (1) strawberry flavour goes up with age, and so does that for (9) chlorophyll. So, too, equally clearly, the placings for (3) lavender and (6) neroli go down with increasing age. No. (2), spearmint maintains a fairly constant placing at all ages. So much and indeed more, can be seen by inspection of Table 59, but there is much more that can be learnt from a detailed analysis. There are, for example, differences in liking between the two sexes in one age group and from one age group to another, notably in the cases of (4) musk lactone and (7) almond; such differences may balance each other so that they are not revealed in Table 59. Furthermore there may be significant and regular variations with age *within* one of the age groups used in Table 59. More detailed study can throw light on such aspects of changes of olfactory preferences with age. Such an analysis is to be found in the remainder of this chapter.

Mean placements of odorants at each age

It is clear enough from what we have seen above, that there are many interesting variations in odour preferences with age. In Table 59 we have considered five age groups, the same as those that were used in compiling Tables 31–50, viz. under 8, 8–14 years, 15–19 years, 20–40 years and over 40 years. Examination of the results of these five age groups shows that preferences often change with age and invites a closer examination in such cases of the changes in preference with age. When, for example, there are big differences in odorant placings between two consecutive age groups, it would be desirable and of considerable interest to examine the incidence of the differences by taking more and smaller age groups. This can be done by reference back to Tables 31–50 which provide material for single ages, with a few exceptions, from 5 to 19 years and then for smaller groups, e.g. 20–29, 30–39, 40–49, and lastly 50 and over. When these different age groups including the individual ages from 5 to 19 are plotted, using the mid-age of the group as the plot (e.g. $24\frac{1}{2}$ in 20–29 group, $34\frac{1}{2}$ in the 30–39 group, $44\frac{1}{2}$ in the 40–49 group, and 60 in the 50 and over group), against the average placement of each odorant, a great deal more information is revealed. It becomes clear that there are changes in olfactory preferences with age which are both interesting and astonishing. For each one of the ten odorants, the placing at the different ages is shown graphically in Figs. 19–31. The conditions of determining the plot points in these figures are as follows:

(1) Up to and including age 19, the plot point is for one age only; i.e. one plot for age 5, another for age 6 and so on.

(2) Over 19 years, the placings are considered in age *groups*: 20–29 years (mid-age $24\frac{1}{2}$), 30–39 years (mid-age $34\frac{1}{2}$), 40–49 years (mid-age $44\frac{1}{2}$), and 50 years and over (mid-age 60).

(3) No plot is shown unless it is the mean of at least six individual subjects' placings: if there are for example, only three individuals of an age, as there are for age 4, then no point is plotted.

(4) In the study of odorants 1, 2, 3, 5, 6, 9 and 10, the considerations in Chapter 9 had shown that there were no great differences in placings for any one odorant by the two sexes, so that in these cases males and females of an age are grouped together. For example, the plots in Fig. 19 are obtained by summing the placings of all (male and female) observers of an age group and dividing by the number of observers in the age group. Odorants 4 (musk lactone), 7 (almond essence) and 8 (naphthalene) which in Chapter 9 had been shown to be ranked unequally by the two sexes were treated in two ways:

   (a) As above, all observers, male and female together and the results are shown in Figs. 22, 26 and 28

   (b) With the sexes considered separately and the results are then as shown in Figs. 23, 27 and 29.

Because the plots for the "both sexes" line are obtained by dividing the sum of the average placings by the total number of observers, they will not necessarily be the arithmetic means of the corresponding plots for the males and females separately in that same age group; only if the age group contains equal numbers of males and females will the "both sexes" plot be the mean of the "males" and "females" plots.

Typical derivation of plots for one of the curves in Figs. 19–31.

The average placing of strawberry essence is plotted against age in Fig. 19. This is a very interesting curve indeed, but before discussing its implications in detail, it may be advisable to show how the plots on which it is based are derived from Tables 31–50. This will be done in detail to make the method perfectly clear. Reference to Tables 31–34 shows that there were twenty-two five-year olds who took part in the tests, six of them are included in Table 31 (introvert males), six of them in Table 32 (extrovert males), nine of them in Table 33 (introvert females) and one in Table 34 (extrovert females). The total placings of No. 1 odorant by the six five-year olds in Table 31 were $1+4+1+1+1+2 = 10$; those by the six five-year olds in Table 32 were $1+1+1+4+2+1 = 10$, so that twelve male five-year olds gave a total of placings of 20 to odorant No. 1, an average of 1·67 each. The females, nine in Table 33

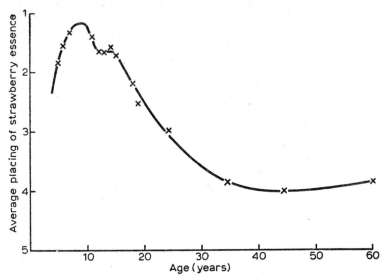

Fig. 19.—Variation in liking (both sexes together) for the strawberry flavour with age.

placed No. 1 odorant thus: $3+1+1+1+1+1+6+5+1 = 20$ and the one female five-year old in Table 34 placed No. 1 odorant: 1; so that ten female five-year olds placed No. 1 odorant so that their placings totalled 21, and averaged 2·10 each. There were twenty-two five-year olds (12 males+10 females = 22) and the total of their placings of No. 1 odorant was $20+21 = 41$, so that the average placing by the whole group of five-year olds was $41 \div 22$ or 1·86. This (1·86) is the figure that is used for the plot. The plots for other ages are obtained similarly. They are set out for No. 1 odorant in detail in Table 60.

Where fewer than six subjects occur in a group, then the average is not given, nor is it used as a plot. Those figures given in the last column of Table 60 form the plots for Fig. 19. Inspection of Table 60 enables the average placing of strawberry essence by the two sexes at each age to be seen separately. There is, therefore, more information in Table 60 than has been used to prepare Fig. 19. But the differences between the sexes are not very great; both sexes follow the same trends in their placings of strawberry essence. There is a more marked liking in the years of adolescence for the fruity odour by the girls than by the boys; that is the only remarkable difference between them.

TABLE 60

Placements of (1) strawberry essence at each age

Age (years)	Males			Females			Both sexes together		
	No. of subjects	Sum of placings	Average placing	No. of subjects	Sum of placings	Average placing	No. of subjects	Sum of placings	Average placing
4	1	5	—	2	2	—	3	7	—
5	12	20	1·67	10	21	2·10	22	41	1·86
6	12	20	1·67	17	25	1·47	29	45	1·55
7	24	31	1·30	20	27	1·35	44	58	1·32
8	1	1	—	—	—	—	1	1	—
9	1	2	—	—	—	—	1	2	—
10	—	—	—	—	—	—	—	—	—
11	11	15	1·36	1	2	—	12	17	1·42
12	23	43	1·87	11	13	1·18	34	56	1·65
13	36	73	2·03	32	42	1·31	68	115	1·69
14	19	35	1·84	27	36	1·33	46	71	1·54
15	26	46	1·77	12	19	1·58	38	65	1·71
16	1	5	—	1	5	—	2	10	—
17	1	2	—	—	—	—	1	2	—
18	7	18	2·57	33	70	2·12	40	88	2·20
19	5	5	—	64	168	2·63	69	173	2·51
20–29	21	57	2·71	42	132	3·14	63	189	3·00
30–39	14	43	3·07	23	102	4·43	37	145	3·85
40–49	9	35	3·89	12	49	4·08	21	84	4·00
50 and over	14	58	4·14	14	50	3·57	28	108	3·86

Tables for the other nine odorants, which would correspond to Table 60 are not included, but they have been prepared and the figures in their last columns (similar to Table 60) have been used in the preparation of Figs. 20, 21, 22, 24, 25, 26, 28, 30 and 31. Furthermore, the division of results according to sex as shown in Table 60, has correspondingly been made for the other odorants (although not shown) and in the case of the odorants (4) musk lactone, (7) almond essence and (8) naphthalene, such divisions have been used to form the basis of Figs. 23, 27 and 29.

(1) Strawberry essence. Fig. 19 shows that the children all like strawberry essence and give it an average placing between 1 and 2. But there is a peak of liking which occurs at an age of eight to ten; younger children do not rate the fruity flavour quite so highly, and after age ten or eleven there is a gradual drop in appreciation which eventually tails off with age to an average placing of about 4. One other remarkable feature is that there is a standstill at adolescence and the average placing is fairly constant between the ages of twelve and fifteen. The picture is of a peak of liking at eight to ten years, a standstill at adolescence and then a gradual onset of a lack of appreciation so that by age forty the average placing is no better than 4.

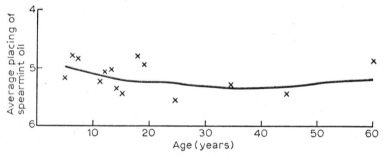

Fig. 20.—The liking for spearmint flavour does not change much throughout life (both sexes together).

(2) Spearmint oil. Fig. 20, the corresponding picture for spearmint, is not very inspiring; throughout the greater part of life from age five to age sixty, there is an average placing that is not far from 5. The liking for spearmint is independent of age and so it is of sex; it is uniform throughout life, at least after the age of five.

(3) French lavender oil. Fig. 21 shows some unexpected behaviour. From age five to fifteen, the children rate lavender oil round about 6; their dislike for it seems to increase a little and a rating of $5\frac{1}{2}$

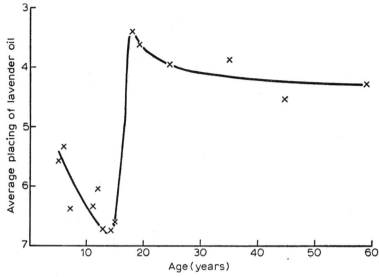

FIG. 21.—Variation with age of the liking for lavender (both sexes together).

at age five, falls to below 6½ at age fifteen. Then quite suddenly a liking develops for lavender and at age eighteen, the rating is between 3 and 4; there is a tremendous reduction of more than three places (from 6·8 to 3·5) between the ages of fifteen and eighteen. Nowhere previously have we encountered such a sudden change in liking. It is inexplicable, but it is inescapable. After age eighteen the placing settles down round about 4 and is steady there into old age. The sudden change, the sudden liking that supervenes between ages fifteen and eighteen is permanent; mature people rate lavender a good two places better than children do. The sudden liking develops in both sexes; it is not confined to one, not even much more noticeable in one than in the other; average placings for the two sexes separately at ages fifteen and eighteen are shown in Table 61.

TABLE 61

The increase in liking for lavender comes quite suddenly and is common to both sexes

Age	Sex	Average placing of lavender
15	M	7·00
18	M	3·14
15	F	5·83
18	F	3·52

(4) Musk lactone. This is one of the odorants which was found in the examination described in Chapter 9 to evoke very different placings from the two sexes. Accordingly, it will be well to examine the results from the two sexes at each age separately, but before doing that we can look at the two together. Fig. 22 shows the

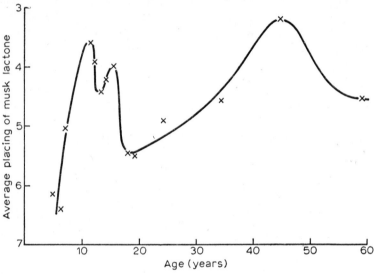

FIG. 22.—Variation with age of the liking for musk lactone (both sexes together).

average placing for musk lactone plotted against age; this curve is for all the subjects, male and female. There is a pronounced peak at the age of adolescence, a rapid fall in liking at the age of eighteen–twenty and thereafter an increase in liking to age forty-five after which there is a fall. It is significant that the two ages of maximum liking for musk lactone occur at about twelve to fifteen and in the forties, both ages having sex significance. In Fig. 23 separate curves for the two sexes are shown; that for the males is always higher than that for the females, but there is some parallelism between the two; there is no doubt that the males show a marked liking for musk lactone at the onset of sexual activity and there seems to be an indication that the females like it best at the termination of their reproductive period. A liking for musk lactone, and doubtless for similar musky smells, is closely associated with male sex characteristics; it is, in fact, probably a secondary characteristic of male sex activity. As was noted in Chapter 9, the male preference for this odorant continues into old age.

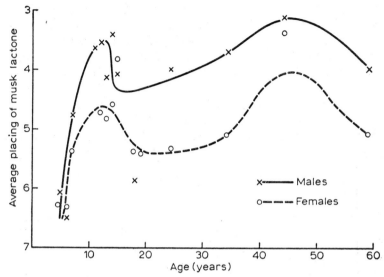

FIG. 23.—Variation with age of the two sexes separately in their liking for musk lactone smell.

(5) Vanillin. The average placings at each age of vanillin are shown in Fig. 24. The curve suggests that there is a maximum liking for it between the ages of seven and fifteen and that by the time eighteen or nineteen is reached, the liking has fallen away and indeed stays at a placing of around 5 thereafter. But the degree of liking around eight to fifteen years is very marked and corresponds

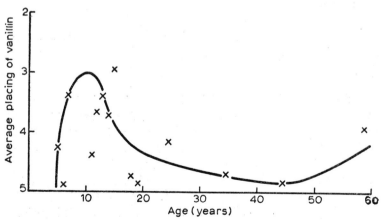

FIG. 24.—Variation with age (both sexes together) of the liking for vanillin.

F

at one stage to an average placing of 3. Quite clearly, vanillin is most highly appreciated by children. There is however more irregularity than usual about the placings for vanillin and as can be seen from Fig. 24, it was impossible to draw a smooth curve which did justice to all the plots. But the main finding of enhanced liking for vanillin over the age range eight to fifteen is clear enough, and the decrease in liking in the late 'teens is also definite.

(6) Neroli oil. Neroli is the essential oil of orange blossom. The outstanding inference to be drawn from Fig. 25 in which

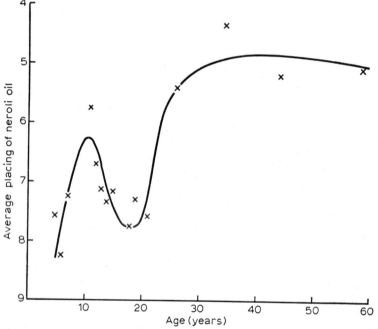

FIG. 25.—Variation with age (both sexes together) of the liking for neroli.

the average placing of neroli is plotted against age is that adults like it very much better than children do. First of all, oiliness (cf. Rule 23) is not a characteristic than endears itself olfactorily to children. Secondly, there is no doubt at all that neroli has a very sophisticated smell; the author ordinarily likes it and considers it a beautiful smell, but there are times when it is too sweet and beautiful and one puts it aside rather overcome. To an adult it is ordinarily a beautiful odour, but it is one that can be tired of and it is perhaps not surprising to find that children do not rate it highly. It is an essential ingredient of eau-de-Cologne, one of the best-liked of perfumes, but in this composition the richness of neroli has been toned down by volatile and spirituous ingredients. It is odd that the liking for neroli develops in the early twenties as can be seen from Fig. 25; we have become accustomed to marked changes in odour preferences occurring at adolescence and also at the age of about eighteen, but the change from near-dislike to positive liking of neroli, takes place when people are considerably older than this. The change has certainly not taken place at age twenty-two and it definitely has taken place at age twenty-seven. There are insufficient subjects of intermediate ages to pinpoint the age of change more precisely, but what figures are available are given below in Table 62 to enable the reader to assess the position for himself.

TABLE 62

The increase in liking for neroli comes in the twenties

Age	Number of subjects of that age	Average placing neroli
20	34	7·47
21	4	8·50
22	7	7·57
23	4	4·75
24	3	9·00
25	1	7·00
26	1	8·00
27	4	2·75
28	1	5·00
29	4	5·00
30	5	5·00
31	2	4·50
32	2	1·50
33	2	4·50
34	2	4·00
35	12	5·08
36	3	5·00
37	2	4·50
38	6	3·50
39	1	2·00

At many of the ages, the number of subjects is too small to allow the average of their placings to have much meaning, but looking down the table one sees clearly enough that a placing of 7 or 8 changes to one of about 5 which is quite a big change, and one sees too that the change has not yet taken place at the age of twenty-two, but that it already has at the age of twenty-seven. Furthermore, the reduction in the average placing, which corresponds to an enhanced liking, persists into old age. Here indeed is a strange change: what is disliked in youth, becomes well-liked in the late twenties. If the placings for the sexes are plotted separately (not shown) it is found that the dislike for neroli is more marked in young girls than in boys, but that after the age of twenty-five the women like it considerably better than do the men. Neroli finds its extremes of liking and disliking in the females; the males are more tolerant when young and less delighted by it when mature. The plots for Fig. 25 have been chosen in just the same way as for the other odorants with this exception; the 20–29 age group has been divided into two groups of 20–22 and 23–29, so that the change of liking will be highlighted. There is, too, a lower peak of relative liking that occurs at about age ten to twelve; if the figures for the two sexes are separated it is found that this peak is due almost entirely to the boys and that the girls hardly contribute to it. The girls whilst they are young uniformly dislike neroli.

(7) **Almond essence.** The average placings of all the observers are plotted against age in Fig. 26; there is an evident rise in appreciation of almond which reaches a maximum at about age twenty and

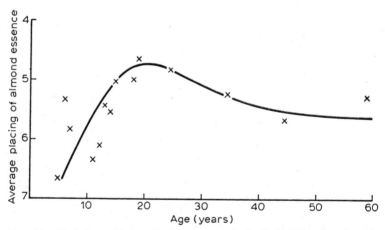

Fig. 26.—Variation with age (both sexes together) of the liking for almond.

thereafter the liking for this odorant falls away a little. But almond essence was one of the three odorants that was found (p. 146) to be rated very differently by the two sexes, and when average placing is plotted against age for the sexes separately as it is in Fig. 27, then more interest develops. It can be seen that the placing by the males (solid line) is fairly steady; the plots are more scattered than one would like, but there are clearly no well-defined peaks; there may be a slight rise in appreciation of almond with increasing age, but it is not well marked. The curve (intermittent line) for the

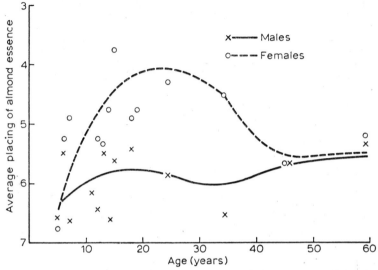

FIG. 27.—Variation with age of the two sexes separately in their liking for almond smell.

females is very different; it starts and it finishes very close to the curve for the males, but in between the extremes of age there is a very evident greater liking for almond. Between the ages of seven and forty all the plots for the females are substantially higher than those for the males.

(8) Naphthalene. This is another of the three odorants which

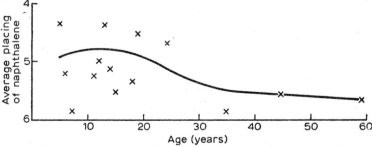

FIG. 28.—Variation with age (both sexes together) of the liking for naphthalene smell.

showed very different responses by the two sexes. In Fig. 28 both sexes are grouped together and the average placing of the whole group is plotted against age. The placings are generally a little lower, that is the curve is a little higher before middle age than after, but the difference is not well defined. The next step was to examine the variation of placing of naphthalene with age in the sexes separately and the results are shown in Fig. 29. The curve (solid line)

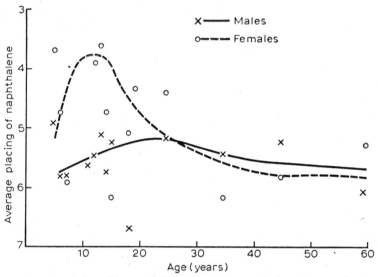

Fig. 29.—Variation with age of the two sexes separately in their liking for the naphthalene smell.

for the males shows little change in the placing of naphthalene with age; it is practically always placed between 5 and 6. The plots (circles) for the females are so scattered that difficulty was experienced in drawing a fair curve; eventually Fig. 18 was used as a guide and the curve shown in Fig. 29 (intermittent line) was drawn. Not much confidence can be felt in the curve itself, but there is no doubt at all that the plots reveal a marked liking for naphthalene amongst girls and women up to the age of twenty-five to thirty. The greater liking by young females, compared with young males, for naphthalene odour is clear to be seen. But it is also clear that there is much more irregularity in the placings of this odorant than has been found with any of the others. The possibility that the inconsistences might be due to a powerful effect of temperament was examined, but no great differences were found: all the intro-

verts grouped together gave an average placing of 5·12 for naphthalene, and all the extroverts one of 5·01, an insignificant difference. (These figures 5·12 for introverts and 5·01 for extroverts are
a little different from the corresponding figures of 5·25 and 5·21
given in Table 65 because they are derived differently; the former
are loaded by some age groups being bigger than others, the latter
are not. But neither set of figures lends any support to the view
that temperament plays much part in the appreciation of the odour
of naphthalene). The variation in responses to naphthalene (79th
in Table 3) were found to be very great in the first part of the investigation, and these irregularities have persisted in the second stage.
What does emerge from the investigation is:

(1) Naphthalene is liked rather better by the under-thirties
than the over-thirties.

(2) It is liked very much better by young females up to the age
of twenty-five or thirty than by males of the same age.

(3) The placings of this particular odorant are considerably
more erratic than usual; it has a sophisticated smell that
does not fall easily into any well-liked, such as fruity, class of
smells, or into any disliked class, such as repulsive smells.

(9) Rape oil. The placing-age curve for rape oil is shown in Fig.
30. The young children tolerate it quite well and place it 5th or

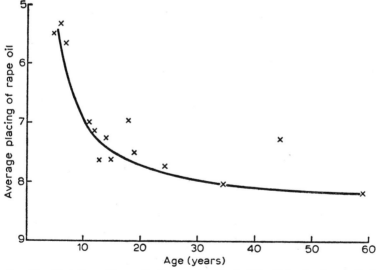

FIG. 30.—Variation with age (both sexes together) of the liking for the smell of
rape oil.

6th, but at adolescence a dislike for it develops and finally it is placed no better than 8th. The change is well defined and the experimental results give a good smooth curve. Rape oil (ranked 112th in Table 1) has a light oily and nutty smell, but its ranking shows that it is not well liked. There was no indication in the first part of the investigation (Table 3) that children tolerated it much better than grown people, but in this part of the research none of the children was younger than ten; in Fig. 30 it can be seen that it is the very young children, aged five, six and seven, who tolerate it well. We have found other instances of very young children tolerating bad smells fairly well (Rule 32). It is true (Rule 23) that children generally dislike oily smells, but even the four older children (ages 10, 12, 14 and 14) did not rank rape oil (Table 18) very differently from adults. It is likely that the general rule (Rule 23) about children disliking oily smells, may have to be modified in respect of very young children, who may tolerate them better.

(10) **Oil-soluble chlorophyll.** The average placings of oil-soluble chlorophyll are plotted against the subjects' ages in Fig. 31. This odorant is uniformly disliked and for most ages it has an average placing between 9 and 10. The very young children (the five and

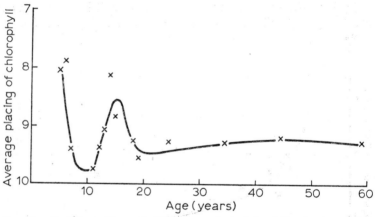

Fig. 31.—Variation with age (both sexes together) of the dislike for the smell of oil-soluble chlorophyll.

six year olds) show better tolerance for it than older people, and this is in line with other evidence that very young children will tolerate quite well what their elders think are very unpleasant smells. Furthermore, although only three four-year-old subjects took part in the tests, one of them (No. 88) placed chlorophyll 2nd; the other two (Nos. 23, 89) placing it 10th. The curve in Fig. 31 shows a well-defined peak at about age fourteen, and there is certainly some considerable change in olfactory preferences at about this age. But for most of the life-span oil-soluble chlorophyll is disliked and given an average placing of worse than 9th.

Comparison of the curves for the ten odorants

In Fig. 32 the curves derived for each of the ten odorants (both sexes together), that is the curves already shown in Figs. 19, 20, 21, 22, 24, 25, 26, 28, 30, 31, are compared in one picture. There is not so much information in Fig. 32 as there is in the individual Figs. for each odorant, because plot points are not shown in Fig. 32 and the degree of agreement of the curve with the plot points cannot be assessed. But Fig. 32 does throw into relief some points that cannot be so easily seen from the individual figures. In particular it can be seen that:

(1) There are very big changes of olfactory preferences with age and apparently it may be exceptional for no such changes to occur. Of the ten odorants used in these tests only two, spearmint and naphthalene, are not subject to these changes, and of these two we have previously seen that naphthalene does show considerable changes if the sexes are considered separately (Fig. 29). However, it should not be forgotten that these ten odorants had been selected from a much greater number as being those most likely to show differences in olfactory preferences according to either sex, age, or temperament.

(2) The biggest changes take place in youth, mostly in the first twenty years of life. There are exceptions, but usually preference changes are slight after the age of twenty.

(3) Of the ten odorants investigated musk lactone and neroli are exceptional in that significant changes do occur later.

(4) There is often a peak either of liking or disliking at about age ten, where very striking differences in odour preferences can occur. Strawberry, vanillin, musk lactone and neroli all show peaks of liking at this age; chlorophyll shows a trough of dislike at age ten and lavender one of dislike at age thirteen.

(5) The approximation to mirror imagery of the curves for chlorophyll and neroli is interesting. It would seem that whatever physiological change is responsible for the development of liking, can work in reverse too.

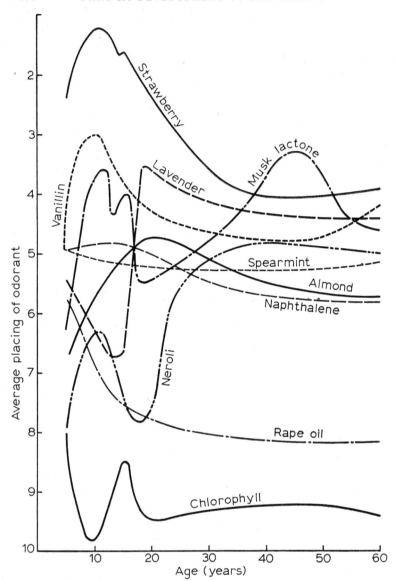

Fig. 32.—The age/liking curve for the ten odorants compared.

(6) There is a placing of nearly 5 at age seventeen for four odorants, a point where the curves for almond, musk lactone, lavender and naphthalene cross. At this age people would probably have considerable difficulty in sorting out these four odorants in order of

preference; it would be of interest to put this specific point to the test.

(7) The extremes of liking and disliking are to be found amongst the children and young people; there is usually a marked tendency for the curves to level off and run parallel and close together after the age of twenty. It would appear that positive delight in odour and flavour may be the prerogative of the young.

First preferences. Most of the subjects placed No. 1 strawberry flavour first; the odd person (subject 525) very exceptional indeed, placed No. 10 chlorophyll first. This last was so odd that at the time we thought he must be joking; however, he assured us that he really did like it best and as he was a responsible and intelligent person, we had to accept it. Indeed, later, two boys, one a fourteen-year-old extrovert (subject 182) and the other a fifteen-year-old extrovert (subject 289) also placed chlorophyll first, and there were additionally seven subjects (10, 34, 53, 89, 119, 136, 137) who placed it second. So some people, especially children, did not find it too disagreeable.

The proportion of subjects at each age who did place No. 1 (strawberry flavour) first can be ascertained from Tables 31–50, and the results are shown in Table 63.

TABLE 63

Proportion of subjects at each age who placed strawberry flavour first

Age	Total number of subjects of that age	Number of subjects placing No. 1 first	Percentage of subjects placing No. 1 first
4	3	2	67
5	22	15	68
6	29	23	79
7	44	35	80
11	12	8	67
12	34	20	59
13	68	43	63
14	46	36	78
15	38	24	63
18	40	16	40
19	69	31	45
20–22	45	13	29
23–29	18	5	28
30–39	37	6	16
40–49	21	5	24
50 and over	28	5	18

It is evident that the proportion of subjects who place strawberry flavour first is high amongst the children, increases to a maximum and then falls away; this can be clearly seen in Fig. 33. The re-

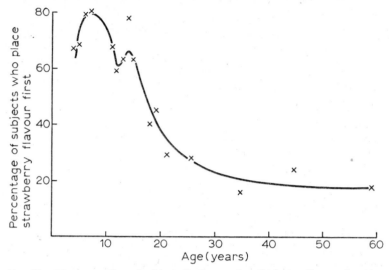

FIG. 33.—The proportion of subjects (both sexes together) at each age who rate strawberry the best of the ten odorants. This curve should be compared with Fig. 19.

semblance of Fig. 33 to Fig. 19 in which the average placing of strawberry essence was plotted against age is very striking. It has naturally to be remembered that the number of subjects who place the odorant first largely determines the average placing, when the proportion placing it first is high, but there are some similarities evident which are not wholly due to this. Apart from the main peak at age seven or eight, there is the same inflection in both curves at the age of adolescence, and the way in which both curves taper away, eventually asymptotically, is very similar.

If a basically similar curve is drawn for No. 5 (vanillin) plotting the percentage of subjects at each age who place vanillin first we obtain Fig. 34. The result is not very satisfying; there are insufficient positive responses; out of a total of 559 subjects, only 47 or 8·4 per cent placed vanillin first. Furthermore, if the percentage of first placings in each of the age *groups* 4–7, 8–14, 15–19, 20–40 and over 40 is plotted against age a very similar curve to Fig. 34 is obtained, so that this latter is apparently representative. When Fig. 34 is compared with Fig. 24 (average placing plotted against

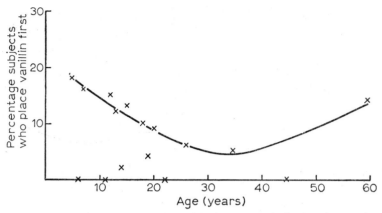

Fig. 34.—The proportion of subjects (both sexes together) at each age who rate vanillin the best of the ten odorants.

age) the depression in the middle age ranges corresponds and so does the rise in liking for vanillin in old age, but the peak at age ten that is so pronounced in Fig. 24 is not to be seen in Fig. 34. There is, of course, a much firmer basis for Fig. 24 than there is for Fig. 34, because in the former, account is taken of every placing, not only as in Fig. 34 of the 8·4 per cent that show a first preference for vanillin.

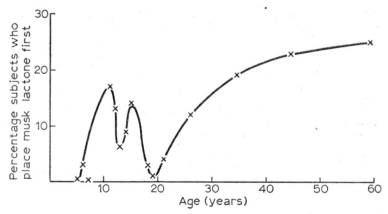

Fig. 35.—The proportion of subjects (both sexes together) at each age who rate musk lactone the best of the ten odorants. The curve should be compared with Fig. 22.

A similarly-drawn curve for No. 4 musk lactone is to be seen in Fig. 35. If this is compared with Fig. 22 in which the average placing of musk lactone is plotted against age, it can be seen that there is a very marked resemblance. There is a rise to a peak at adolescence with a dip in the centre of the peak, a fall to age twenty and thereafter a rapid rise. But musk lactone was one of the odorants that was found to be particularly susceptible to the subjects' sex and if the percentage of first placings for each sex separately is plotted against age, we obtain Fig. 36. The resemblance of this

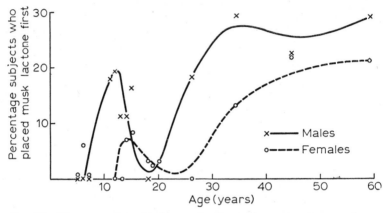

Fig. 36.—The proportion of subjects of each sex separately who at each age rate musk lactone the best of the ten odorants.

curve to Fig. 23, in which the average placings by the two sexes are plotted separately against age, is striking.

The proportion of subjects at each age who place each of the ten odorants first is of interest and is shown in Table 64.

Some of the odorants, notably strawberry, lavender, musk lactone, neroli and almond show clearly-defined trends in Table 64; in some cases there is an increasing, in others a decreasing, liking for the odorants as age increases, but these trends follow along the lines already discussed (pp. 158–171). Sometimes, notably for lavender, there is a preference in the very young that soon fades away; often too there are significant changes at adolescence and in the twenties.

Rules

The following general rules may be derived from the contents of this chapter.

Rule 50. Olfactory preferences may change significantly with age; in some instances the changes are very considerable (cf. Rule 29).

TABLE 64

Proportion of subjects, at each age, who place each of the odorants first

Age	Percentage of subjects who place first each of the odorants									
	Strawberry flavour	Spearmint	Lavender	Musk lactone	Vanillin	Neroli	Almond flavour	Naphthalene	Rape oil	Oil-soluble chlorophyll
5	68	0	10	0	18	0	0	5	0	0
6	79	3	7	3	0	0	7	0	0	0
7	80	0	0	0	16	0	5	17	0	0
11	67	6	0	17	0	0	0	9	0	0
12	59	3	0	13	15	0	0	9	0	0
13	63	4	2	6	12	0	6	0	0	2
14	78	3	0	9	2	0	2	5	5	3
15	63	8	0	14	13	0	5	9	5	0
18	40	7	18	3	10	1	13	9	2	0
19	45	7	20	1	4	2	12	6	0	0
20–22	29	17	24	4	7	17	16	8	0	0
23–29	28	5	5	12	6	11	11	5	0	0
30–39	16	0	27	19	5	5	8	7	0	5
40–49	24	0	14	23	0	0	23	5	0	0
50 and over	18	4	11	25	14	11	11	7	0	0

Rule 51. Sometimes the changes in preferences with age are different for the two sexes; examples are provided by almond and musk lactone.

Rule 52. The fruity smell, exemplified by strawberry essence is well-liked by children; there is a maximum liking at age ten or eleven, and thereafter a slight falling away to adolescence, where the liking stands still for a few years. Thereafter it falls away fairly rapidly. At all ages the fruity smell is liked, but the liking is very much greater in children than it is in adults (cf. Rule 21).

Rule 53. The liking for some odours changes very little with age; spearmint affords an example (cf. Rule 23).

Rule 54. Occasionally, but not usually, there is a very sudden change in liking for an odorant. Examples are provided by lavender for which liking increases enormously between the ages of fifteen and eighteen and by neroli (orange blossom) for which the liking increases greatly between the ages of twenty-two and twenty-seven.

Rule 55. Odours which have sex significance, such as musk lactone, evoke two changes in preference among the subjects; the first occurs at the age of adolescence and the second at the end of the reproductive period, that is the forties for women. This second change is more marked in women than in men.

Rule 56. Odours which are characteristic but which do not fall easily into a recognized group of pleasant or unpleasant types, evoke responses that are more irregular than usual. Naphthalene provides an example (cf. Rule 8).

Rule 57. Odours which are commonly disliked such as rape oil and oil-soluble chlorophyll are tolerated very much better by very young children up to about six years old (cf. Rule 32).

Rule 58. Generally the biggest changes in olfactory preferences take place in youth, in the first twenty years of life, and thereafter the changes are less marked. But there are many exceptions to this rule (cf. Rule 54).

Rule 59. The biggest differences in olfactory preferences occur in the young; they are more emphatic in their likes and dislikes. Older people exhibit clear cut preferences, but they are slighter in degree. Delight and disgust are more noticeable in the young than the old, and these emotions steady down with increasing age to a more moderate degree of liking and disliking.

Rule 60. When preference placing is plotted against age, curves can result which are almost mirror images of each other e.g. neroli and chlorophyll. Identical, or at least simultaneous, physiological changes can both enhance and diminish liking for different odorants.

Rule 61. Examination of the proportion of subjects who place any one odorant first (i.e. they prefer it absolutely to the others) yields preference–age curves generally similar to those obtained by plotting average placing against age. This is of interest because it is much easier and quicker for a subject to pick out the odour he likes best of all from a group, than it is for him to place all the odours in a group in their order of preference.

CHAPTER 11

ODOUR PREFERENCE VARIATIONS WITH TEMPERAMENT (TEN ODORANTS, MANY PEOPLE)

So far in this second part of the investigation, a study has been made of the variation in olfactory preferences with sex and with age. Sex is well defined; there was never any doubt about which subjects were male and which female. Age is also accurately known; there may have been one or two minor adjustments made by some subjects; for example, the frequency of age 38 in women was noticeably greater than that of age 40, but the great majority of subjects gave their ages unconcernedly and doubtless correctly. Temperament is rather different; one has to judge, and in judging may make mistakes. In practice the testers found no difficulty in classifying most of the subjects either as introvert or extrovert, but there were a few subjects who were both introvert and extrovert, thoughtful and reflective and also bright socially. Such subjects were classified according to that side of their nature which seemed to be most evident. Usually, there was no apparent difficulty in classifying appropriately, but, nevertheless, classification according to temperament cannot hope to be so clear cut as classification by sex or age.

The information on which this chapter is based is contained in Tables 31–50. Because, at the moment, we are interested mainly in the effect that temperament has on the individual's odour preferences, we can sum together and average the males' and females' results in what are otherwise similar groups. An example may make this clear.

From Table 31 we have for introvert males under eight years, average placings for the ten numbered odorants of:

No. 1	No. 2	No. 3	No. 4	No. 5	No. 6	No. 7	No. 8	No. 9	No. 10
1·36	5·45	6·18	5·23	3·14	7·32	7·18	5·64	5·32	8·18

From Table 33 we have for introvert females under eight years, average placings of:

1·58	4·53	5·42	6·00	4·53	8·21	5·70	5·13	5·18	8·69

Averaging these two lines, we get for all introverts under eight years:

1·47   4·99   5·80   5·62   3·83   7·77   6·44   5·38   5·25   8·44

If we do the same for the groups in Tables 32 and 34–50, we arrive at the summary shown in Table 65. As before (compare the opening of Chapter 9) the fact that one group, for example, of male introverts, may contain fewer subjects than another group, for example of female introverts, is disregarded; it is the average of each group that is taken as the significant figure and that is used in the compilation of Table 65. That way, there is no unfair loading by there being an unusually large number of subjects in any one group, e.g. the seventy-seven introvert females aged 15–19 in Table 41 compared with only eighteen otherwise similar males shown in Table 39. The figure given for 15–19 year old introverts in Table 65 for (1) strawberry flavouring is 2·06 which is the mean of the values 1·72 from Table 39 and 2·40 from Table 41.

The first impression one gets from Table 65 is that the differences between the placings of the introverts and the extroverts are only small. The difference figures in the extreme right-hand column are smaller than those in the corresponding column of Table 56 which is concerned with sex differences and are much smaller than the differences due to age that are displayed in Table 59. It seems fair to say that age changes are responsible for the greatest differences in olfactory preferences, that the differences in preferences between the sexes are smaller but still very considerable, and that the two temperaments yield still smaller differences. The most powerful determinant of olfactory preferences is age; next comes sex; and lastly temperament.

Spread of placings greater by introverts

In the first part of the investigation it was found (Rule 33) that although many of the odorants were rated nearly equally by introverts and extroverts, it was noticeable that introverts spread out their placings more uniformly than the extroverts. Is this true for the second part of the investigation, that part concerned with many subjects and only ten odorants? The first statement as to the frequency of equality of rating by the two temperaments is undoubtedly borne out, as Table 65 so clearly shows; the differences in placings between introverts and extroverts shown in the extreme right-hand column are much smaller than the differences determined by either age or sex.

TABLE 65

Placing of the ten odorants according to the subject's temperament

Odorant no.	Average placing by introverts of years:						Average placing by extroverts of years:						Difference in average placings of introverts—extroverts
	0–7	8–14	15–19	20–40	Over 40	All groups	0–7	8–14	15–19	20–40	Over 40	All groups	
1 (strawberry essence)	1·47	1·47	2·06	3·14	3·63	2·35	1·53	1·69	2·19	3·30	4·47	2·64	−0·29
2 (spearmint oil)	4·99	5·00	5·11	5·54	4·97	5·12	4·89	5·38	4·70	5·06	4·89	4·98	+0·14
3 (lavender oil)	5·80	6·86	4·67	4·15	4·47	5·19	6·22	6·35	5·14	4·04	4·38	5·23	−0·04
4 (musk lactone)	5·62	4·36	5·11	4·58	3·46	4·63	5·51	4·21	4·98	4·63	4·26	4·72	−0·09
5 (vanillin)	3·83	3·68	3·89	3·86	4·58	3·97	4·13	3·58	4·37	5·01	4·15	4·25	−0·28
6 (neroli oil)	7·77	7·20	7·09	6·32	5·15	6·71	7·26	7·01	7·09	5·44	5·04	6·37	+0·34
7 (almond essence)	6·44	5·57	5·04	5·31	5·70	5·61	5·17	5·62	4·89	5·18	4·88	5·15	+0·46
8 (naphthalene)	5·38	4·82	5·36	5·12	5·59	5·25	5·32	4·59	5·00	5·21	5·94	5·21	+0·04
9 (rape oil)	5·25	7·13	7·35	7·81	7·77	7·06	6·32	7·71	7·57	7·79	8·18	7·51	−0·45
10 (chlorophyll oil-soluble)	8·44	8·92	9·34	9·20	9·70	9·12	8·65	8·84	9·07	9·33	8·81	8·94	+0·18

As to the spread, once again we find that the introverts spread out their results more than do the extroverts. In Table 65 the average placing in the "All groups" column is (as it must be) 5·50; in the introverts' all groups column the average placing difference from this mean is 1·30, in the corresponding extroverts' column it is only 1·26; the introverts' spread is a little greater. Both of the best placings of all, anywhere in Table 65, 1·47 for strawberry essence and the worst placing of all, 9·70 for chlorophyll, are to be found in the introverts' columns. The average difference between the worst and best placings for any one odorant by the introverts is 1·71, whereas for the extroverts it is only 1·55. To make this last observation quite clear, it may be noted that the greatest difference for rape oil is 7·81–5·25 = 2·56 for the introverts (worst in 20–40 age group, best in 0–7) and 8·18–6·32 = 1·86 for the extroverts (worst in the over forties, best in the 0–7); if similar treatment is accorded to the results in Table 65 for the other odorants the average greatest difference for introverts is found to be the figure already given of 1·71 and that for extroverts one of 1·55. The differences are not great, but they do support the earlier finding, already expressed in Rule 33, that introverts spread out their olfactory placings more, and more uniformly, than do the extroverts.

This can be seen, too, in Fig. 37 in which average placing is plotted separately for introverts and extroverts against odorants and the odorant numbers are arranged along the ordinate in order of preference. As can be seen from Table 65 the order of preference is for the introverts 1 5 4 2 3 8 7 6 9 10 and for the extroverts is 1 5 4 2 7 8 3 6 9 10; the placings of Nos. 3, 7 and 8 are very similar; those of the other odorants are identical. Examination of Fig. 37 shows that the differences between the two curves (solid line for introverts, dotted line for extroverts) are very small, but such as they are, they support the statement that the introverts spread out their placings more uniformly. But the best evidence for this greater spread by introverts comes from Part I in which Rule 33 was deduced, and wherein is discussed a much bigger range of odorants. Fig. 37, aside from its primary purpose of comparing introverts' and extroverts' preferences, is really of much more general interest because it illustrates well, even on such a small number of odorants as ten, that there is a wide middle "indifferent" group between the relatively few well-liked and the few disliked odorants (cf. Rules 8, 10). In a real sense the two curves in Fig. 37 are typical of the

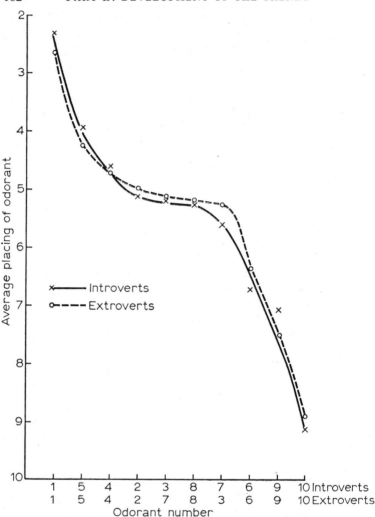

FIG. 37.—The placings (both sexes together) of the ten odorants by the two temperament groups shown separately.

range of olfactory preferences; like and dislike shine brightly and warningly at the top and bottom, and in between is a greater number of indecisive reactions. For the purpose for which it was drawn, to show differences between introverts' and extroverts' preferences, the one thing that Fig. 37 demonstrates admirably is that such differences are only very small; but it does also illustrate the greater crowding that occurs in the middle ranges of the extroverts' preferences and the rather better spread of the introverts' preferences, although these effects are no more than marginal. The curve for the extroverts is certainly flatter than that for the introverts, but only slightly so.

Detailed comparison of preferences of the two temperaments

Examination of the "all groups" column in Table 65 suggests that there are only two well-marked differences in olfactory preferences between the temperament groups; the introverts like rape oil better than the extroverts and the reverse is the case for the almond flavour. It is almond flavour that the females like better than the males (Chapter 9), and it is this same odorant which the extroverts like better, although not so much better, than the introverts. Rape oil showed no considerable sex differences, but it can fairly be said to have an unusual odour, one not frequently met and it is, therefore, in line with Rule 36 that such an odour should be less acceptable to extroverts than to introverts. After these two odorants, almond and rape oil, which show well-marked differences, come neroli, which is preferred by the extroverts, and strawberry and vanillin, both of which are preferred by introverts, but the differences are small. There is nothing in the results of this comparison of the preferences of the temperament groups towards ten odorants to support the earlier findings expressed in Rules 34 and 35 that if there are differences between the two temperament groups, then the extroverts will be found to rate the pleasant odours, more like the children do, whilst it is the unpleasant odours that are rated more like the children by the introverts.

Differences in corresponding age groups

Even if the separate age group columns in Table 63 are used as a basis for the comparison of introverts' and extroverts' preferences, there are no very striking differences to be found. Those differences that are the most evident are:

Strawberry essence. The introvert over 40's give to strawberry essence a placing of 3·63 on average, but the extroverts do not appreciate it so much and give it a placing of 4·47. Yet in the younger age groups there are no big differences between the two temperament groups for strawberry essence; the difference only shows up in the over 40's.

Musk lactone. A very similar state of affairs prevails here. In the younger age groups, introverts and extroverts place musk lactone very similarly, yet in the over 40's, the placings are 3·46 by the introverts and 4·26 by the extroverts; quite considerably different.

Vanillin. The introverts show a marked preference compared with the extroverts for vanillin in the 20–40 age group where the placings are 3·86 and 5·01 respectively; in the other age groups the differences between the temperaments are smaller.

Almond. The under 8 extroverts rate almond (5·17) distinctly better than the corresponding introverts (6·44). Throughout (except marginally in the 8–14 years group) the extroverts rate almond flavouring better than the introverts do.

Rape oil. Here again the major difference comes in the under 8's. The introverts place rape oil 5·25, but the extroverts place it 6·32. The introverts accept better the unusual character of the odour.

In all these five instances, there is a difference in placing of about one place. But four of the five are concerned with extreme age groups, two with the very youngest and two with the oldest.

First placings

In considering, as we have just done, the occasional notable differences between introverts' and extroverts' placings, one is assailed by the thought that there is a factor that has been forgotten. Perhaps it may be sex; musk lactone and almond which as odorants are peculiarly susceptible to sex influences, both occur in the five examples just discussed of considerable differences in preferences by the two temperaments. This can be put to the test by the method of first preferences. In all, 165 out of 311 introverts, corresponding to 53 per cent, and 123 out of 248 extroverts, corresponding

TABLE 66

Proportion of subjects who prefer strawberry essence absolutely

Age group (years)	Percentage of subjects placing strawberry essence first			
	Male introverts	Male extroverts	Female introverts	Female extroverts
0–7	82	70	76	82
8–14	54	58	87	74
15–19	56	50	45	45
20–40	32	14	18	30
Over 40	22	8	36	9

to 50 per cent, place strawberry essence first, i.e. they prefer it absolutely, so that a slightly higher proportion of introverts than of extroverts prefer strawberry essence absolutely. If the subjects' results are divided into their two sex groups, two temperament groups and five age groups, the results appear as shown in Table 66. There is really very little new to be derived from these figures. We already knew that the fruity odour of strawberry essence was much more highly appreciated by children than by grown people, and we already knew (p. 148) that in the 8–14 years group, the girls think more highly of strawberry essence than the boys do. The only other feature that emerges is the relative lack of appreciation in the over 40 extroverts for strawberry essence. The introduction of the sex factor has not proved helpful in the case of strawberry essence; no further information about the effect of temperament has been revealed.

But still, strawberry essence is not one of the odorants whose appreciation is largely influenced by sex. Is it possible that in the case of an odorant which is susceptible to sex differences more information about the effect of temperament would be revealed? The corresponding information about musk lactone is given in Table 67, which looks rather more interesting for the study of temperament differences. In passing, it may be noted that both Tables 66 and 67 afford strong support for what has already been written about the influence of both sex and age on olfactory preferences. However, Table 66 did not prove helpful for the study of the influence of temperament on olfactory preferences. Will Table 67 be better?

TABLE 67

Proportion of subjects who prefer musk lactone absolutely

Age group (years)	Percentage placing musk lactone first			
	Male introverts	Male extroverts	Female introverts	Female extroverts
0–7	0	0	3	0
8–14	22	7	3	3
15–19	11	14	4	0
20–40	14	21	6	12
Over 40	33	23	14	27

The male introverts like musk lactone better than the male extroverts; the female introverts like it less than the female extroverts.

All the males like it, as we already know, much better than all the females. But it is the introverts who provide the extremes: males with the greatest liking, females with the least, enclosing between them the two extrovert groups. The study is not without interest and one feels that there may be more information in Table 67 than has been deduced. But if the matter is taken a step further and the percentage of absolute preferences (first placings) at each age is plotted against age, separately for each of the four groups: introvert males, extrovert males, introvert females and extrovert females, then nothing additional emerges. Only the dominance of the introvert males in their liking for musk lactone is emphasized. Those who place the musky smell first are mostly either round the age of puberty or over thirty. Men place it first more often than women; the order of the groups is: introvert males > extrovert males > extrovert females > introvert females. Some resemblance can be seen between the preferences in this respect of the extroverts, males and females, but the peak of liking that occurs in males at adolescence never shows in females.

If the results for No. 7 (almond essence), which also showed some susceptibility to the influence of sex, are treated similarly, Table 68 results.

TABLE 68

Proportion of subjects who prefer almond essence absolutely

Age group (years)	Percentage placing almond essence first			
	Male introverts	Male extroverts	Female introverts	Female extroverts
0–7	0	4	3	18
8–14	0	4	6	3
15–19	11	0	10	15
20–40	9	8	15	12
Over 40	11	15	14	27

There are some big differences here and they support what we have previously learnt about the influence of age and sex on olfactory preferences. But what light do they throw on the influence of temperament? Certainly the extrovert females place almond essence first more often than the introvert females. The order of the groups in their liking for almond essence is: extrovert females > introvert females > extrovert males > introvert males.

Almond: effect of temperament on average placing

If curves are prepared for the four groups, plotting the average placing for each age against that age, there is obtained Fig. 38.

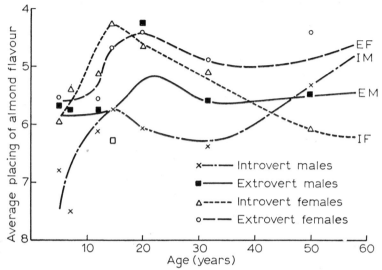

FIG. 38.—The average placing of almond odour by the two temperament groups in each sex shown separately as it varies with age.

This takes the investigation described immediately above a little further: that was concerned with variation of the proportion of *first* placings of almond by the different sexes and temperaments; this next stage concerns itself with variation of the *average* placing of almond by the different sexes and temperaments. As the total number of subjects has to be split into four groups, those ages where there are not many subjects are grouped together, and the age groups that have been used for the preparation of Fig. 38 are: 4–6, 7, 11–13, 14–15, 18–22, 23–40 and over 40; all the basic information is contained in Tables 31–50. This grouping of ages undoubtedly has the effect of smoothing out irregularities in the curves. It is not a very desirable way of smoothing the curves; the alternative would be to make many more tests and assemble more information. The available information taken from 559 subjects is beginning to look rather thin when these are divided according to age, sex and temperament all at the same time. The most reasonable way of stretching the information is to group results of adjacent ages and this is what has been done; if it had not been done, the curves would have been too erratic to be read usefully. But the need to group the ages may be an indication that most of the useful information in Tables 31–50 has now been extracted from them.

Examination of the four curves in Fig. 38 suggests at once that two of them, those for EF (extrovert females) and for EM (extrovert males) are very similar in shape to each other and different from the curves for IF (introvert females) and IM (introvert males) which are themselves similar to each other up to age thirty. It does seem that the two temperaments have different odour preferences when the odour is one that is susceptible to sex differences, as musk lactone and almond are. There is some indication that if an odorant is preferred by the females, then the extrovert females like it better than the introvert females; if it is preferred by the males, then the introvert males like it better than the extrovert males. But, if the odorant is one to which the sexes respond not very differently, then the influence of temperament on odour preferences is only slight or perhaps does not exist at all.

Effect of intelligence on olfactory preferences

When the researches that have been described were started the inclusion of intelligence as well as sex, age, and temperament as a possible determinant of olfactory preferences was considered. At the time it was thought that intelligence could have little or no bearing on whether a subject liked or disliked an odour; there was purposely to be no analysis of liking or disliking, no questioning of the subject as to why he disliked or liked this, that or the other odour; on the contrary, all that was asked for was the initial -im mediate response—I like or I don't like—that comes automatically. So, intelligence did not seem to be a criterion that it was necessary to include in the researches. Furthermore, it did not need much effort to call to mind instances of people of quite different degrees of intelligence who had apparently similar preferences in odours; the laboratory staff provided examples. So, with the aim of keeping the research within reasonable confines and excluding any factors whose exclusion would simplify the research, it was decided to omit intelligence as a possible determinant of olfactory preferences. Nevertheless, at first at least, an eye was kept open for any marked dissimilarity in preferences that might be due to intelligence differences. None was noticed. A few of the subjects were a shade simple, but their odorant arrangements showed nothing unusual; they might have been made by anybody. Another few of the subjects were scientists known in their own fields throughout the world, but their arrangements of odorants, too, were not evidently unusual; they could have been made by anybody. Liking, it was thought, had little to do with intelligence.

However, an opportunity to make easily some comparative tests on people of different intelligence presented itself to one of the testers whilst she was carrying out work in a local school, and with considerable presence of mind, she seized the opportunity. There were in one form at the school four intelligence "streams" each consisting of eight girls of roughly the same age; the first stream was the brightest, the second stream next, the third next, and the fourth the least intelligent. Each of the eight girls in each stream arranged the ten odorants in order of preference and the results of the four streams were kept separate. The results are shown in Table 69.

TABLE 69

Does intelligence help to determine olfactory preferences?

Odorant		Average placing by girls of:			
No.	Name	1st stream (most intelligent)	2nd stream	3rd stream	4th stream (least intelligent)
1	Strawberry essence	1·00	1·25	1·13	1·00
2	Spearmint oil	4·75	4·88	5·00	4·88
3	Lavender oil	4·50	5·25	5·25	7·75
4	Musk lactone	5·25	6·50	5·00	4·75
5	Vanillin	2·88	4·88	3·88	3·13
6	Neroli oil	8·13	7·00	8·00	8·13
7	Almond flavouring	6·88	3·62	5·13	4·63
8	Naphthalene	4·50	4·75	4·50	4·13
9	Rape oil	8·00	8·00	8·38	8·13
10	Chlorophyll oil-soluble	9·13	8·88	8·75	8·50

There is not much in Table 69 which points to intelligence being a determining factor of olfactory preferences. The consistently better tolerance of oil-soluble chlorophyll with diminishing intelligence is interesting and the poorer tolerance by the fourth stream of lavender suggests that they were a little backward, less grown-up than the other streams. What these thoughts really point to is that some of the children are undeveloped, that their mental age is rather lower than their body age. This, of course, is simply another way of saying that their I.Q. (intelligence quotient) is low. It may be that in people who are still growing, intelligence does affect olfactory preferences, but only in so far that low intelligence children behave like younger children, so that whatever mental growth determines their intelligence, also has some influence on their olfactory preferences:

Rules

Those general rules that can be drawn from the contents of this chapter are:

Rule 62. Differences in olfactory preferences that are due to temperament differences are much less frequent and much smaller than those due to age or sex differences (cf. Rule 33).

Rule 63. The liking for the fruity odour of strawberry essence lasts longer through life in the introverts than it does in the extroverts; the latter lose interest in it after forty years of age.

Rule 64. The biggest differences between the two temperament groups in respect of their olfactory preferences occur towards those odorants which one sex likes better than the other, such as musk and almond.

Rule 65. Intelligence differences have little or no effect on olfactory preferences, with the reservation that intelligent children exhibit preferences more in line with those of normal children who are a little older.

Rule 66. The most powerful determinant of olfactory preferences is age; next comes sex which also has a powerful effect; then comes temperament which has only a slight effect, and finally intelligence which has practically no effect.

PART III

Comparison of the Findings with the Prior Art

CHAPTER 12

PLEASANTNESS AND UNPLEASANTNESS OF SMELLS

MANY PEOPLE might well think that pleasantness and unpleasantness are spontaneous and involuntary reactions and so far as odour is concerned unambiguous as well. When a flower or a bottle is held to the nose and a sniff taken, the reaction is immediate. If the flower is a rose, the smell is liked, it is indisputably pleasant; no analysis is necessary, the reaction of liking and pleasantness comes without thought; and even if an analysis is attempted, if the subject says in effect "Why do I like this smell?" he will not get much further. He may remind himself that flowers have smells that are usually liked; he may recall occasions when he was happy and when the rose smell was present: perhaps in a sunny garden, at a flower show, or in the scent worn by a woman companion. But none of these recollections has much depth of meaning as an answer to his question. He knows surely enough that he likes the smell of the rose, but he does not know why. If instead of being a rose, the flower that is held to the nose, perhaps in a bunch, is the ramson which flourishes in shady hedgerows and woody places in May, the reaction will likely be one of dislike of the strong garlicky, rather offensive smell. There is more to liking or disliking of a smell than knowing whether it belongs to a flower or not.

Bodily requirements as a determinant of liking

Some food smells can be pleasant or nauseating to the same person at different times; if he is hungry roast pork can smell delicious, if he is sick it can be nauseating; the smell of good beer can be admirable to a thirsty man, but anathema to him at the onset of next day's hangover. Instances such as these, and the further one that some people have what is almost a passion for such flavours as olives and horseradish, point to the liking or disliking of smells being in part dependent on the body needs. The principle is sound enough, but is it capable of extension? Can we say that the rose smell is delectable because it provides a minute trace of some such material as geraniol that the body can use with benefit and correspondingly that the garlicky odorant present in the ramsons is unpleasant because it will have a deleterious action on the body, even in the microscopic quantities in which it is inhaled. It seems to be an unlikely and far-fetched idea, but we must not forget that the body has been built to match its environment, that it will when possible adjust itself to compensate for a change of environmental conditions, and that when this is not possible it will endeavour to change its environment by moving away. There may be more than is commonly thought to support the view that pleasant smells are pleasant because the inspired odorants have a beneficial effect on the body, and that unpleasant smells are unpleasant for the contrary reason.

Emotional requirements as a determinant of liking

Particularly in young children and in animals bodily requirements may be a powerful determinant of liking or disliking, but in adults more abstract faculties have developed, an aesthetic sense has come, an ability to appreciate beauty: of scene or figure, of music or of the wind in the trees, of the texture of fabric or the touch of old wood, and doubtless too of the perfume of honeysuckle or the sweet mellifluous scent of the countryside in the May sun. These last two are doubtless of considerable practical use to the bee, but to the human their value is mainly what we call aesthetic and think of as abstract although it may have value, as yet unknown, in building up some emotional maturity that will be a characteristic of our future development. Certainly odours affect the emotions; ylang-ylang will soothe anger born of frustration and wild rose will lift one out of a depression. It has to be remembered, too, that children do not think nearly so highly of flower smells (Rule 20) as adults do, and that their main interests olfactorily seem to be tied to what is delicious to eat (Rule 21).

So that what this preliminary examination of pleasantness and unpleasantness in odorants suggests is:

(1) Reactions of the subject to odorants are usually spontaneous and involuntary, either of liking, or disliking, or perhaps of indifference.

(2) Analysis of the reasons for liking or disliking cannot usually be taken far. Usually the liking or disliking seems to be without reason.

(3) Association of ideas with some former experience may occasionally play some small part in determining the reaction, whether of liking or not.

(4) Food smells may be coloured with pleasantness or unpleasantness according to the needs of the body.

(5) Usually aesthetics is the factor that determines the olfactory reaction. It seems possible that this in turn depends on the requirements of the emotional apparatus in the body and brain. Perhaps it is true that the emotional system needs "food" as much as the body does, and that such food consists of seeing, hearing, touching, smelling and tasting what is pleasant. In the last two, the chemical senses, there is the added possibility that the very small quantities of pleasantly odoriferous substances taken into the body may have a nutritional action on the neuro-physiological apparatus.

The psychology of pleasantness and unpleasantness

Pleasantness and unpleasantness are not strong emotions like fear and anger, but are referred to either as "affective states" or "hedonic tone". According to Boring et al[15] they "correspond to broad attitudes of acceptance or rejection that the organism assumes toward various aspects of its environment. Pleasant things are the things that we like, that we desire and seek to obtain. Pleasant situations are ones that we attempt to maintain and prolong. Unpleasant things are not liked. We strive to avoid them. Unpleasantness is a condition that we try to terminate."

Often, pleasant stimuli are those that are beneficial to the body, e.g. the sweet taste associated with the nutrient value of sugar and conversely the unpleasant bitter taste of harmful alkaloids. But the relationship is not exact. Not everybody likes cod-liver oil however beneficial it may be, and diabetics continue to crave for the sugar which will hurt them. Intensity of stimulation whether of smell, flavour, or taste, has an effect, too; we are indifferent to very dilute solutions of salt, we like those that are a little stronger and then we dislike those that are very salty, but these changes in liking with intensity may not be at variance with the thesis that what is good for us is usually liked.

In 1932 Beebe-Center[16] wrote a book on the psychology of pleasantness and unpleasantness. He considered then that it was a potential body of knowledge rather than an actual one, and it may well be that this view is as true today, more than thirty years later, as it was then. Pleasantness, wrote Beebe-Center, is probably but one aspect of well-being. It might be fair to extend this statement to say that anything that will tend to promote well-being, of the body or of the emotions, will also be pleasant: that what we need, we also like. There is a close connection here with what has just been suggested, namely that some odours may be pleasant because they feed either the body or the mind.

Both from the same matrix

It has been suggested by Nafe[17] writing of smells that "pleasantness and unpleasantness are inherently alike as if made from the same matrix. Their differences are of the sort that occur within one and the same modality. Pleasantness and unpleasantness do not occur together, they may appear in rapid alternation." It is hard to think there is anything in common between the emotions derived from smelling a bunch of roses and a pigsty—the sense is the same but the emotions are diametrically opposite.

Alternation of two sensations

Just as Nafe thought that pleasantness and unpleasantness occur not together but in rapid alternation, so other workers have thought that two smells presented together to the nose can be experienced in rapid alternation. Zwaardemaker frequently referred to this alternation as a contest or competition between the two smells: he related[18] that if ethyl mercaptan and coumarin (both highly diluted) were smelled, one in each nostril, simultaneously, then the garlic smell of the mercaptan would be perceived first, then the woodruff smell of the coumarin and then the two alternately. Zwaardemaker thought that the time taken for a smell to be detected, the reaction time as he called it, was a determining factor, e.g. when the garlic smell was predominant its reaction time was 0·94 sec. whereas for woodruff the time of reaction was 0·99 sec. so that the garlic smell appeared first and then that of the woodruff. A translation of the relevant paragraph is "it can be seen that the contest between the two smells alternates, that there is a peculiar kind of a mixed smell with first one and then the other odorant predominating". Sometimes there was contest or alternation, sometimes there was mutual compensation. Zwaardemaker stated quite definitely that the two sensations alternated "now I perceive the garlic smell of the ethyl mercaptan, and now the woodruff smell of the coumarin; they alternate," and later he refers to a rapid alternation. The present writer has experienced alternation of this sort but has the impression that the alternation is determined by a shift of attention; if one thinks of the coumarin then one can smell it almost to the exclusion of the mercaptan, and contrarily if attention is focussed mentally on the mercaptan, it is that that is smelled and the coumarin is not noticed. But it is impossible today to go along with Zwaardemaker when he thinks of reaction times of the order of a second; it is commonplace that smell comes and disappears apparently instantaneously; the times involved are of the order of one-hundredth or one-thousandth of a second and are not ordinarily noticeable.

Although the idea of alternation of two sensations has attracted several philosophers notably Valentin,[19] Aronsohn,[20] Zwaardemaker[18,21], and Henning,[22] there seems to be little real evidence to support it. What undoubtedly does sometimes happen is the simultaneous perception of different sensations.

Simultaneity of perception

Often two smells, sensed in the two nostrils, will feed to the brain persistent and simultaneous messages intimating their presence. Henning[22] actually made a relevant experiment with mustard oil in his right nostril (unpleasant) and jasmine oil in his left nostril (pleasant). He stated that he experienced the smell of jasmine together with a general sensation of pleasantness, a mixture but not a fusion of the two sensations. Similarly while sensing the mustard oil olfactorily, he was aware of a sensation of unpleasantness. The pleasantness and the unpleasantness were not experienced simultaneously but appeared to alternate. Very often the two smells can be separated mentally and identified; the brain directs its attention to one and then to the other; it is awkward for it to identify two smells at the same time just as it is awkward for it to make two simple little calculations at the same time; many people would have no difficulty at all in multiplying say 23 by 7 mentally, or in subtracting say 17 from 54, but they would find it quite impossible to do the two things at the same time; one after another quickly is easy, but the two together quite impossible. There are, of course, many instances where the brain carries out two, or perhaps a dozen, jobs simultaneously: it regulates the body temperature, indicates warmth of environment, maintains the body mechanically in balance, controls the rate of breathing, hears a call, sees the daylight, feels the wind, smells the summer scents in it and so on, but these actions are done by different parts of the brain designed and built to function autonomously and in some of the examples involuntarily. One part of the brain that is designed to do one thing at a time cannot do two things simultaneously: if two people talk to another one at the same time they are both incomprehensible and they may even cause mental disquiet which can bring violent reactions; an intermittent light with a defined flicker frequency can bring on an epileptic fit in some people (the two sensations are "light" and "no light"). When two smell messages, say those of ethyl mercaptan and coumarin, reach the brain continuously and simultaneously, the brain cannot recognize them both simultaneously; it can identify one and a split second later the other. There is absolute simultaneity of stimulation but there cannot be simultaneity of recognition; there is succession of recognition and it is this which has been labelled alternation by the early workers. There is, in fact, no regular alternation, but there is a succession of attentive acts on the part of the brain now to one stimulus and then to another. The pleasant smell, and the unpleasant smell, cannot be both identified at once, although it may be possible to identify them successively.

The sensation shining through

Although two stimuli of similar nature, which are the concern of one part of the brain must be dealt with successively, it is nevertheless possible for two stimuli that are quite different in nature to be experienced simultaneously; they are received by different parts of the brain which can function independently. We feel the heat of a flame that touches us and simultaneously we feel the pain; there are separate receptors and nerve pathways for heat and for pain. Similarly, if we hold ethyl mercaptan to the nose we can simultaneously perceive its dull pervasive rotten cabbage smell and also the unpleasantness that we associate with this smell. We smell a rose and the olfactory equipment takes note of the volatiles and announces the rose smell, but shining through, and perceived simultaneously and independently is the emotion of pleasantness. Even as we smell the rose, so at that very same instant, the mind is suffused with happiness. Perhaps it was something like this that Becher[23] had in mind when he wrote:

> "Die Unlust des Schwefelwasserstoffgeruchs z.B. erscheint durchaus durch die Geruchsempfindung fundiert" and we translate it:

"The unpleasantness of the hydrogen sulphide smell, for example, shines clearly through the smell sensation that this substance arouses."

The pleasant and the unpleasant we cannot smell as separate odours simultaneously, but we can experience the olfactory sensation due to one of them and the associated feeling of pleasantness (or unpleasantness) due to that one at the same time.

Compensation of pleasant and unpleasant smells

In the above considerations, we have imagined two odorant substances, for example the mercaptan and the coumarin that Zwaardemaker used, presented singly but simultaneously to the nose. Precautions have to be taken to bring about this state of affairs and the obvious one is to present one odorant to each nostril. This is, in fact, what Zwaardemaker did with his double olfactometer; pictured in Fig. 39. The two nozzles to be inserted into the

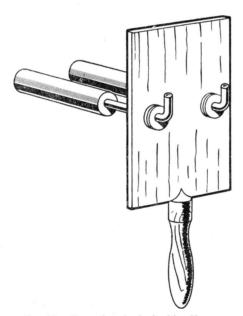

Fig. 39.—Zwaardemaker's double olfactometer.

two nostrils can be seen and the tubes at the back of the picture will slide in such a way that the time of contact of the inspired air which passes through them with an odorant surface is altered;

accordingly the smell strength on the two sides of the double olfactometer can be adjusted. Zwaardemaker found that the simultaneous inspiration of two odorants would sometimes greatly reduce their apparent smell strength: each seemed to reduce the other and with some mixtures he found no resultant odour at all. A translation of his own description of this is:

> "According as one or the other sensation predominates, either the one or the other smell is noticed, and when they are exactly counter-balanced, then either no precise sensation is experienced, or only a very weak impression, quite indefinite, which was noticeable only by great effort and corresponded with neither of the components."

Some of the pairs of compensating odorants that Zwaardemaker reported were: cedarwood and indiarubber, indiarubber and Tolu balsam, skatole (an odorous principle of faeces) and coumarin, caproic acid (goat-like smell) and ethyl mercaptan, and ethyl mercaptan and eucalyptol. Zwaardemaker's work on compensation has lived, it has been used to support commercial claims of one odour compensating another, but it has never been adequately followed up; for sixty years one writer after another related what Zwaardemaker had found and nobody gave the subject much practical investigation. In fact, many people interested in smell had wondered how much truth there really was in Zwaardemaker's work. For one thing, Zwaardemaker had very unwisely included in his tests such a pair as ammonia and acetic acid; these two would obviously react chemically and neutralize each other at the top of the nostrils (where the two nostrils join) if nowhere else. The evident possibility in such a case of the odour counteraction being due to chemical neutralization had caused people to wonder if in the other examples such as coumarin and mercaptan there had been true neutralization of odours or some other adventitious phenomenon.

The present author has carried out some practical work on which two preliminary reports have been published.[24,25] It transpired that complete compensation could be obtained to the degree that neither of the two odour components could be recognized but there was never found that condition of no sensation at all which Zwaardemaker had reported; on the contrary there was always a vague olfactory awareness. Nevertheless, when two air-streams carrying respectively the unpleasant sweaty butyric acid and the pleasant gin-like oil of juniper were mixed in certain proportions and an observer was asked to say what he could smell (not knowing if the air mixture contained either butyric acid or juniper oil or both) the answers were often negative, such as "pleasant neutral smell", "faint, neither recognizable". Another odour "pair" that was found was pyridine (rank tobacco smell) and oil of wintergreen. There is no doubt at all that odour compensation does take place so that neither of two odorants, present in sufficient quantity to be easily recognized alone, can be recognized in the mixture. What is the significance? A pleasant smell and an unpleasant smell will sometimes neutralize each other so that neither can be recognized. The only possible explanation is that the compensation is internal, that it takes place in the central nervous system, in the olfactory nerves, at the nerve junctions or on the cortex. It is an important observation that such internal compensation of pleasant and unpleasant smells can take place. Such compensation may take place in our ordinary life as a matter of routine. The animal olfactory apparatus was never designed for objective odour measurement, but rather to keep the animal as comfortable in his environment as is consistent with the warning functions of the smell sense.

Reactions to olfactory pleasantness and unpleasantness

We undergo various spontaneous reactions when presented with olfactory stimuli; these reactions are more noticeable and can even be violent if the stimuli are very unpleasant. Kenneth, indeed, expressed the opinion that the mental effects of perfumes may be studied merely by observing the contraction or relaxation of the facial muscles. One should perhaps add to this that the more experience a person gains in smell tests, the less easy is it to make deductions from his behaviour; practised subjects tend to become poker-faced. But this applies only to professionals; the average person who unselfishly becomes a subject in olfactory tests for an odd occasion has no such inhibitions, and it is true enough that his expressions may reflect his opinion of the smells. Children especially express their likes and dislikes facially, and of their reactions to odorants it would be difficult to improve on the description given by Kniep, Morgan & Young[26] who reported:

> "the behavior which goes with liking an odour includes: smiling, speaking in a 'pleasant' tone of voice, laughing, nodding head, opening of the mouth, looking up, slight sucking movements (one case), taking a longer and deeper smell of the substance. Expressions of dislike are more

numerous and include: turning the head in various degrees, turning away the entire body, jerking head back suddenly, wrinkling nose together with raising the upper lip, shaking the head, speaking with disgust ('ugh', 'uff', 'ooo', 'ahh'), leaning back in chair away from bottle, twisting mouth, speaking very definitely 'no', clearing throat and coughing, compressing lips, rubbing nose with finger or arm, frowning, putting hand over mouth or nose, pinching nose, spitting, wrinkling face, a 'pained, unhappy look', waving the bottle away with the hands."

Sometimes, too, for a pleasant smell the eyes light up as was noted for taste by Gauger[27]. It has been pointed out by Bull[28] that people pull faces, tighten the nostrils, turn up the nose, and get ready to spit out of the mouth, if they experience a bad smell or taste, but that these "muzzle" reactions are often associated with dislike or disgust even when no real smell is present, e.g. to show disapproval, disgust or scorn of a person. Such disgust reactions, similar to those produced by smell, are used to train children to avoid dirt and disorder, and the reactions of adults to dirt and disorder are often those that they would use towards a smell that they disliked. As Bull puts it "Thus in the presence of anything that seems to be disorderly, confused, or messy, we tend to act as if the offending situation were to be ejected from the mouth or rejected by the nose. The very notion of a flaw or imperfection can become effective in producing this reaction to disorder, and the 'perfectionist' is one who gets disgusted by almost everything."

The opposite reactions are less apparent but Bull has reported in certain cases "a widening of the nasal openings, a definite extension or spreading of the outer walls of the margin of the nostrils . . . at the time they are well pleased with something, particularly if it is of a sensory nature, not necessarily an odour".

Racial characteristics

The hedonic tone of odours depends to some extent on racial characteristics; what one race finds pleasant another may not. The Phoenicians are said to have mixed pepper in their perfumes. Orientals find pleasure in valerian which is disliked by most Europeans. The Japanese like camphor and borneol; the former is said to keep away certain worms that destroy bamboo which is much used as a wood. Reference to Table 3 shows that in the author's experiments camphor was ranked 47th by introverts and 92nd by extroverts. It was liked much more by the introverts than by the extroverts; possibly the Japanese as a race are introvert more than extrovert and if so the author's finding would fall into line with their traditional liking for camphor. According to Leitch[29] some natives of the Torres Straits presumably as yet uninfluenced by the views of Western communities were carefully examined by a Cambridge Anthropological Expedition; their olfactory sensitivity was found to be only slightly greater than that of Europeans. Their favourite smells were violet, musk and thyme; they violently disliked asafoetida, valerian and civet because of their similarity to faecal smells. And yet according to Johnston[30], on the borders of Asia asafoetida is not considered unpleasant but is extensively collected, sold and used as a condiment for food. (Asafoetida is the sap of two umbelliferous trees and is collected by cutting the plant just above the root, leaving the root in the ground and scraping off the sap as it collects and dries on the cut root.) In the West, civet (glandular secretion of the civet cat) is not pleasant to many people, and yet it is a common ingredient of many good perfumes. In Table 3 it can be seen that civet was placed 118th by the children, 129th by the men and 132nd by the women; the children's placing is in line with Rule 32. Yet in the East civet is appreciated; perhaps Eastern likes and dislikes are more in line with the children's in the West. There are big differences between different races of mankind in their olfactory preferences.

People themselves have odours: the early saints exhaled an odour of violets, an odour of sanctity, negro races have a characteristic smell, white people have a buttery smell to the negro. Plutarch relates that a Spartan lady visited Berenice, wife of Dejotarus, but that one smelled so much of sweet ointment and the other of butter, that neither of them could endure the other. There are, too, individuals who have strange likes and dislikes; it is recorded that Cardinal Olivieri Carafa who died at Rome in 1511, aged 81, had an invincible repugnance to the smell of a rose. One has to be careful not to attach too much credence to what is mainly anecdotal, and to look with some scepticism on the many reports of people who would faint when some particular odour was brought into a room. But it is true enough that the different races of the world vary in what they find olfactorily pleasant. Almost certainly they do not vary much in their ability to smell, i.e. in sensitiveness to tenuous smells, but that is of the body more than of the mind and in their assessments of the pleasantness or unpleasantness of smells they do vary. Personal odour matters; it is important that it should be pleasant. Armpit stink was at one time a cause of rejection for army recruits in Japan. In the Song of Solomon "my beloved is unto me as a bag of myrrh". If personal odour is pleasant that is fine, but body odour has become almost unmentionable and the arch way in which it is handled by TV commercials is enough to make most of us squirm. Perhaps Plautus[31] was nearest the truth in "mulier recte olet, ubi nihil olet". One observation that may perhaps have some significance is that cinnamon leaf and bark oil were found (Table 3) to be preferred by Western males (24th leaf, 28th bark) to females (36th leaf, 49th bark); Western males (14th) like musk ambrette much better than females (64th) as can be seen from Table 3; they also like musk lactone much better than do the females as can be seen from Fig. 16. Perhaps there is some evidence that Western males may be closer than the females in their approach to the olfactory preferences of the Orientals.

The part played by association

It may be doubted whether the powers of association of smells are sufficiently great to change to unpleasant what is normally pleasant, and vice versa. That the power of association is great enough to alter preferences there can be no doubt, and this aspect of the subject will be discussed in Chapter 14. Kenneth in Edinburgh has probably done most of the work on olfactory associations. In a review of the subject[32] he considered that the reactions of a person to smell stimuli depended on the quality and quantity of the odorant, and on the physiological and psychological condition of the subject. "Direct reactions are chiefly the perception of the quality and the quantity of a smell and the effect immediately produced. Indirect reactions are the associations, with or without affective tone, subsequently evoked." Often associations with a particular odorant were much the same with different subjects: usually menthol reminded them of peppermints, asafoetida reminded them of onions, and ferric valerian reminded them of gorgonzola. But it was impossible to predict individual associations: "The smell of vanillin may remind one subject of chocolate, another of his grandmother, and another of a few bars of Chopin's music". The emotional effect was measured with a d'Arsonval galvanometer and sometimes extreme reflexes would indicate an individual's idiosyncratic association of one specific odorant with some intense emotion such as fear. In one such case the association derived from some thirty-years' old emotional incident that the subject associated with the smell of camphor; thereafter it made him afraid. Thus thought Kenneth, but the student's revulsion from the smell of camphor may have had a more fundamental cause. According to Watson[33] camphor is an anaphrodisiac:

"Camphora per nares castrat odore mares."

Sometimes there is a natural and well-founded dislike of a smell; one may be educated out of it by a psycho-analyst explaining that it is caused by some forgotten and unimportant incident, but the real reason may go much deeper than either subject or psycho-analyst guesses.

Adaptation and habituation

The nose quickly adapts itself to any smell. The bunch of violets. delightful at first, appears to lose its odour after some seconds, The change is not in the violets which continue to emit vapours of irone and kindred ketones, but in ourselves; our olfactory apparatus becomes exhausted, the sites in it for adsorption of the irone molecules are soon filled and when this happens, sensation diminishes. If a series of solutions of acetone in water are prepared it is just possible to distinguish one that contains 0·03 per cent acetone from pure water, but if one prior inspiration is taken of pure (100 per cent) acetone, then with the next inspiration, nothing more dilute than 5 per cent acetone can be smelled consistently; the adaptation is so great that the threshold concentration of the acetone is raised by 170 times.[34] Acetone has an indifferent, neither pleasant nor unpleasant smell, but similar considerations apply to odorants both pleasant and unpleasant. Olfactory adaptation takes place very rapidly; it is a manifestation of the sorptive nature of the olfactory stimulus[35]; it protects us from what might become tiring and long-continued sensation of the smell of the rose or the foetor. Long continued pleasantness or unpleasantness of olfactory sensation is unlikely to persist because of the onset of adaptation.

Habituation is a somewhat similar experience in its conscious manifestations but there must be a different mechanism that brings it about. Long-continued exposure to smells seems to make the subject unaware of them; he becomes habituated. Pfaffmann[36] has related that medical students in the dissecting rooms soon become adapted to the odours of the cadavers. The writer was once appalled on entering the insect breeding room of a research establishment by the warmth, closeness, and unpleasant sickening smell, but enquiry of a scientist who was sitting there working in it all day long, elicited the reply that he no longer noticed it. There is a factory in Northern Ireland which processes the bodies of dead animals, making blood hydrolysate for firefoam, fertilizers and so forth; the smell to a visitor is nauseating and so it is even after having been there for a few hours, but after a few days long periods elapse without it being noticed. The men who work in the factory never notice it, not even first thing in the morning—they have become habituated. The mechanism of this habituation must be central, some part of the nervous system assesses the smell as consisting of part of the normal environment, as having no news value and as not being worth reporting to the cortex of the brain. Other and similar instances will probably occur to the reader. There is no doubt that the supreme physical (not psychical) function of the nervous system is to keep the body in equilibrium with its environment, and this means that pleasantness or unpleasantness whether of the olfactory or of any other sense is unlikely to persist for long.

The basic reason for pleasantness of odour

Why are some substances pleasant to smell, some unpleasant? Ultimately perhaps this is all part of the Creator's grand design of keeping the body in a state compatible with its environment. On a rather more workaday basis, is there any relation that we can discern between the chemical and physical properties of odorants on the one hand and the pleasantness or unpleasantness of the olfactory sensations to which they give rise?

The relation between chemical constitution and odour has been studied by the present author[37] and a series of rules has been formulated. With these rules in mind it is possible, for example, to say that sulphur, selenium, and tellurium compounds often have vile smells, whilst their oxygen analogues are often odourless. Compounds of phosphorus, bismuth and arsenic often have garlicky odours. Esters often have fragrant fruity odours. Ketones generally have pleasant odours. Lactones have fragrant ester-like odours. An oxygen linkage is frequently associated with a pleasant odour, e.g. esters, lactones, nitrates. Compounds in which an element functions at a valency lower than its maximum usually have offensive odours, e.g. hydrogen sulphide and the isonitriles. Many sulphur compounds, particularly when the sulphur is divalent, have offensive odours, e.g. mercaptans. The olfactorily offensive and delicious are often closely related chemically. Arsenic compounds are usually garlicky or ill-smelling (cacodyl) but not if the arsenic is a hetero-cyclic member of a ring. The 1,3,4-arrangement in the benzene ring usually leads to a pleasant odour, but not if the substituent groups are heavy. The foregoing are examples taken from the rules that were formulated. Studying them and other common and accepted relations between chemical constitution and pleasantness of odour, sometimes it seems possible to catch a glimpse of a general design, but nobody so far, despite a good deal of effort, has succeeded in enunciating it precisely. Within limits the general rules enunciated twenty years ago by the present writer[37] are true but exceptions do occur and still worse, attempts to generalize the rules or generalities themselves into one golden rule have failed.

A more speculative suggestion, but one of much wider application has been made by the writer[38]; it is that pleasantness of smell may be associated with uniformity of adsorption on different kinds of receptors, whilst unpleasantness is associated with extremes of difference. In a study of certain odorants and some inorganic adsorbents, pleasant smells such as lemongrass were adsorbed fairly uniformly on five different adsorbents (characteristics of 4 2 4 4 6) whilst unpleasant faeces odour was adsorbed rapidly on some adsorbents, hardly at all on others (0 0 9 9 9). There is a big jump between inorganic adsorbents such as those that were used and the protein adsorbent in the olfactory epithelium, but adsorption is a physical process and slight differences in structure between the olfactory receptors may yield differences of adsorptive properties equivalent physically to those that exist between one inorganic adsorbent and another. The general idea is that there is a plurality of kinds of receptor in the nose and that those odorants that affect all the different kinds fairly equally are pleasant odorants. Contrarily, those odorants that are very easily adsorbed by some of the kinds of receptors, but are not adsorbed or only adsorbed with great difficulty by the other kind of receptors are supposed to have un-pleasant odours. Uniformity and balance of stimulation give pleasantness; high specificity of stimulation gives unpleasantness. At present the idea is not much more than a guess, but it is one that might attract the philosopher.

Rules

Those general rules that can be discerned in the subject matter of this chapter would seem to be:

Rule 67. Liking or disliking when it occurs of a smell is involuntary, spontaneous, immediate and unambiguous, but to many odorants the normal reaction is one of indifference.

Rule 68. Liking or disliking of an odour, especially of food, is partly determined by the requirements of the body. What will be good for the body will usually be liked.

Rule 69. Liking or disliking of an odour may be partly determined by the emotional requirements of the subject. These may be transient as of anger or misery or may perhaps be long-term needs for the growth of a desirable condition of emotional maturity.

Rule 70. Association of a particular smell with some former experience may occasionally play a part in determining the reaction, whether of liking or not.

Rule 71. Most often there is no apparent reason for liking or disliking a smell, even although the reaction is clear and unmistakable.

Rule 72. Liking and disliking of odours are not strong emotions like anger and fear; they are gentler reactions that are referred to as "affective states".

Rule 73. Two separate smells, e.g. one pleasant and one unpleasant, cannot be simultaneously perceived as two individual smells; they can be perceived in alternation due to a shift of attention.

Rule 74. Two or more separate smells may be perceived simultaneously as a composite whole, as in a perfume, but not as separate individuals.

Rule 75. The sensations of pleasantness and unpleasantness cannot be experienced simultaneously but only in alternation.

Rule 76. A smell sensation and the pleasantness or unpleasantness that it arouses, can be experienced simultaneously.

Rule 77. Some pairs of odorants present in small and suitable proportions in air, may when mixed give an air in which neither odorant is recognizable, and of which the odour is weaker than that of either component separately. This is known as odour counteraction, and its mechanism is one of compensation in the central nervous system.

Rule 78. Reactions to pleasantness or unpleasantness of odours can be very marked particularly in children. Generally a contraction of the facial muscles indicates dislike, whilst their relaxation indicates liking.

Rule 79. Reactions to unpleasant odours are more violent than to pleasant odours.

Rule 80. Reactions that belong properly to olfactory unpleasantness or disgust are frequently used to signify dislike of any disorderly or messy situation or person even although no smell is present.

Rule 81. The different races of mankind show some, probably minor, differences in olfactory preferences. Orientals generally think more highly of heavy spicy and animal perfumes than do Western people, especially Western women.

Rule 82. People of different races have different body odours; usually those of their own race are the least objectionable.

Rule 83. Olfactory pleasure is unlikely to continue for long, because fatigue ensues rapidly and the intensity of perception wanes. Olfactory unpleasantness also fades for the same reason but more slowly.

Rule 84. Even very unpleasant odours lose their apparent intensity in time; the subject becomes habituated and eventually unaware of the olfactory unpleasantness of his environment.

Rule 85. Many relations between chemical constitution and type of odour, often pleasant or unpleasant, have been enunciated, but it has not yet been possible to weld them into a general theory. The fragmentary relationships are, however, often unassailable.

Rule 86. There are indications that pleasant odorants may stimulate receptors of different kinds uniformly, whereas unpleasant odorants have high specificity of stimulation, exciting some receptors and hardly affecting others. If this is true, and it is still unproved, our olfactory preferences are for those odorants that stimulate all kinds of receptors fairly uniformly.

REFERENCES

15. E. G. Boring, H. S. Langfeld & H. P. Weld, *Foundations of Psychology*, p. 90, 1948, Wiley, New York.

16. J. G. Beebe-Center, *The psychology of pleasantness and unpleasantness*, 427 pp., 1932, Van Nostrand, New York.

17. J. P. Nafe, Experimental study of the affective qualities; unpleasantness or pleasantness of various odours with description of accompanying sense-feelings other than the sensation itself, *Amer. J. Psychol.*, 1924, 35, 507–544.

18. H. Zwaardemaker, Die Compensation von Geruchsempfindungen, *Arch. Physiol., Leipzig (Arch. Anat. Physiol., Physiol Abt.)*, 1900, 423–432.

19. A. Valentin, *Lehrbuch der Physiologie*, 1848, 2nd Edn., 2, 292.

20. E. Aronsohn, Experimentelle Untersuchungen zur Physiologie des Geruchs., *Arch. Physiol., Leipzig (Arch. Anat. Physiol., Physiol abt.),* 1886, 321–357.

21. H. Zwaardemaker, *Die Physiologie des Geruchs,* Chapter 10, "Die Compensation des Gerüche", p. 167, 1895, Engelmann Leipzig (translated from the Dutch).

22. H. Henning, *Der Geruch,* p. 172, 1916, Verlag von Johann Ambrosius Barth, Leipzig.

23. E. Becher quoted by Henning in reference 22.

24. R. W. Moncrieff, The counteraction of odours, *Chemistry in Canada,* 1959, 11, No. 9, 66–72.

25. R. W. Moncrieff, Odour counteraction, *Perfumery Essent. Oil Record,* 1958, 49, 808–811.

26. E. H. Kniep, W. L. Morgan & P. T. Young, Individual differences in affective reactions to odours, *Amer J. Psychol.,* 1931, 43, 406–421.

27. M. E. Gauger, The modifiability of response to taste stimuli in the preschool child, *Columbia Univ. Contrib. to Educ. Teachers Col. Series,* 1929.

28. N. Bull, The olfactory drive in dis-like, *J. Psychol.,* 1944, 17, 3–9.

29. N. Leitch, The science of smells, *Middlesex Hospital J.,* 1934, 34, 166–183.

30. J. F. W. Johnston, *The Chemistry of Common Life,* p. 449 of 1894 Edn., Blackwood, Edinburgh.

31. Plautus, *Mostellaria,* 1, 3, 116.

32. J. H. Kenneth, Mental reactions to smell stimuli, *Psychol Rev.,* 1923, 30, 77–79.

33. W. S. Watson, On the therapeutic influence of odours, *The Medical Press & Circular,* 1875, 71 (old series), 143–144.

34. R. W. Moncrieff, Olfactory adaptation and odour intensity, *Amer. J. Psychol.,* 1957, 70, 1–20.

35. R. W. Moncrieff, The sorptive properties of the olfactory membrane, *J. Physiol.,* 1955, 130, 543–558.

36. C. Pfaffmann, cf. p. 358 on Reference 15.

37. R. W. Moncrieff, *The Chemical Senses,* pp. 300–304, 2nd Edn., 1951, Leonard Hill, London.

38. R. W. Moncrieff, The characterization of odours, *J. Physiol.,* 1954, 125, 453–465.

CHAPTER 13

THE CLASSIFICATION OF ODOURS

THE STUDY of any new subject: plants, insects, stars, or odours, calls early on for some system of classification, a first attempt to bring some order into the chaotic. Odours have been studied for a very long time indeed and each classification that one looks at seems to have had its conception in some earlier classification. Our main concern is their division into pleasant and unpleasant classes, but this has equally been the most obvious and generally chosen division that the various classifiers have seen in front of them. It has had, too, the merit that there is not usually any doubt as to whether a smell is pleasant or unpleasant. True there are many indifferent ones that are neither, but if pleasantness or unpleasantness is present it is quite evident (cf. Rule 67). Perhaps we might start with Bain's classification; it included most of what was good in earlier attempts, it broke new ground by its inclusion of much new thought and it is very largely based on opposite sensations, on the pleasant and unpleasant aspects of the particular characteristic that is being considered.

Bain's classification. Alexander Bain, Professor of Logic at Aberdeen a hundred years ago, had an immense literary output. One of his books which can still be read with much profit and pleasure is "The Senses and the Intellect"[39] published in 1855, one which ran to four editions. In it he gives a classification of odours derived largely from first principles, a classification which must have been a source of inspiration to later and more widely-known workers on smell. Bain's classes of odours were:

(1) Fresh; those tending to increase the activity of the lungs, such as the balmy odours of the field and garden, and the perfume Eau-de-Cologne.

(2) Close or suffocating, such as the effluvia of crowds, of warehouses, stores and mills.

(3) Nauseous or disgusting, such as hydrogen sulphide.

211

(4) Sweet or fragrant, that represent the pure and proper pleasures of smell, such as the violet.

(5) Stinks such as the cadaverous odour of asafoetida, or the smell derived from squeezing in the fingers the brown scum of a stagnant pond.

(6) Pungent, such as ammonia and snuff.

(7) Ethereal, such as alcohol and chloroform.

(8) Appetizing as of flesh.

Bain considered other possibilities but rejected them as main classes: the sulphurous and electrical class he classed with ethereal; acrid odours were only mixtures of pungency and bad smell, and so were the so-called empyreumatic odours resulting from the action of heat on vegetable bodies. Pleasantness and unpleasantness are the keys to the classification: there is the pleasant class of fresh odours, e.g. fresh air and its unpleasant analogue the close or suffocating class. There are appetizing and nauseating classes, and sweet odours and stinks. The two remaining classes of his eight are ethereal and pungent; there was probably no intention that they should be opposites, but one is pleasant and the other unpleasant and furthermore if one were to say that "ethereal" and "pungent" are two qualitative adjectives that have some antithetic quality, one might be right in the majority of cases. Pleasantness and unpleasantness were Bain's two aspects of olfactory freshness, appetizing quality, sweetness, and soft smoothness. Such a basis of classification should be of help in a study of olfactory preferences.

Zwaardemaker's classification. In 1895 Zwaardemaker[40] put forward a systematic classification in which odours were divided into nine general classes: ethereal, aromatic, fragrant or balsamic, ambrosial, alliaceous, empyreumatic, caprilic or hircine, repulsive and nauseating or foetid. The first four classes are pleasant, the last four are unpleasant, and the middle class—alliaceous—is often unpleasant but is liked when associated with onion and garlic food smells. This classification has received a great deal of attention, largely because Zwaardemaker thought that those odorants in the same class would cause olfactory adaptation (cf. p. 88) one for another. Furthermore each class was divided into two or more sub-classes and members of any one sub-class were supposed to exercise a great degree of adaptation one on the other. Thus one of the sub-classes of the aromatic class contains camphor, eucalyptol and eugenol and it was later claimed by Ohma[41] that these three would give almost perfect adaptation for each other. It is true enough that the degree of cross-adaptation that two odorants will exhibit is a measure of their likeness and this criterion has been used both by Cheesman & Mayne[42] and by the author[43] for determining the likeness of odours. But there is no need, first of all, to attempt to classify the odorants as Zwaardemaker did, putting such unlikely bedfellows as chloroform and the fruity odours in the same class. Looking back on the work that has been done in the present century it is difficult to see that Zwaardemaker's classification has been inspiring or even useful. Nor did it have the sound logical basis of Bain's classification with its four factors and their pleasant and unpleasant aspects. It seems to be impossible to find much in Zwaardemaker's classification that will help us along in a consideration of olfactory preferences.

Heyninx's classification. In 1919 Heyninx[44] put forward a classification of odours which has some points of interest to our subject. His classes were acrid, rotten, foetid, burning, spicy, vanillar or ethereal, or garlicky. He was clearly a specialist in the unpleasant odours, and was content to lump most of the pleasant odours into one class. Is there any justification for such a method of division? At first we are reminded of the greater impact of bad smells on the human emotions, of the greater violence (cf. Rule 79) of our reactions to unpleasant odours. Are they therefore of such importance that they warrant a classification that the pleasant odours do not? Further reflection shows that the differences in kinds of odours in the pleasant group are just as real as those in the unpleasant group. Heyninx held fast to his classification and discussed it again fourteen years later,[45] but it is difficult to feel any conviction that there is much in it that is likely to be useful in a consideration of olfactory preferences. It lacks the simplicity and logic of Bain's early classification and it lacks the empiricism that might have enabled it to be tested. This characterized Henning's classification; one which we must now discuss.

Henning's prism. Henning[46] in his book "Der Geruch" divides odours into six classes and assigns to each class a characteristic linkage. The six are shown in Table 70.

Henning did not consider that the six classes were quite separate and distinct; he thought that they merged into one another. This is acceptable because there is no other evidence that we have to suggest the existence of quite separate classes; a gradual merging of one into

TABLE 70

Henning's odour classification

Odour class		Chemical linkage (Geruchsbindungen)		Examples
Original description	English equivalent	Original description	English equivalent	
Würzig oder gewürzhaft	Spicy, aromatic	Gegenstellung	Para	Anisaldehyde, CH_3O—⟨ ⟩—CHO *p*-Tolyl acetylene CH_3—⟨ ⟩—C:CH
Blumig oder duftend	Flowery, bloomy	Seitenstellung	Ortho	Ionone Me_2C ⟨ CH_2—CH_2 / CH—CMe ⟩ CH CH:CHCOCH$_3$ also irone, jasmone
Fruchtig	Fruity	Gabelung	Forked	Methyl heptenone Me_2C:CHCH$_2$CH$_2$COCH$_3$ also citral
Harzig oder balsamisch	Resinous, balsamy	Innenstellung	Internal linkage	Camphor CH ⟨ CH$_2$—CO / — CMe$_2$ — CMe \ CH$_2$—CH$_2$ ⟩ also pinene
Faulig	Rotten, foul	Aufsplitterung der Ringe	Opened ring	Mercaptan R-SH and Cacodyl As$_2$(CH$_3$)$_4$
Brenzlich	Burnt, empyreumatic	Glatte Ringe	Smooth ring	Nicotine ⟨N⟩—CH ⟨ CH$_2$—CH$_2$ / NMe—CH$_2$ ⟩ also pyridine

another is more in line with everyday experience. Fig. 40 is copied from Henning's "Der Geruch" and shows "Das Geruchsprisma". It is common in discussion of Henning's olfactory prism to find references to face FESR, lines FR and ER and so on. These are derived from the usual English translations of Henning's corner stones, thus:

blumig	ethereal	or E
faulig	putrid	or P
fruchtig	fruity	or F
würzig	spicy	or S
brenzlich	burnt	or B
harzig	resinous	or R

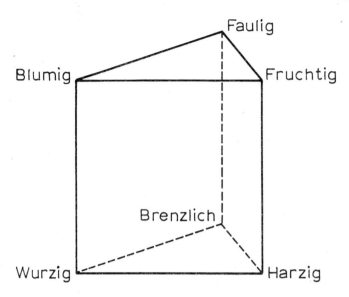

FIG. 40.—Henning's olfactory prism showing his original descriptions of the type odours.

So that the analogous figure with the usual English identification is as shown in Fig. 41.

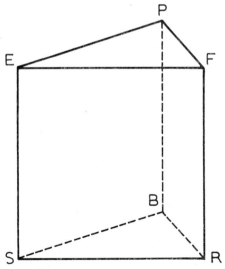

FIG. 41.—Henning's olfactory prism showing the nomenclature used by English-speaking authors.

Henning also conceived the idea that the figure might be irregular in shape, e.g. the edge EF might be shorter than the edge SR. Whether this has any real meaning is perhaps questionable; can one imagine that the difference between ethereal and fruity is less than that between spicy and resinous. Conceivably this might be meaningful but so far there is not a grain of evidence that it is true. Henning's prism is usually thought of as hollow, with the various odours grouped at the corners, along the edges and on the surface of the sides. But Leitch[29] views it differently and has criticized Henning's arrangement on the ground that the number of smells lumped together in the centre of the prism is out of all proportion larger than those worked in along the edges; another criticism he raises is that two of Henning's six basic smells (occupying the six corners of the prism) are themselves complex.

As can be seen from Figs. 40 and 41, the four pleasant types of odour; flowery, fruity, spicy and resinous lie on one face EFRS, and the two unpleasant ones; putrid and burnt, along the edge PB. It should therefore be possible as Beebe-Center has pointed out, to divide the prism by a secant plane, cutting edges EP, PF, SB and BR into two "halves", one pleasant and one unpleasant, with indifferent odours lying along the section (along its edges if the prism is thought of as hollow). All one can say about this is that the high proportion of odours that excite neither great pleasure nor displeasure would require a considerable area either on or close to the secant plane to represent near-indifference. It seems unreasonable to group a large proportion of all odours into such a small area of the model.

A careful study of the properties of the Henning prism was made by Findley.[47] She employed ten subjects and thirteen odorants and asked the subjects to rate the pleasantness of the odorants on a scale of $+2$ very pleasant, $+1$ more pleasant than unpleasant, 0 indifferent, -1 more unpleasant than pleasant and -2 very unpleasant. Some of the odorants which she conceived would lie on the EFRS face had high average values and some that would lie on the PB line had low average values. Examples are shown in Table 71.

Apart from ethyl ether which has a typical ethereal (but certainly not flowery) smell the correlation is reasonably good; the odorants on the EFRS face have values indicating pleasantness and those on the PB line have values indicating unpleasantness. Findley concludes "our experiment accords with Henning's conclusion that

TABLE 71

Values of pleasantness assigned to odorants variously placed on Henning's prism

Odorant	Position on prism	Average value (max. poss. +2; min. poss. −2)
Tonka bean	EFRS face	1·4
Orange oil	„	1·4
Peppermint	„	1·0
Amyl acetate	„	1·0
Hop flowers	„	0·5
Ether	„	−1·3
Tar oil	PB line	−1·0
Pyridine	„	−1·8
Hydrogen sulphide	„	−2·0

fragrant, ethereal, spicy, and resinous odours are usually pleasant, and that putrid and burned odours are usually unpleasant". The basic weakness of the investigation is that a decision has to be made subjectively as to the position of any odorant on the prism. For example, Findley places ether (diethyl ether) on the EFRS face, but it would seem to the writer that ether has a smell that contains a "burnt" component and that it might more suitably be placed on the EPBS face where its found affective value of −1·3 would be more appropriate. There might even be some justification for placing it right at the E corner. Until some way is available of locating the odorants objectively on the prism it is difficult to see how much more can be got out of it. Findley went to great trouble and appears to have extracted the greatest possible information from Henning's idea, but the results are still a bit shaky: as she herself says "Judgements of the qualitative similarity of odours are very variable and it is thus impossible to verify Henning's qualitative theory with any great degree of precision". One can, however, say without fear of contradiction that the further away from the PB line an odorant falls the more it will be preferred olfactorily.

Crocker-Henderson classification. An ambitious attempt to resolve the difficulty of classifying and characterizing odours was made by Crocker & Henderson.[48] They postulated that there were four fundamental types of smell, just as there are four fundamental tastes of sour, sweet, salt and bitter and that these four fundamental smells were served by four kinds of olfactory nerve endings. The four postulated fundamental odours were fragrant, acid, burnt, and caprylic (goaty) and any given odour could be built up from these four fundamental odours. Any of the fundamental odours could be present in any given composite odour in intensity varying from one (very weak) to eight (very strong) and its absence could be denoted by zero. Consequently all the numbers from 0000 to 8888 represented odours, e.g. the rose smell was represented by the number 6423 indicating that the:

fragrant smell is stimulated to a degree of 6

acid   „   „   „   „ „   „   „ 4

burnt   „   „   „   „ „   „   „ 2

caprylic   „   „   „   „ „   „   „ 3

Clearly fragrance is a constituent odour that is to be preferred and one might expect many pleasantly smelling odorants to have a characteristic number starting with a high (fragrant) digit. That this expectation is justified can be seen from the following characteristic values:

Vanillin	7122
Safrole	7343
Citral	6645
Damask rose	6523
α-Terpineol	6323
Acetic acid (20 per cent)	3803
Toluene	2424
Anisole	2577

Crocker[49] points out that careful distinction must be made between the terms "fragrant" and "pleasant"; thus, methyl salicylate (wintergreen) 8453, does not compare in pleasantness with many floral odours that may have "fragrant" values of only 6 or 7 (rose 6523) but which have more favourable values of the other components, Crocker & Henderson evolved four ranges of comparison standards for each of these fundamental odours; comparison of the odorant to be characterized with the standards for the "acid" component was made with the series:

Vanillin	7122
Cinnamic acid	7212
Resorcinol dimethyl ether	5335

Toluene	2424
Isobutyl phenylacetate	5523
Methyl phenylacetate	5626
Cineole	5726
Acetic acid (20 per cent)	3803

The other three components of the odorant to be characterized were determined by comparison with the three other sets of standards, to which reference can be conveniently made in Crocker's book[49].

The method has been used by Dorough et al[50] to compare the odours of some isomeric octanols and it gave reasonable results. The method is, however, entirely subjective and the author has found it confusing when an attempt is made to analyze the smell of ginger or cloves or hyacinth into so many parts fragrant, so many burnt and goat-like. But with practice more meaning comes into the method and the results that it gives.

Adsorption method. The principles on which odours might be classified according to their adsorption characteristics on different adsorbents has previously been outlined by the author.[38,51] The initial work was carried out on inorganic adsorbents which are clearly very different indeed from the parts of the animal olfactory system on which odorants are adsorbed. Later this method was developed and the use of organic adsorbents in film form was described.[52] It would seem that this method has the basic requirements for a proper classification to be made, although a great deal of experimental work would be necessary. It has the great advantage that the method is analogous to that which brings about smell sensation in an animal or a human and it is built into an instrument which inspires air. The instrument in operation behaves very much like a nose. It will suddenly catch, due to a favourable air current, a smell from a nearby open bottle of acetone or ammonia and will respond to it. It will, in fact, with suitable sensitive adsorbent films respond to any odorant. What it will not do is demonstrate an affective tone. Pleasantness and unpleasantness are meaningless to it. They might not however eventually be meaningless if it was found that pleasant odours were more easily picked up by specific kinds of films, or even if it was shown as is not unlikely that pleasant odours were picked up by films of a greater variety than unpleasant ones. Here is the possibility of an approach not only to a logical and firm classification of odours, but also to the objective measurement of olfactory pleasantness and unpleasantness.

Assessment. From the standpoint of olfactory preferences Bain's classification seems to be most useful, based as it is on the pleasant and unpleasant aspects of the four odour qualities: freshness (and closeness), appetizing (and nauseous), fragrance (and stinks), etherealness (and pungency). Zwaardemaker's classification offers less that is of value to any consideration of olfactory preferences, partly because it is sometimes possible to find the olfactorily pleasant and unpleasant in one and the same sub-group. Heyninx's classification has little to offer to our present considerations. Henning's prism is the classification that has received most attention and experimentalists who have worked hard with it give it mild praise; there is no doubt at all that empirically it seems to classify reasonably well. Its defect is that it is absolutely subjective; in order to fix a point on the prism for any particular odorant one must first mentally analyse its smell into so much fruity, so much resinous, so much spicy and so on, and that it is almost impossible to do. One does one's best and after a lengthy research arrives at the rather unhelpful conclusion that smells that are both putrid and burnt are unpleasant. A point that sometimes escapes attention is that Henning's prism forbids certain combinations of "fundamental" odours; thus an odorant which contained some part of spiciness, some of burnt and some of resinous could not also have as a partial component ethereal, putrid or fruity notes. A glance at Fig. 41 will show that this is so and that there are other similar exclusions; the complexity of many odours lends no support to the validity of such exclusions. The Crocker–Henderson arrangement also suffers from the disadvantage that a difficult mental analysis has first to be made of an odour into four components; it does however have the interesting result that the final characteristic number gives some indication of pleasantness or unpleasantness; pleasantness is mainly determined by the "fragrance" value but is subject to modification by the "acid", "burnt" and "goaty" values.

The inherent trouble with all these classifications is that one has first of all to assign an odorant to a class which is inherently pleasant, such as flowery or unpleasant such as foul, and then one concludes that nearly all the members of the flowery class are pleasant and those of the foul class are unpleasant. Very little is added. Bain's classification adds something in the way of logical understanding. Crocker & Henderson's adds something in the way of modification of "fragrance" by other constituents, which simultaneously modify the pleasantness. The other approach that has been indicated, that of correlating pleasantness of odour with defined adsorption characteristics may offer a more soundly-based classification. It has to be remembered, though, that the several methods of classification that have been described have not aimed specifically at separation of pleasant from unpleasant odours. The feeling of pleasantness that comes with beauty, whether of vista, of symphony or of odour ultimately varies from one person's assessment to another's; so does that of unpleasantness and the two cannot be arbitrarily and exactly separated. All that can be done is to find rules of application as wide as possible that correlate odours of different kinds with pleasantness and unpleasantness. Precise instrumental determination of odour quality should be possible in the near future; precise instrumental determination of pleasantness and unpleasantness will always be difficult because it must take account of individual variations in preference, even of idiosyncrasy.

Rules

The only rule, and that a little diffuse, that we can derive from the contents of this chapter is:

Rule 87. The most successful classification of odours is based on the division of several odour properties into their pleasant and unpleasant aspects. There is, as yet, no classification that provides a reason for the difference between pleasantness and unpleasantness of odours, nor one which provides a clear-cut boundary between them.

REFERENCES

39. A. Bain, *The Senses & the Intellect*, 1855, Parker, London.

40. H. Zwaardemaker, *Die Physiologie des Geruchs*, pp. 207–238, 1895, Engelmann, Leipzig.

41. S. Ohma, La classification des odeurs aromatiques en sous-classes, *Arch. néerl. Physiol.*, 1922, **6**, 567–590.

42. G. H. Cheesman & S. Mayne, The influence of adaptation on absolute threshold measurements for olfactory stimuli, *Quart. J. exp. Psychol.*, 1953, **5**, 22–30.

43. R. W. Moncrieff, Olfactory adaptation and odour likeness, *J. Physiol.*, 1956, **133**, 302 (cf. Ref. 14).

44. A. Heyninx, *Essai d'Olfaction physiologique*, 289 pp., 1919, Larcier, Brussels.

45. A. Heyninx, La physiologie de l'olfaction, *Rev. d'oto-neuro-ophtalmol.* 1933, **11**, 10–19.

46. H. Henning, *Der Geruch*, p. 94 (see Ref. 22).

47. A. E. Findley, Further studies of Henning's system of olfactory qualities, *Amer. J. Psychol.*, 1924, **35**, 436–445.

48. E. C. Crocker & L. F. Henderson, Analysis and classification of odours. An attempt to develop a workable model, *Amer. Perfum.*, 1927, **22**, 325–327, 356.

49. E. C. Crocker, *Flavor*, pp. 12–16, 1945, McGraw-Hill, New York.

50. G. L. Dorough, H. B. Glass, T. L. Gresham, G. B. Malone & E. E. Reid, Structure–property relationships in some isometric octanols, *J. Amer. chem. Soc.*, 1941, **63**, 3100–3110.

51. R. W. Moncrieff, The sorptive nature of the olfactory stimulus, *Proc. 2nd Intern. Congr. Surface Activity*, pp. 321–328, 1957, London.

52. R. W. Moncrieff, An instrument for measuring and classifying odours, *J. appl. Physiol.*, 1961, **16**, 742–749.

CHAPTER 14

SOME PREVIOUSLY DISCUSSED ODOUR
PREFERENCES

L IKING and disliking, pleasantness and unpleasantness are relative. It is easy enough to say: "I like this smell better than that", when given the two to compare, but very difficult to say by how much; quantitative treatment of pleasantness is difficult. Furthermore, what one person prefers may be different from what another prefers. Can one nevertheless get some sort of expression of average pleasantness? Can it be said that for most people their preferences are similar? An attempt was made by Beebe-Center[53] on the problem of assigning to an odour a general affective value (pleasant or unpleasant); one, and this is important, which was not dependent upon a particular observer. The work was carried out experimentally at Harvard in 1925–1926. Beebe-Center determined the rank order of fourteen odorants which was assigned to them by each one of his eight observers. The fourteen odorants were sweet orange (most pleasant), extract of carnation, oils of jasmin, bergamot, ylang-ylang, cloves, Ceylon cinnamon, synthetic white rose perfume, neroli, cananga, petitgrain, thyme, rosemary, and geranium (least pleasant). He found that five of his eight observers judged olfactory substances for pleasantness far more in accord with their general affective value (average value) than the other three did. He considered that these five people were aesthetically more sensitive to odours than were the other three whose rankings seemed to be confused. His work did show that there is a large measure of agreement between many observers as to which odours are pleasant and which are unpleasant but that there are some subjects who disagree. He did not however give details of the age and sex of his subjects which it would have been interesting to know. In view of the protracted nature of the work it is most likely that he enlisted the help of some of his students and whether psychology students make good subjects is questionable. But he did find that five out of the eight subjects agreed well about the rank order of pleasantness of the fourteen odorants and that is a significant finding and suggests that the term "general affective value" does have a real meaning.

Percentage of pleasantness

In a later and more ambitious study Beebe-Center[54] assigned coefficients of percentage of pleasantness, P, to olfactory stimuli; he defined the coefficient, P, as:

$$P = \frac{p + \frac{1}{2}i}{p + i + u} \times 100$$

where p is the number of "pleasant" and

　i is the number of "indifferent"; and

　　u is the number of "unpleasant" reactions to an odorant elicited from the subjects.

This is simple enough; all it consists of is giving 1 point for each "pleasant" response, $\frac{1}{2}$ point for each "indifferent" response, nothing for each "unpleasant" response, dividing the sum of these points by the total number of responses and then converting to "per hundred". Similarly the "percentage of pleasantness" for a *set* of stimuli is the average of the percentages of pleasantness for the individual stimuli in that set or series.

Experimentally, Beebe-Center used the following set of twenty-one olfactory stimuli; anise oil, sweet orange oil, clove oil, cassie extract (acacia), bergamot oil, cinammon oil, jasmin synthetic, ylang-ylang oil, cananga oil, carnation extract, white rose synthetic, juniper oil, petitgrain oil, geranium oil, fennel oil, neroli bitter oil, nutmeg oil, thyme oil, patchouli oil, rosemary oil, and cumin oil. Only three observers (male students) took part in the trials and their opinions as to what was pleasant and what unpleasant varied tremendously. Each was asked to give a response to

TABLE 72

**Effect of pleasantness or unpleasantness of previous experience
on reactions to olfactory stimuli**

Observer	Percentages of pleasantness of set of stimuli after:	
	Pleasant determination	Unpleasant determination
No. 1	73	82
No. 2	14	33
No. 3	38	65
All	125	180

the set of odorants: (a) after first smelling those members of the set that he considered pleasant, (b) after first smelling those he considered unpleasant. The results were as shown in Table 72.

After smelling only the pleasant members of the set, the whole set seems not quite so pleasant (125 against 180) as after smelling only the unpleasant members; this result is not unexpected. But what is unexpected is the magnitude of the differences of responses between the three observers. One cannot help suspecting that there was too much opportunity for introspection, and not enough prompt service paid to the immediate first response of pleasantness or unpleasantness. Perhaps the choice of psychology students as observers was unfortunate. However, three other male observers, presumably also students, did rather better; they compared their reactions to the twenty-one stimuli (a) without previous experience and (b) after previously smelling the unpleasant members of the set. Their results are shown in Table 73.

TABLE 73

**Effect of previous unpleasant experience on reactions
to olfactory stimuli**

Observer	Percentage of pleasantness of set of stimuli after:	
	No previous determination	Unpleasant stimuli determination
No. 4	32	44
No. 5	53	58
No. 6	49	58
All	134	160

Once again the result is not unexpected. A previous relatively unpleasant olfactory experience makes a standard olfactory experience seem a little more pleasant than usual. Beebe-Center puts things more generally and more professionally in his law of affective equilibrium which states that "The affective value of the experiential correlate of a stimulus varies conversely with the sum of the affective values of those experiences preceding this correlate which constitute with it a unitary temporal group".

This work was followed by some along similar lines by Kniep, Morgan and Young[26]. First experiments were made with 100 observers, 50 men and 50 women, all students within the age group 18–24 years, and the percentage of pleasantness as defined by Beebe-Center was determined for fifteen odorants and for a sixteenth empty control bottle. This last should obviously have been "indifferent" to all the subjects and should have given a percentage of pleasantness of 50; in fact it yielded one of 61 which is not too close to the expected figure. Experimental results (pleasant and unpleasant odorants were arranged at random) were as shown in Table 74.

TABLE 74

Quantitative description of pleasantness of smell

Odorant	Percentage of pleasantness
Camphor	70
Wintergreen oil (methyl salicylate)	90
Vanillin	93
p-Dichlorbenzene	83
Menthol	62
Phenol	31
Acetophenone	56
Nitrobenzene	15
Geraniol	81
Ethyl cinnamate	31
n-Caproic acid	9
Quinoline	15
Heptyl aldehyde	7
o-Bromtoluene	20
Diphenyl ether	44
Empty bottle	61

There are six of these fifteen odorants that were included in the investigation described in Part I of this book and it will be of interest to compare the preferences there described with those found by Kniep *et al.* For example Kniep *et al* give a figure of 81 per cent as the percentage of pleasantness of geraniol which has a lovely rose-like smell; in our investigation (Table 1) geraniol was found to have an average placing of 44·8 out of 132 odorants and was ranked 39th. The corresponding values for all of the odorants that figured in both investigations are as shown in Table 75.

The high values of pleasantness assigned by Kniep to wintergreen (methyl salicylate) and to paradichlorbenzene are difficult to accept; the other values agree reasonably with those found by the author. Crocker, it may be remembered, gave maximum "fragrance" value

TABLE 75

Comparison of Kniep et al's preferences with those found by the author

Odorant	Percentage of pleasantness (Kniep et al)	Average placing out of 132 odorants (Author)	Ranked out of 132 odorants (Author)
Vanillin	93	43·3	37th
Geraniol	81	44·8	39th
Camphor	70	60·5	66th
Methyl salicylate	90	71·1	82nd
Nitrobenzene	15	72·3	85th
Paradichlorbenzene	83	90·2	107th

(8) to wintergreen but was at pains to point out that although it had maximum "fragrance" it did not have maximum pleasantness. Furthermore, that any group of people should rate paradichlorbenzene better than geraniol is astonishing. Once again, one cannot help questioning if psychology students, with their habits of introspection, make the best, or even passable, subjects for simple expressions of olfactory preferences.

Recognition of smells

There is no doubt at all that most people, when requested to express preferences for one odorant over others, try to identify the smells, and are very pleased with themselves, and look for praise, if they succeed. In the author's work described in the first two parts of this book, attempts by the subjects to recognize smells were always discouraged until after they had arranged the odorants in order of preference; what was asked for was always the first instantaneous reaction, "I like" or "I like better" or "not so well", and this was simplest and most convincing if the subject did not try to identify the odorant and bring in the loading factor of associations that previous experiences may have given it. Other workers seem sometimes to have permitted, if not encouraged, recognition of odorants; there is a probability that what is identified may be given a better rating than what cannot be identified. But unpractised people find it not so easy to identify smells quickly, even although they may be reasonably familiar.

An investigation of the capacity of unpractised people for identifying smells was carried out by Sumner.[55] Tests were carried out with twelve odorant materials on 200 people who were asked to identify the odorants. Of the 200, fifty were doctors, nurses, and students, and the other 150 were patients; the patients did no worse than the medicals. The work was done at the General Infirmary at Leeds. Some substances, such as coffee, were identified by most people, others like eucalyptus by only a few; asafoetida was identified by only two out of the 200, the other 198 had never met it previously. Results were as shown in Table 76.

TABLE 76
Identification of odorants

Odorant	Identified by per cent of observers
Coffee	82
Chocolate	75
Almonds (benzaldehyde)	72
Tar	63
Lemon oil	57
Peppermint oil	50
Camphor	31
Aniseed oil	24
Clove oil	20
Nutmeg	18
Eucalyptus oil	5
Asafoetida	1

All of the subjects were supposedly free from organic defects in their sense of smell—there was no known anosmia—so that their performance was apparently rather poor.

In a way this is true enough, but anyone who has worked for long on the sense of smell knows how much a little practice can do. The olfactory sense is very acute and very discriminating and, with practice, individuals soon learn to recognize a large number of smells. A laboratory assistant with whom the author worked was so very poor at identifying smells when she started to work amongst them that some doubt was felt as to whether she could really smell at all. After a few .months she was identifying smells exactly and instantaneously and affected to be frightfully bored at having to do such childishly simple work. With smells, practice makes perfect.

The smells that are used in hospitals to test a patient's olfactory ability are most frequently peppermint, camphor, cloves, and asafoetida. As Sumner rightly says it would be much better to use coffee, almonds (benzaldehyde), tar, and oil of lemon; these the normal person will probably recognize. No one will recognize asafoetida if he has never met it before, and cloves and camphor are not so easy as might be imagined for the unpractised to identify.

Pleasantness and ease of recollection

Gordon[56] has looked into the question of whether pleasant or unpleasant odours are the more likely to be recalled. The work was carried out at the University of California, Los Angeles. Ten odours were investigated: lemon, cinnamon, bergamot, lavender, tansy, peppermint, creosote, eucalyptus, valerian, and asafoetida but there was not a great deal of difference under the experimental conditions adopted in the ease of recollection; some 49 per cent of pleasant odours, 50 per cent of unpleasant and 56 per cent of indifferent odours were recalled (p. 258). There was however considerable variation between the likes and dislikes of individual testers; for example, eighty-four subjects (out of 200) thought lemon best of all, fifty-one gave it second place, thirty-six gave it third place etc. down to eight who gave it sixth place; poorer than this it never ranked and the average of all the positions assigned to it was 2·175. The most disliked odour was asafoetida; 139 persons gave it tenth place, but one person ranked it as high as fifth. The average rankings for the ten odorants were:

lemon	2·175	eucalyptus	5·885
cinnamon	2·835	tansy	6·665
peppermint	3·380	creosote	7·725
bergamot	3·925	valerian	8·345
lavender	4·535	asafoetida	9·530

The distribution of the placings for lemon, eucalyptus and asafoetida are shown in Figs. 42.–44. The group of 200 people who gave their opinions was composed almost entirely of students and no correlation between type of person and odour preferences was attempted.

There are four odorants out of the ten that Gordon used, which were included in the first part of the author's investigation. They were put in the order (best-liked first): lemon, cinnamon, peppermint, lavender by Gordon, but in Table 1 they appear in the order lemon, peppermint, lavender, cinnamon, which affords some sort of agreement although cinnamon is rated unexpectedly favourably by Gordon's subjects. This would suggest (cf. Table 3) that Gordon's 200 subjects included a high proportion of young males, but she does not say.

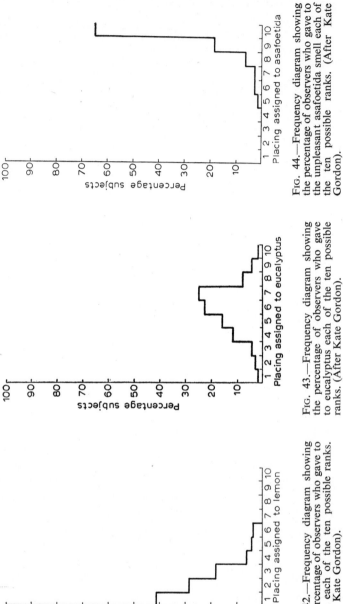

FIG. 42.—Frequency diagram showing the percentage of observers who gave to lemon each of the ten possible ranks. (After Kate Gordon).

FIG. 43.—Frequency diagram showing the percentage of observers who gave to eucalyptus each of the ten possible ranks. (After Kate Gordon).

FIG. 44.—Frequency diagram showing the percentage of observers who gave to the unpleasant asafoetida smell each of the ten possible ranks. (After Kate Gordon).

Findley's observations

Findley[47] whose study of Henning's classification of odours has already been discussed (p. 216) found that a large group of people placed nineteen odorants in the following order of preference (best first):

> lemon oil, cinnamon, (Tonka bean, orange oil), jasmine oil, cardamon, peppermint, amyl acetate, coffee, (tansy oil, hop flowers), turpentine, (benzol, xylol, tar oil), ether, ammonium valerate, pyridine, hydrogen sulphide.

Those odorants in the same brackets were ranked equal. No attempt was made to correlate individual preferences with type (age, sex, or temperament) of person. Seven odorants that were similar to seven out of Findley's nineteen odorants were included by the author in his investigation (Table 3). Their comparative rankings in the two investigations are shown in Table 77.

TABLE 77
Comparison of rankings of odorants

Odorant	Ranked by Findley		Ranked by author	
	Out of 19	Per cent	Out of 132	Per cent
Lemon oil	1	6	(flavour) 11	8
Cinnamon	2	11	27	20
Tonka bean	3	16	(tincture) 56	42
Orange oil	3	16	10	8
Peppermint	7	37	(flavour) 13	10
Amyl acetate	8	42	57	43
Pyridine	18	95	118	89

Comparison of the two "per cent" columns shows good agreement for lemon, amyl acetate and pyridine, fair for cinnamon and orange and great discrepancies for Tonka bean and peppermint. In these two last the form in which the odorant was presented was different. Once again cinnamon is placed better, that is by Findley as well as by Gordon, in the earlier work than it was by the author (Table 3).

Kenneth's observations

Kenneth[57] carried out experiments in the Psychology Dept. at Edinburgh University, with sixty men and women students as subjects. In his own words: "it was found that odour preferences, while subject to fluctuations, could be determined with some degree of accuracy" but later "the order of preference is difficult to establish with accuracy, unless a large number of persons are tested, but the experiments under review reveal the following order: Oil (otto) of roses, amyl acetate, oil of lavender, terebene, cassia (like cinnamon but coarser), eucalyptus, clove oil, menthol, camphor, origanum (marjoram), musk, citronella, pine oil, cedarwood oil, benzole, ethyl alcohol, sandalwood oil, ferric valerian, asafoetida, carbon bisulphide."

The subjects agreed unanimously that carbon bisulphide was without a trace of pleasantness and almost unanimously that otto of roses was without a trace of unpleasantness: "the only subject who disliked otto of roses associated the smell with a motor accident in which he had been very seriously injured, and which it was found, had taken place near a rose garden". Does this strain credence?

One observer's preferences are almost constant

Kenneth[58] later compared his own odour preferences, for a group of twelve odorants, measured in the two periods 1922–1923 and 1927, that is with an interval of four or five years between the observations. The number of observations that he made on any one odorant in the two periods varied from two to twelve; in order to illustrate the excellence of agreement both within each of the two periods, and of the two sets one with the other, his first four observations (when he made so many) are shown for each of the two periods in Table 78. The judgments are indicated thus: $+ +$ entirely pleasant, $+ -$ not quite pleasant, $- +$ not quite unpleasant, $- -$ entirely unpleasant. Each of the four judgments were made on a different day.

Kenneth's results as he himself points out confirm Young's[59] earlier conclusion that "the most variable odors are in the region of indifference while the most constant are either 'very pleasant' or 'very unpleasant' ". Kenneth was obliged to substitute in 1927 a synthetic rose oil for the natural attar that he had used in 1923, but even so his preference for the rose smell persisted. The only other odorant, for which he had what he called an idiosyncratic liking, and which gained full marks in both series of tests, was cedarwood. But it is difficult to pick out any odorant which showed big differences between the two periods; there was a slightly better tolerance of amyl alcohol in the first period, a little doubt arising

TABLE 78

Constancy of affective preferences

Period	Amyl alcohol	Camphor	Cassia oil	Cedar-wood oil	Citronella oil	Menthol	Musk	Origanum oil	Pine oil	Rose oil	Sandal-wood oil	Xylol
1922–1923	− + + + / − − + −	− − − − / + + + +	− − / + +	+ + + + / + + + +	− − − − / + + + +	+ − − − / + + + +	+ − − + / − + + −	− − − − / + + + +	+ + + + / + + + +	+ + + + / + + + +	− + − + / − − + −	− + + − / + − − +
1927	− − − − / − − − −	− − − − / + + + +	+ − + − / − + − +	+ + + + / + + + +	− − − + / + + + +	− − − − / + + + +	− − + + / + + − +	− − + − / + + + +	+ + − − / + + + +	+ + + + / + + + +	− − + + / + − − −	− − + + / + − − −

in the second period as to whether pine oil really was entirely pleasant, but the best defined observation and the surest inference that can be drawn from Table 78 is that there had been very little difference in Kenneth's own olfactory preferences over a period of four or five years. Both sets of tests were made when Kenneth was a grown man; had he done them much earlier, say the first test in his early 'teens and the second in his late 'teens, then we should have seen some very much bigger differences.

His orders of preference in the two periods were as shown in Table 79.

TABLE 79

Constancy of an individual's olfactory preferences

Rank	1922	1927
1st	Rose oil	Rose oil
2nd	Cedarwood oil	Cedarwood oil
3rd	Pine oil	Origanum oil
4th	Citronella oil	Pine oil
5th	Origanun oil	Citronella oil
6th	Menthol	Menthol
7th	Camphor	Camphor
8th	Musk	Musk
9th	Cassia oil	Cassia oil
10th	Xylol	Sandalwood oil
11th	Sandalwood oil	Xylol
12th	Amyl alcohol	Amyl alcohol

"The constancy of judgement after several years' interval is very striking, and the table also reveals the idiosyncratic preference of the subject for cedarwood oil and his relative dislike of cassia oil."

So far as concerns Kenneth's own placings in 1922 and 1927 they bear out very well the good agreement between first and second arrangements of odours noted in Chapter 8 (Rule 39) and really extend this rule because there was such a long interval of time between Kenneth's two successive arrangements. Seven of his twelve odorants were, in fact, given identical placings in the two arrangements and four of them differed, one arrangement from another by only one place; the one odorant, origanum oil which moved by two places in order of preference was the one that is to most people, and possibly also to Kenneth, the least familiar. Rule 43 would have predicted 5 instead of 7 odorants to have taken identical placings and 4 odorants as actually found to differ by one place only.

A bigger range

Kenneth, in the same paper,[58] extended his studies to a consideration of thirty different odorants; he arranged them twelve times in order of preference and found that there was good agreement. Rose oil he always placed first, cajeput oil always last. In the middle of the series there was more variation; for example his twelve successive placings of citronella oil were: 12, 9, 5, 8, 11, 6, 6, 16, 11, 13, 12, 8. And yet in straight comparisons of pairs he preferred citronella to fir oil 6 times out of 12, to menthol 8 times out of 12, to sassafras 7 times out of 12, to Pumilio (pine) oil 8 times out of 12, to rosemary and camphor each 11 times, to caraway 10 times, and then to 14 other odorants 12 times out of 12. Similarly three other odorants were always preferred to citronella; two, neroli and bergamot oils 11 times out of 12, sylvestris (pine) 8 times, origanum 10 times and juniper 6 times. So that when citronella was paired with 17 other odorants the preference was always (12 times out of 12) the same, with four other odorants it was the same 11 times out of 12, and with the other eight odorants there was less regularity. Truly it is amongst the indifferent odours that the variations are greatest. Just as a group of people agree well amongst themselves about the odours they like best (Rule 6) and about those they dislike most (Rule 5) and become confused and disagree about their preferences in the intermediate range (Rule 8), so does one individual subject behave on repeated testing. He is consistent about the odours that he really likes or dislikes but becomes confused about the arrangement of the indifferent odours.

It may be of interest to list Kenneth's thirty odorants, best-liked first, most disliked last; they are: rose, neroli, bergamot, cedarwood, thyme, pine oil (sylvestris), origanum, juniper, citronella, fir, menthol, sassafras (rich in safrole), pine oil (Pumilio), rosemary, camphor, caraway, dill, musk, patchouli, nutmeg, cassia, sandalwood, benzaldehyde, methyl salicylate, toluene, xylene, anise, amyl alcohol, fennel, cajeput. Kenneth pointed out that the odours of musk, benzaldehyde and citronella gave especially variable reactions. Two of these, musk and benzaldehyde which is the essential constituent of almond odour, we have already found (Chapter 9, Rules 46, 47) to have sex significance. Perhaps their effect even on one individual can vary according to his sex tone, his state of health. Cajeput, Kenneth's least-liked odorant, is a pungent oil that is distilled from the leaves of some East Indian trees.

Constancy of preferences

There were other workers besides Kenneth who investigated the constancy, or the variation if there was little constancy, of odour preferences with time.

Young[59] in 1923 in Minnesota made experiments with four subjects, two men and two women, and eight odorants which were presented to them three times a week for five successive weeks. The odours were scored on a basis ranging from +3 for very pleasant to −3 for very unpleasant and intermediately. The average scoring, of many tests, given by each of the four subjects to each of the eight odorants was as shown in Table 80.

TABLE 80

Average scorings of odorants

Odorant	Average scoring by			
	A (man)	C (man)	B (woman)	D (woman)
White rose perfume	+2·8	+2·5	+0·8	+2·9
Oil of anise	+2·6	+3·0	+2·9	−2·1
Spirits of camphor	+2·5	+1·1	+1·7	+2·2
Oil of bergamot	+2·1	+0·9	+2·1	−0·2
Creosote	−1·0	−1·3	+1·2	+1·4
Asafoetida	−1·3	−3·0	−0·4	−2·8
Caproic acid	−2·9	−2·1	−3·0	−3·0
Cod-liver oil	−2·9	−2·1	−2·7	−2·8

The outstanding sex difference is the much better rating given by the women to creosote. Subject D repeatedly stated that oil of anise suggested liquorice candy which she disliked greatly. Her rating of oil of anise is very different from those of A, C, and B. Young found that for any one subject the variation from one day to another (and even from one week to another) for one odorant that was very pleasant or very unpleasant was small, but that variation in the indifferent range was much greater. In 1928[60] he confirmed this finding and agreed with Kenneth and with Beebe-Center both of whom had intermediately worked on the constancy of preferences, that the most variable odours in respect of their affective judgments are in the region of indifference, and the most constant are either very pleasant or very unpleasant. In 1931 Beebe-Center returned to the subject, as described below.

Different observers more variable than one at different times

Beebe-Center[61] compared the variability of judgments in one observer at different times with that of different observers. Tests were made on fourteen odorants by eight observers on three occasions; the first was followed by the second after two weeks, and the second by the third after some few (about $4\frac{1}{2}$–$7\frac{1}{2}$) months. In the intervals between the three series of tests the subjects took part in many olfactory experiments, which might perhaps have been expected to modify their preferences. Agreement for any one individual at the different times of test was very much better than that between different individuals. Beebe-Center was inclined to attribute the considerable differences between individuals to unlike past experiences and to attribute agreement primarily to like organic constitution. One thing he noticed was that the shift in the later series was in the direction of greater disagreement between the several observers.

It is interesting, too, that in Young's earlier investigation of the constancy of olfactory preferences,[59] one of his four subjects stated that recognition of an odour increased its pleasantness. This is true enough in the sense that inability to "place" an odour that one is sure one knows is frustrating and unpleasant, and when recognition does come it is pleasant. But the real answer to this difficulty is to get the subjects to give first impression answers, "I like" or "I dislike", before they have time to sort out why they like or dislike.

One last observation to which further discussion will be afforded in Chapter 20 is that olfactory preferences change with the times. What was well liked a hundred years ago may not be thought of so highly today.

Rules

Those rules that can be derived from the subject matter of this chapter are as follows:

Rule 88. There is sufficient agreement between different people of the same kind, e.g. female students, on their olfactory preferences to justify making an average assessment, known as a "general affective value" (cf. Rules 5 and 6). The use of such an average value would not usually be justified without some accompanying statement of the kind of people engaged, e.g. men, women or children.

Rule 89. The apparent pleasantness of an odorant is appreciably increased by just-prior smelling of unpleasant odorants. Conversely it is apparently reduced by just-prior smelling of pleasant odorants.

Rule 90. Recognition of an odour enhances its pleasantness. Unpractised people usually find it difficult to put a name to odours with which they are quite familiar.

Rule 91. Recollection, that is recognition after previous experience, of odours is nearly independent of pleasantness or unpleasantness; it is no more easy to remember one kind than the other.

Rule 92. An adult individual's odour preferences are very constant over a period of years.

Rule 93. Often-repeated testing on one adult individual reveals excellent consistency of preferences amongst the liked and the disliked odours, but considerable variability amongst the indifferent odours (cf. Rules 5, 6, and 8 for *groups* of people).

Rule 94. Constancy of preferences in one individual at different times is greater than that between several individuals.

REFERENCES

53. J. G. Beebe-Center, General affective value, *Psychol. Rev.*, 1923, **36,** 472–480.

54. J. G. Beebe-Center, The law of affective equilibrium, *Amer. J. Psychol.*, 1929, **41,** 54–69.

55. D. Sumner, On testing the sense of smell, *The Lancet*, 1962, II, 895.

56. K. Gordon, The recollection of pleasant and unpleasant odours, *J. exp. Psychol.*, 1925, **8,** 225–239.

57. J. H. Kenneth, Some experiments on mental reactions to odours, *Perf. Essent. Oil Record*, 1924, **15,** 85–87.

58. J. H. Kenneth, A few odour preferences and their constancy, *J. exp. Psychol.*, 1928, **11,** 56–61.

59. P. T. Young, Constancy of affective judgments to odours, *J. exp. Psychol.*, 1923, **6,** 182–191.

60. P. T. Young, Studies in affective psychology, *Amer. J. Psychol.*, 1928, **40,** 372–400.

61. J. G. Beebe-Center, The variability of affective judgments upon odours, *J. exp. Psychol.*, 1931, **14,** 91–93.

CHAPTER 15

WHAT IS KNOWN OF THE INFLUENCE OF SEX
ON ODOUR PREFERENCES

IT IS surprising how little experimental work has been carried out
and published about the effect of sex on odour preferences.
Most of the well-known workers on smell seem to have written in
very general terms at one time or another in the last century drawing
attention to the function of smell in bringing together the two
sexes especially in animal and primitive human societies; they have
had much to say about the animal components (musk, civet, and
ambergris) of perfumes, and they have given renewed life to many
anecdotes of questionable truth. Some workers with a scientific
leaning have investigated such secondary points as the influence
of the menstrual period on olfactory acuity in women. Elsberg,[62]
for example, thought that they possessed an unusual acuteness of
smell just before and during the menstrual period. Workers with a
descriptive leaning have spread themselves on the function of
smell in sex relations; Millen[63] provides a ready example in Chapters
13 and 14 of his book. There is a wealth, or at any rate a very large
quantity of anecdotal and imaginative material about the relations
between sex and smell. And yet the amount of work that has been
published dealing with the straightforward subject of differences
between the sexes regarding the smells they like and dislike is small
indeed. Do men and women have different olfactory preferences?
Everybody seems to have taken it for granted that they have, and
imagination has run riot as to the depth and amplitude of these
differences. Kenneth[58] in Edinburgh forty years ago is about the
only worker who seems to have done very much to examine the
differences experimentally.

Comparison of Kenneth's preferences with sex groups

The same twelve odorants which were arranged in order of preference by Kenneth himself in 1922 and in 1927 (p. 232) were also
used for the investigation of sex differences. In the period 1922–
1924 a group of males and a group of females had arranged the same

TABLE 81

Order of preference of twelve odorants

Subjects	Amyl alcohol	Camphor	Cassia oil	Cedar-wood oil	Citronella oil	Menthol	Musk	Origanum oil	Pine oil	Rose oil	Sandal-wood oil	Xylol
Kenneth in 1922	12	7	9	2	4	6	8	5	3	1	11	10
Kenneth in 1927	12	7	9	2	5	6	8	3	4	1	10	11
Group of males 1922–1924	12	8	2	5	7	3	9	6	4	1	10	11
Group of females 1922–1924	12	6	2	10	5	3	9	4	7	1	11	8

twelve odorants in their orders of preference and their placings, as well as those of Kenneth, are shown in Table 81. Some sixty subjects took part in the tests.

There are certain differences between the rankings made by the men and women, notably the male preference for pine and cedarwood and the better female tolerance of xylol. There are, too, even bigger differences between the results of Kenneth himself and the group of males. Kenneth's pronounced dislike of cassia oil (cassia is rather like cinnamon but not so fine), his dislike of menthol and his idiosyncratic liking for cedarwood oil are all remarkable.

Unfortunately, not one of the three odorants, pine oil, cedarwood oil and xylol which Kenneth found would give the biggest differences in reaction according to the subject's sex, was included in the 132 odorants used by the author in the first part of his investigation and accordingly none of these three is to be found in Table 3. Therefore any straight comparison of results with these three is impossible at present.

There were, however, four of Kenneth's twelve odorants that did appear in Table 3. They are shown in Table 82 with the rankings given by men and women (from Table 3) and by men and women in Kenneth's groups. Remembering that Table 3 contained 132 odorants and that Kenneth used only twelve the rankings from Table 3 can be divided by ten or eleven to be equivalent to Kenneth's.

TABLE 82

**Olfactory preferences by sex: comparison of
Kenneth's and author's results**

Odorant	Author's rankings		Kenneth's rankings	
	Male	Female	Male	Female
Rose oil	37th	23rd	1st	1st
Citronella	80th	60th	7th	5th
Camphor	68th	61st	8th	6th
Musk	83rd	75th	9th	9th
Cassia (Author used cinnamon bark)	19th	49th	2nd	2nd
Xylene (Author used toluene)	114th	82nd	11th	8th

The first four odorants in Table 80 were similarly used both by Kenneth and the author and the comparison is direct. If one is prepared to admit that the odour of cassia is of the same type as cinnamon bark (as it is, but it is coarser), and that xylene and toluene have odours of the same kind, one can get, in addition, the last two lines in Table 82.

There is nothing in Table 82 to rouse much enthusiasm, but it can fairly be said that wherever Kenneth found a difference in ranking by the two sexes of an odorant, the author found differences in the same direction; the three odorants concerned are, citronella, camphor and (possibly) xylene.

Assessment

It seems to be fairly generally recognized that there are considerable differences between men and women in respect of their olfactory preferences. But what they are or how great they are has been a matter of speculation rather than of exact knowledge. Kenneth made a start on the task of gathering the necessary knowledge; the author has taken the investigation further. Between these results of the two workers there is some measure of agreement and no direct disagreement. How great the differences can be between the sexes in their olfactory preference is shown in Chapters 3 and 9. The known dependence of selling on pleasant olfactory associations (Chapter 21) should encourage wider and deeper investigation of the sex differences in preferences.

It may be noted that an investigation of changes in taste preferences with sex and age has been reported by Laird & Breen[64]; the tests were made with pineapple drinks ranging from tart to sweet, and are concerned with taste rather than olfaction. If the tests had been made with sugar solutions they would have been in the sphere of taste and definitely not of olfaction, but the introduction of the pineapple flavour means that we cannot disregard them and they are discussed in Chapter 19.

REFERENCES

62. C. A. Elsberg, Newer aspects of olfactory physiology and their diagnostic applications, *Arch. Neurol. Psychiat. Chicago*, 1937, **37**, 223–236.

63. J. K. Millen, *Your Nose Knows*, 1960, Cunningham Press, Los Angeles.

64. D. A. Laird & W. J. Breen, Sex and age alterations in taste preferences, *J .Amer. Dietetic Assn.*, 1939, **15**, 549–550.

CHAPTER 16

WHAT IS KNOWN OF THE INFLUENCE OF AGE
ON ODOUR PREFERENCES

WHAT WE have seen in Chapters 4 and 10 has been that there are great differences between the olfactory preferences òf children and adults. How does this knowledge knit into the prior art? The first observation is that unfortunately there is not very much of it, that is of prior art. It is absolutely astounding that variations of olfactory preferences with age should have received so little attention from the experimentalists. As was the case with sex, so it is with age; there is a general but diffuse belief that olfactory preferences do change, but exact knowledge is at a premium. It seems to the author all the more surprising in that knowledge of such changes must be of interest and value to manufacturers, especially to those who make foods and beverages. Such information as has been discovered and printed will be discussed now, but it is very thin.

Percentage of pleasantness

The work by Kniep, Morgan and Young[26], which was discussed in Chapter 14, and which concerned the determination of the percentage of pleasantness of fifteen different odorants, was extended by them to throw light on the olfactory preferences of children in the following way. Similar trials to those already outlined in Chapter 14 (pp. 225–7) were made with children at a local school (Champaign Illinois), 50 within the age group 7–9 years inclusive and 50 within that of 10–13 years (or possibly 11–13 years; the paper is not clear on this point). The odorants used were the same fifteen as had been used before for the adults except that two of them, nitrobenzene and diphenyl ether, were now omitted. As before, an empty bottle (no odorant) was included as a control. Results were as shown in Table 83.

The totals, i.e. the sum of the percentages for the three columns are respectively 780, 735 and 709 (excluding nitrobenzene and diphenyl ether). The children, especially the younger children, give higher percentages of pleasantness to the odorants. Are young

TABLE 83

Percentage of pleasantness of some odorants according to different age groups

Odorant	Percentage of pleasantness given by age group		
	7–9	10–13	18–24
Camphor	66	78	70
Methyl salicylate	84	94	90
Vanillin	84	89	93
p-Dichlorbenzene	76	86	83
Menthol	56	52	62
Phenol	47	52	31
Acetophenone	54	48	56
Nitrobenzene	—	—	15
Geraniol	80	79	81
Ethyl cinnamate	47	32	31
n-Caproic acid	26	14	9
Quinoline	10	12	15
Heptyl aldehyde	38	8	7
o-Bromtoluene	30	24	20
Diphenyl ether	—	—	44
Empty bottle	82	67	61

children more easily pleased than adults? ask the authors, but they do not answer the question. The authors conclude that "the experiment shows that children and adults are similar in their likes and dislikes for odors" and they bolster up this opinion with some statistical correlations. But they really do less than justice to their own work. They overlook the much better tolerance of the very young children for the unpleasant odour (pungent, persistent, slightly fruity) of heptaldehyde (oenanthaldehyde) and the goat-like caproic acid. The children, too, liked phenol better than did the adults. The really worrying feature about these otherwise excellent experimental results is that both groups of children assign unduly high percentages of pleasantness to the empty bottle; what can one say about the 7–9 year olds who give it 82 per cent pleasantness? Are they anxious to please, to give positive results? Do they live in a world peculiar to themselves of unpleasant smells where "no smell" is a pleasant relief? Do they subscribe to the view that "he smells best who smells of nothing"? In the order in which the bottles of odorants were presented to the subjects, the empty bottle always followed the phenol bottle; phenol especially with its associations of hospitals and surgeries is slightly unpleasant, and the immediate previous experience of a mildly unpleasant odour (cf. Rule 89) might be expected to lead to a percentage of pleasantness in excess of 50. But a figure of 82 per cent would certainly not be expected; it may indicate that the young children were unreliable. Regrettably what it indicates all too plainly is that there was something sadly wrong with the experimental work. Controls are absolutely essential for research work on smell; if they give reasonable results, one feels that the rest of the work is sound; if they give unreasonable results, the rest of the work is highly suspect, and it should all be done again, and again, until the discrepancy is cleared up. One factor that may have contributed to the difficulty is that the time interval between successive presentations of odorants was only 50 seconds; it could have been longer with advantage, but this should not have led, one feels, to such big discrepancies. There are, too, indications that the children were under some mental stress; they seemed to think they were required to like the smells and that testing would continue until they did like them or at any rate until they said that they did. In one's own experiments on children's olfactory reactions one recalls the thought given to the design of the experiments and the sympathy shown by the testers to the children; one cannot doubt that similar care was taken by other workers, but even so the results must be looked at objectively. It is impossible to forget that the young children in the 7–9 years group gave a percentage of pleasantness of 82 to an empty bottle and only very slightly higher values of 84 per cent to methyl salicylate and vanillin, with all the other odorants rated lower. Not only did the empty bottle follow phenol, but this followed ethyl cinnamate, which followed o-bromtoluene so that the empty bottle followed three unpleasant smells. This in itself, although it goes some way to explaining the anomalies, was a bad arrangement and indicated poor design of experiments. It is regrettably impossible to feel much confidence in the remainder of the figures of Kniep et al.

In attempting a comparison of the results of Kniep, Morgan & Young with those of the author (Chapter 4) there are five odorants that figure in both Kniep et al's work and the authors (Table 3) and that can be used for comparison. They are: vanillin, geraniol, camphor, methyl salicylate, and paradichlorbenzene. Both workers find that the appreciation of vanillin rises as age increases; its percentage of pleasantness is 84, 89 and 93 in Kniep's age groups and its placing is 66·0 (under 15 years), 46·8 (15–25 years) and 30·0 (over 25 years) in the author's. If comparisons of the same type are made for the other four odorants, common to both workers, there are no other instances of consistent agreement to be found. If comparisons on a broader basis are made, e.g. with Kniep's 18–24 age group and the author's 15–25 age group there are no adequate resemblances; Kniep's students place vanillin, geraniol, methyl salicylate, camphor and paradichlorbenzene in the order 1, 4, 2, 5, 3, whilst the author's subjects (15–25 years) put them 1, 2, 3, 4, 5. Kniep's young children (7–9 years) put them in the order 1, 3, 1, 5, 4 (two of the odorants were rated equally first); his older children (11–13 years) put them 2, 4, 1, 5, 3 and the author's under 15's put them 4, 1, 3, 2, 5. There is no correspondence.

Very young children's tolerance

There is a very interesting paper by Stein, Ottenberg, and Roulet[65]; it concerns mainly the olfactory tolerance of children of 3 and 4 years old for odorous materials that when older they will think unpleasant. The three odorants used experimentally were synthetic faeces (a chemical mixture built up to have a faecal odour), synthetic sweat, and amyl acetate. The method of test was to offer to the subject (the child) who had closed his eyes, a bottle containing one of the odorants; the subject inhaled twice and then rated the odour as to "like" or "dislike". The subjects consisted of 300 healthy children between the ages of three and twelve approximately half boys and half girls, and they were tested at Pennsylvania. "A group of adult workers", their number and sex not stated, also took part in the test. The most important finding was that most of the three- and four-year olds rated all three odorants as pleasant; at the age of five there was a significant change and they then disliked faeces and sweat. There was, too, a slight drop in their appreciation of amyl acetate but after age six this picked up again; the amyl acetate reminded boys of model airplane "dope" and the girls of fingernail polish remover.

Stein *et al* comment "In early childhood it has been observed that all variety of objects are tasted and smelled, and usually no avertive response to odorous substances is apparent. Quite often a child may derive pleasing olfactory sensations from things which later in life, as an adult, are perceived as unpleasant." In Fig. 45. the results that Stein *et al* obtained from the faecal and sweat smells are shown, the responses being expressed as the percentage of pleasant (I like) reactions. The graphs have been drawn as the original authors drew them, discontinuously, but it looks fairly

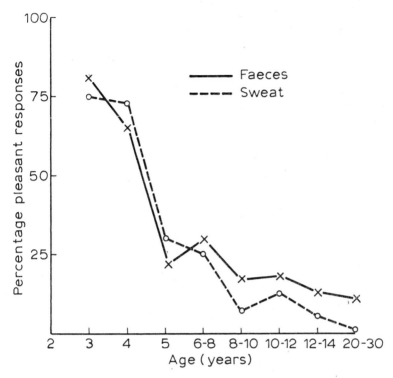

Fig. 45.—Showing the much better tolerance by very young children for two unpleasant odours of physiological significance.

clear that a smooth curve could be drawn close to the plots for each of the two odorants. Whatever physiological changes take place doubtless do so not discontinuously but gradually. The author's work described in Part I included no very young children, and even in Part II in which 559 subjects took part there were only three four-year olds and none younger. It is an interesting field and one in which more work with very young children is required.

There was, however, some general concordance between the author's results and those just described of Stein *et al*; for example, (Rule 32) in Part I it was observed that children exhibited a remarkable tolerance for odours containing a faecal note, to which they seemed to be indifferent. Furthermore (Rule 57) in Part II it was found that odours which are commonly disliked such as rape oil and oil-soluble chlorophyll are tolerated very much better by children up to about six years old.

Elderly people miss the gas smell

Perhaps the connection between the smell of town gas or coal gas and olfactory preferences is rather tenuous. But a great deal of town gas today comes not from the coke retorts but from the oil refinery, in the form of propane, butane etc., and is nearly odourless. It must be made odorous to be safe, so that a leak in the house will not go undetected and so suffocate the occupants. Various agents have been suggested: Pentalarm, a mixture of amyl mercaptans was one of the first and was needed only in very small quantity (12 oz. per million cu. ft. of gas) to give an unpleasant although not a nauseating smell; a smell that would be observed unmistakably but would not sicken. Ethyl mercaptan has also been used; so has tetrahydrothiophen. It is odd that this last has a powerful mercaptan-like odour because thiophen, of which it is a reduction product, has only a slight smell. What is necessary for the odorization of propane to make it suitable for domestic use is something that is unpleasant, and that suggests "gas" but is not nauseating. It may be that even more care than hitherto will have to be exercised in choosing an odorant for gas, because apparently some old people cannot smell town gas, or at least they do not notice it.

Chalke and Dewhurst[66] looked into the ability of old people to recognize the odour of town gas. In 1955, out of a total of 8,000 fatal home accidents, 892 were due to domestic gas, and three-quarters of these happened to people who were over 60 years old. Chalke and Dewhurst found that 95 per cent of the under 65's that they tested could recognize 20 parts of gas per 10,000 of air, but that 30 per cent of subjects (or of the 61 subjects that they tested) who were over 65 were unable to recognize the odour of town gas in any concentration that was lower than 50 parts per 10,000 of air. The writer has found, in the limited number of smell tests that he has made on old people, that the greatest difficulty is to get them to pay attention and take a good sniff. Too often they say "No, I can't smell it" to finish the business so that they can be left alone. But let them get interested in what is going on, and they are found to be able to smell pretty much as well as anyone else. This does not much reduce the problem of old people and town gas smell; largely through inattention, partly through living an inward-looking life, partly through their dislike of making any effort, they become unconscious of external stimuli. But there will be some who disagree and who maintain that olfactory acuity does fall off with age. It may be so; it is something on which more work is needed. The author believes that the falling off is in attention rather than ability but there is insufficient evidence available to be sure.

Inability to smell some odorants

As an extension of what has just been written, there may be reasons other than defects in the olfactory equipment that can cause people to show no response to an odour. The author knew a girl student who could smell quite normally; she got a holiday job picking freesias in some local greenhouses; at first the smell was fine, soon it was a bit overpowering, and at the end of the fortnight she could not smell freesias at all. Blakeslee,[67] who seems to have specialized in finding odd cases of unusual smelling capacity, in his work in the Genetics Dept. at Washington discussed the odour of freesias. He found two varieties of freesia, Golden Treasure and Golden Daffodil to which there were both smellers (the majority) and non-smellers, the last a small minority of the subjects. There were, too, other flowers such as verbenas and azaleas and wild crab-apple blossom that yielded similar results. Blakeslee accepts unhesitatingly that there are real differences in the capacity to smell: "The peculiarity of floral odors in that certain odors can be detected by some but not by all people is probably common" and he thinks that the differences in odour sensitivity are innate and hereditary. He also considers such differences to be in line with the well-known existence of tasters and non-tasters for the bitter taste of phenyl thiocarbamide and some related substances. Blakeslee is probably right but it is so hard to believe that another person cannot smell at all the flower that is so fragrant to oneself, that one feels the subject would bear a little more investigation. One must rule out habituation as in the case of the girl picking freesias, and rule out sheer laziness as in some of the very old. It would be of particular interest to see whether cases of smellers and non-smellers occurred with smells of all kinds, or only with pleasant smells like the freesias, or only with unpleasant smells like the coal gas. One feels intuitively but perhaps unwarrantably, that something of considerable psychological significance might emerge from such an investigation. It might conceivably show that pleasantness and unpleasantness had common boundaries with sensitivity.

Rules

The general rules that can be derived from the subject matter of this chapter are:

Rule 95. There may be a tendency for young children to give higher coefficients of pleasantness (to say "Yes, I like" more often) to a group of odours, than older people would.

Rule 96. Old people are prone not to notice smells, even dangerous smells such as of escaping gas. This may be due partly to inattention.

REFERENCES

65. M. Stein, P. Ottenberg & N. Roulet, A study of the development of olfactory preferences, *A.M.A. Arch. Neurol. Psychiat.*, 1958, **80**, 264–266.

66. H. D. Chalke & J. R. Dewhurst, Accidental coal-gas poisoning: loss of sense of smell as a possible contributory factor with old people, *Brit. Med. J.*, 1957, II, 915–917.

67. A. F. Blakeslee, Are freesias fragrant? *National Horticultural Mag.*, July 1932, **11**, 211–212.

CHAPTER 17

WHAT IS KNOWN OF THE INFLUENCE OF
TEMPERAMENT ON ODOUR PREFERENCES

A s WAS pointed out in Chapter 11, temperament in the author's studies of olfactory preference was assessed as introvert or extrovert on a rather empirical basis. The division is that suggested (p. 12) by Jung but it had no deeper psychological significance; it required neither acceptance nor even understanding of Jung's theories. It has indeed been pointed out by Gray and Wheelwright[68] that Jung's type theory "was based on normal people and therefore does not necessitate acceptance or even consideration of his theories about the unconscious". This opinion reinforces the point that the author's division of subjects into introvert and extrovert groups is empirical and real and simple to carry out, without carrying any diffuse psychological postulates as inevitable corollaries.

The division was made and the results that it yielded so far as concerns olfactory preferences were described in Chapters 5 and 11; they were less clear cut than the results of comparisons of olfactory preferences with either sex or age but there were some differences of olfactory preferences between the two temperament groups that were easily observable. In the earlier literature, the prior art, there are no similar comparisons to be found; no earlier worker appears to have divided a group of subjects according to their temperaments and then compared their olfactory preferences. There have been, nevertheless, many connections noted between temperament and olfaction and these bear some relation to our more immediate issues.

Affective tone

As Leitch[29] has pointed out, smells are strongly loaded with what the psychologists call affective tone. Vision and hearing convey spatial and temporal relations accurately but they are often devoid of meaning in an emotional sense, whereas smell carries with it a liking or disliking. Sometimes, of course, vision (a lovely statue

251

or a sick animal) and hearing (music or the distracting noise of a stream of aircraft) carry pleasant or unpleasant associations but not nearly so often as smell. It is nothing uncommon for an appetizing smell to make us salivate or for an unpleasant one to make us feel sick, but sights and sounds that induce such violent reactions are less common. It is because olfactory sensation is so heavily loaded with affective tone that it is so closely linked with temperament.

Temperament affects responses

Some people are much more affected by smells than others. Sensitive people may be intensely moved by the perfume of a bowl of flowers while others are looking round for the drinks. One man can stand in ecstasy by a hedgerow in which the year's first honeysuckle is flowering; another could not be bothered to negotiate the ditch so as to reach the flower. If beauty is in the eye of the beholder, so is fragrance in the nose.

As to the idiosyncratic sensitiveness of some individuals, anecdotes abound. One[69] is of a lady, 58 years old who suffered badly from the smell of linseed if a decoction of it was prepared in her room; there was a sudden swelling of the face and loss of consciousness, the swelling lasted for a day. Orfila, master of poisons, tells other unexpected anecdotes. It seems a pity to translate his lively French, and as it is so commonly read nowadays, perhaps he may be quoted in the original, plus the bracketed meaning of any uncommon words:

"Les parties subtiles et odorantes, de la bétoine (betony) fleurie sont si vives, que l'on assure que les jardiniers qui arrachent (grub up) cette plante deviennent ivres et chancelants (unsteady) comme s'ils avaient bu du vin."

"Lorsqu'on se repose à l'ombre d'un noyer (walnut tree) ou d'un sureau (eldertree) on ne tarde pas à s'endormir et on éprouve une céphalalgie (headache) intense."

"Des effets purgatifs produits par l'odeur que répandent l'ellébore noir (Christmas rose) et la coloquinte (bitter apple) que l'on pile (on being ground)".

Danger was widely believed to reside in keeping flowers in a room at night; their odours were poisonous and could even act fatally on certain sensitive persons. According to Pouchet,[70] in 1779 a woman in London died during the night from having kept a large bouquet of lilies in her room. A young girl perished in the same way from the effects of a bouquet of violets. Workmen who have imprudently fallen asleep upon bales of saffron have died in consequence. Catherine de Medici four hundred years ago could not endure the scent of roses; if she saw a painting of a rose she was seized with some degree of nausea. Even worse, her contemporary and political opponent the brave Chevalier de Guise fainted at the sight of a bunch of roses. All these Pouchet gives. One can smile and be a little superior and label him a credulous savant, but one might be wrong. One of the author's testers (Part II) reported that a thirteen-year-old negro boy was sick after smelling the ten test odorants which had had no effect on some 500 whites. He might have been unwell and nearly sick before he made the test, although there was no reason to think so. So with Pouchet's cases, although it is impossible to feel convinced that it was smell and smell alone that caused death, it is equally impossible to deny significance to them. Extreme cases such as these are undoubtedly rare, and must be looked at critically. The question must be faced: were the symptoms including the distress really caused by smell, or was there some other cause at work. Was there possibly some absorption of the odorous vapours into the blood stream? It is possible, too, that association of ideas may lead to distress. Undoubtedly as everyone knows, some odours can produce revulsion and nausea. And it is beyond doubt that some people are very much more sensitive to smells than others, that they are idiosyncratic. Whether Pouchet's anecdotes were exactly true is unimportant. That they, and many like them, are extant is evidence of the existence of people who are peculiarly susceptible to odours. Their olfactory preferences must be very unusual indeed, when a rose can cause revulsion. There is even a certain amount of evidence that odours can cause physiological changes at the same time as they rouse the emotions.

Thus, it has been shown that the sudden appearance of an odour can cause measurable change in the resistance of the skin of a person, quite similar to that which takes place if he is suddenly startled. Kenneth[57] was perhaps the first to make use of the D'Arsonval or moving-coil galvanometer to record differences in the electrical resistance of the hand when a person was exposed to a smell. He reported that one person caused the galvanometer to fluctuate extremely when he was exposed to the smell of benzol; the person associated the benzol smell with the smell of petrol and he owned a car which had played some part in his life. The author[71] investigated the psycho-galvanic reflexes, as these electrical responses are called, a little further and found:

    (1) that an unpleasant odour will cause a more pronounced reflex than a pleasant one, and

    (2) that the reflexes vary from one individual to another, and

    (3) that with the same individual different kinds of response can be caused by different odorants.

In all cases the reflex is due to an emotional disturbance caused by perception of the odour, followed within a second or two by sweating, and the sweat reducing the electrical resistance along the skin. One would hardly think that the perception of an unpleasant smell would cause the hands to perspire, but it does. Other emotions have been shown to cause sweating not only on the hands but also on the soles of the feet and these and other parts of the body have been used to measure responses by various workers; there can be no reasonable doubt that some odours can cause sweating not only on the hands, but on all parts of the body which are rich in sweat glands. Fig. 46 shows two traces from a psycho-galvanometer

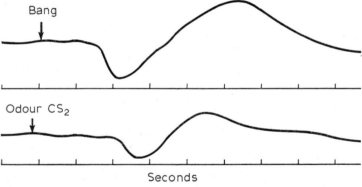

Fig. 46.—Psycho-galvanic reflexes to "startle" induced (top) by an unexpected bang, and (bottom) by an unexpectedly unpleasant odour.

record; in either case the subject was the same (the author) and the electrical resistance of a part of his skin is shown on the trace; where the line is horizontal the resistance is unchanged. In the upper trace there was a "startle", an unexpected bang, at the point indicated by the arrow; a second later (the divisions at the bottom of the Figure indicate seconds) the resistance drops and then rises again. In the lower trace there was the sudden appearance of the odour of carbon disulphide in the inspired air: the subject knew that an odour was to be expected but he did not know that it would be carbon disulphide which has a high unpleasant note. Either with the startle or the unpleasant odour there is an emotional response that causes sweating. Some people, depending on their temperament, give much bigger psycho-galvanic responses than others do; the responses have been fairly thoroughly explored for some stimuli such as "startle"; it is a fair inference that odours have a measurable physiological action on the subject who perceives them and that this action varies not only with the nature of the odorant but also with the temperament of the observer.

That some people are greatly affected emotionally by odours there is no doubt but whether we all react in the same way is more doubtful. The author has recourse to smelling ylang-ylang when angered or frustrated and finds it soothing, and has found that to smell wild roses will lift him out of a depression, and that to smell honeysuckle in a hedgerow will suffuse him with an ecstasy (the effect varies from time to time according to the weather and the tone of the subject, but sometimes it is truly ecstasy). Kenneth[57] on the other hand has found musk and cassia exciting, rose soothing, and pine bracing. There is room here for a lot more work to be done.

Therapeutic possibilities

The effect of odours on the emotions, at least of some people, is very real indeed and is not at all well understood. Many people, indeed, would question if there was much or any effect but this is mainly an indication of how greatly the subject has been neglected. Very little is known about it.

Ninety years ago Watson[33] discussed the healing possibilities of odorants. He suggested the use of exhilarating odours in nervous conditions and the treatment of the insane with agreeable odours. He drew attention to the exhilarating influence of new-mown hay and of seaweed after a storm, to the voluptuous scent of roses and of the musk plant and suggested that dyspeptics and hypochondriacs could be treated with such delightful smells. The odour of young animals was thought to have an enlivening effect on aged and feeble persons; butchers still attribute their good health to the ever-present smell in which they work of the meat.

Watson said that asthma was sometimes relieved by the smell of the skunk. Since then other workers, notably Brown & Colombo[72] and Feinberg & Aries[73] have drawn attention to the connection between odours and asthma. Stein & Ottenberg[74] have suggested "that in some patients the asthma attack is a means of physiologically defending against the activation of odours of unresolved childhood conflicts". However, the symptoms of asthma are induced by a variety of substances and circumstances and opinions still vary a good deal as to the importance of the role played by odours, some authorities maintaining that it is negligible. With hay-fever sufferers the use of an odorous aerosol mist has been found by the author[75] to be helpful.

Cigarette smoking

Tobacco brings consolation; it puts a screen against reality and affords a refuge and some respite. It turns thoughts inwards and enhances the introvert and depresses the extrovert characteristics in a smoker. It might reasonably therefore be expected to modify the olfactory preferences. In one respect it certainly does: smells of a burnt and rank nature, e.g. pyridine, are tolerated much better by a smoker than a non-smoker. Anyone who has been a cigarette smoker and then abstained even for a few days will be surprised to find how his sensitivity to such odours has been enhanced; after a few weeks he will find the smell of a cigarette that someone else has smoked in the house quite unpleasant. The simple explanation, as has been described by the author,[76] is that the habit of cigarette smoking enhances the olfactory threshold concentration of tobacco-like odours whilst a few days' abstention from the habit increases the sensitivity to equal that of a non-smoker. Over a wider range of odours, smoking seems to have little effect: some perfumers smoke, others do not. Probably the effects of tobacco vary from one to another. Ruckmick[77] when first taking to tobacco reported that the mind appeared extraordinarily clear but probably most people would say that tobacco blunts perception and takes the edge off unpleasant experience. Its known effect on olfactory preferences is limited to increased tolerance of pyridinous odours but it is quite possible that there are other and more significant changes due to the drug's tendency to provoke introversion.

Abstract recollection of perfumes

It is probably true that those sensations that we can recall at will, even without the normal stimulus, are those that we like best. We can call to mind the face and figure of a loved one; we create a mental picture of a place, coastline, wood, or house without difficulty; of touch, too, the softness of hair, the burning lips, the held catch. If we try to recall the taste of shrimps of which we may be very fond, it is not quite so easy; to recall the odour of roses on the author's part at least requires a definite effort of concentration; it does not come as readily as one might expect it to and even whilst the effort is being made it is confused by mental pictures (vision coming in) of red roses, of bottles of geraniol and citronellol on the laboratory bench and of the gardens at Kew. Musk which the author likes very much is easier to recall; it requires a far greater effort to recall in abstract the odour of hydrogen sulphide which has been experienced a thousand times more often than musk. On the basis of his own experiences the author would say that smells of any kind are very difficult to recall in the abstract and that those that are the most liked are those that present the least difficulty.

Ribot[78] had much earlier remarked on the difficulty of remembering smells and on the associated rarity of olfactory hallucinations in the insane. Ribot estimated that about one person in eight could recall most odours at will but that 40 per cent of people could not recall any by any effort of will.

There is, of course, a big difference between recalling in an abstract way, when no stimulus is present, and recognition when the stimulus is present. This last is where one of the main requirements in a perfumer enters: an excellent memory for smells. We smell something new; there is a note in it that is familiar; what is it? The practised perfumer will remember what it was and where he smelled it; most of us will probably not remember. But most of us improve rapidly at this test of recognition and recollection with a little practice and effort.

It has been suggested that pleasant odours should be used to help learning. Jerome & Ludvigh[79] thought that pleasant odours had a retroactive facilitative effect on learning and unpleasant odours had a retroactive inhibitory effect. They thought that the degree of facilitation or of inhibition was proportional to the degree of pleasantness or unpleasantness of the odours. But they do not say which pleasant and which unpleasant odours they used for test. Watson[33] suggested that agreeable odours might be used to help teach deaf mutes.

The most ambitious investigation of the recollection of pleasant and unpleasant odours was that made by Gordon[56] at California with 200 subjects testing ten odorants, giving 2000 responses in all. She found that of 1020 pleasant olfactory impressions experienced

I

49 per cent were recalled, and of 882 unpleasant impressions 50 per cent were recalled and of ninety-eight indifferent ones 56 per cent were recalled (p. 229). As she herself put it, no correlation was found between memory value of odours and their affective value (pleasantness or unpleasantness). But if Gordon's paper is studied in detail it can be seen that she asked a lot of her subjects and it may well be that the "found" percentages of 49 per cent pleasant and 50 per cent unpleasant were a little at the mercy of chance. Gordon's paper was very valuable in respect of her findings, which have already been discussed in Chapter 14, on the rankings in preference given to some odorants, but that part of it which relates to memory counts is perhaps less convincing.

Odour preferences an indication of temperament

One of the most stark discussions of odour preferences and temperament was written by Peck[80] at the end of the last century. Peck argued that men ransacked the whole world for wines of an exquisite bouquet in order to please the palate, but smell was often ignored. "To give any thought to the cultivation of this sense or to its delectation is regarded by the Anglo-Saxon race especially, as being at the best decidedly effeminate and at the worst as something that is positively low." And yet the bouquet of wines depends mainly on their smell.

"If the sense of smell has an important function in associational psychology, and if it has a direct relation, as it certainly does have, to temperament and motive, it must be possible to derive from its study innumerable clues to character, and a means whereby the moral attributes of individuals can be approximately known."

Peck goes on to suggest that in judging character and in classifying individuals we can employ a formula that can be constructed from a careful study of their odour preferences. Probably many people would agree that the type of perfume that is used is an indication of temperament and one can agree that violet and frangipani are often used by discerning women. But to condemn as Peck does, the user of eau-de-Cologne as commonplace or the user of White Rose as insincere seems to be simply stupid. Peck has the right idea in that perfumes can reveal temperament but he has made some wild guesses instead of laboriously collecting evidence and then sifting and analysing it. There is a lot of work to be done here that might have therapeutic value and that could very nicely be carried out by post-graduate psychology students. It would be wise however not to include many psychology students amongst the subjects; they are too reflective and introspective. The subjects should give first reaction immediate responses—I like, I dislike, indifferent, or I prefer—and the person carrying out the research, the post-graduate research student, should do the reflecting and the wondering why. If ever there was a neglected field of study this is it.

Rules

Those general rules that may be derived from the contents of this chapter are:

Rule 97. Some people, probably only a small minority, are very susceptible emotionally to odours, and can be upset or made ill by their presence.

Rule 98. Physiological changes due to the play of odours on the emotions can be measured on a galvanometer as changes in the electrical resistance of the skin.

Rule 99. Some odours will affect the emotions beneficently, soothing anger and uplifting the downcast.

Rule 100. Odours probably have an important part to play in the future in healing the sick, especially in diseases of the breathing apparatus and in mental illness. The possibilities have been, and still are, much neglected.

Rule 101. Cigarette smoking greatly depresses the sensitivity to odours that resemble tobacco smoke, but has no marked effect on sensitivity to odours of other kinds. If a regular smoker abstains from tobacco for a few days his sensitivity to tobacco-like odours rapidly increases to equal that of a non-smoker.

Rule 102. It is difficult to recall a smell in abstract (that is without the smell being present). Those smells that are the most liked are those that present the least difficulty to recall.

Rule 103. Knowledge of a person's olfactory preferences may give clues to the sex, age, and temperament of that person.

REFERENCES

68. H. Gray & J. B. Wheelwright, Jung's psychological types, including the four functions, *J. gen. Psychol.*, 1945, **33**, 265–284.

69. M. J. B. Orfila, *Traité de Toxicologie*, 4th Edn., **2**, 542–543, 1843, Fortin, Masson et Cie, Paris.

70. F. A. Pouchet, "L'Univers", p. 231, 1865, Hachette, Paris.

71. R. W. Moncrieff, Psycho-galvanic reflexes to odours, *Perf. Essent. Oil Record*, 1963, **54**, 313–316.

72. E. A. Brown & N. J. Colombo, The asthmagenic effect of odours, smells, and fumes, *Ann. Allergy*, 1944, **12,** 14

73. S. M. Feinberg & P. L. Aries, Asthma from food odours, *J. Amer. med. Ass.*, 1932, **98,** 2280.

74. M. Stein & P. Ottenberg, Role of odours in asthma, *Psychosom. Med.*, 1958, **20,** 60–65.

75. R. W. Moncrieff, Effect of odorants on hay-fever symptoms, *Perf. Essent. Oil Record*, 1962, **53,** 616–618.

76. R. W. Moncrieff, Smoking: its effect on the sense of smell, *Amer. Perfumer*, 1957, **69,** No. 4, 40–43.

77. C. A. Ruckmick, Experiences during learning to smoke, *Amer. J. Psychol.*, 1924, **35,** 402–406.

78. T. Ribot, Le goût et l'odorat, *J. Psychol. norm. path.*, 1920, **17,** 5–16.

79. F. D. Jerome & E. J. Ludvigh, Retroactive effect of pleasant and un-pleasant odours on learning, *Amer. J. Psychol.*, 1931, **43,** 102–108.

80. H. T. Peck, The morality of perfumes, *The Cosmopolitan* (New York), 1898, **25,** 585–590.

CHAPTER 18

ODOUR PREFERENCES OF ANIMALS

THERE IS a mass of information about the sensitiveness of some animals to smell; that of tracker dogs is legendary. But there is not much published work about the odour preferences of animals, and most of what there is in this short chapter is an account of the author's own observation, and much of that again concerns observations on his own dog, Spindle, a beautiful and sensitive creature. He is like a greyhound, but smaller and with blackish spots on a white coat, a true descendant of the dogs to be seen in Landseer's pictures and in old sporting prints, a hunting whippet.

Olfactory reactions can be violent

Whilst the preference tests described in Part II were being carried out, the arrangement of ten odorants in order of preference by some 500 people, the possibility was discussed of ascertaining Spindle's order of preference. The wide-neck bottles, unstoppered, were held out to him one at a time; he investigates anything that is held out for him to sniff and he came at once to each bottle. Some of them obviously had little interest for him; he took a casual sniff and wandered off— couldn't care less. But when the musky bottle was offered he evinced very great interest; came nearer to make a closer examination and then licked the neck of the bottle in evident appreciation. On the other hand, when the bottle containing oil-soluble chlorophyll was held out to him he approached and sniffed as usual, but immediately shot back and then slunk away as if he had been physically hurt. It looks as though to a dog, a good smell is as good as a meal, a bad one as bad as a beating. Certainly the dog's reactions are much more emphatic, than those of a man. Many of the men had really liked the musk lactone, but none had shown any wish to lick the bottle; most of the subjects had disliked the oil-soluble chlorophyll, but none of them had backed away from it as if they had been struck. The dog's reactions were far more emphatic than the human's.

Between the bottle licking and the slinking away, there were

261

grades of behaviour; these were sorted out as well as could be (in the middle of the series the preferences were very diffuse) and the conclusion was reached that Spindle's order of preference for the ten odorants was:

- (4) musk lactone (liked best)
- (3) lavender oil
- (5) vanillin
- (6) neroli oil
- (2) spearmint oil
- (1) strawberry flavour
- (7) almond flavouring
- (8) naphthalene
- (9) rape oil
- (10) oil-soluble chlorophyll (disliked most).

Spindle's order of preference using the numbers assigned to the different odorants, as shown in the list above and also at the beginning of Chapter 7 was not very different from that of the author (subject 518 in Table 49) and may be seen:

Spindle's preference order   4 3 5 6 2 1 7 8 9 10

Subject 518's preference

| order | 1st run | 4 3 6 1 2 5 9 7 8 10 |
| | 2nd run | 4 2 3 6 1 5 7 8 9 10 |

It has to be admitted that the degree of correspondence is quite good and at the time it was pretty generally thought to be very funny indeed. Looking at the placings today, the biggest difference seems to be in the positions assigned to (5) vanillin and in the author's second run to (2) spearmint oil. One must not push the resemblance too far, but the definite liking for (4) musky and (3) lavender odours and the dislike of (10) oil-soluble chlorophyll are common to dog and man.

Some major differences

In some measure the agreement found between dog and man was fortuitous and dependent on the rather suitable choice that had been made of the ten test odours. It is evident enough that dogs do not like fruit or fruity odours and that most flower smells leave them cold, whereas humans, as can be seen from Tables 1 and 3, find their chief olfactory delights in fruit and flowers. When the author and Spindle walk in the country, the former often picks a flower to smell: honeysuckle, clover, dog rose, herb Robert, ramsons, whatever there is, and then holds it for Spindle to smell; invariably the dog comes, puts his nose to it and most often finds no interest in it and leaves it at once. There are a few flowers that earn a second confirmatory sniff, just to make sure that they really are of no interest and these are the ones that are not typically floral in odour, such as privet, buckthorn and agrimony. In the garden, too, he will take a second sniff at herbs like sage and thyme, but they never hold him for more than a second or two. There is some musk mallow (*Malva moschata*) that flowers at the end of June in a near-by gravel pit. Spindle's predilection for musk lactone being known, it was hoped that musk mallow might interest him: but no, one sniff and he left it, evidently quite unimpressed. To the author the smell of musk mallow varies. Some, picked on a hot sunny afternoon had a high top note, reminiscent of the sizzle of freesia's top note, although altogether the smell was not like that of freesia, but was more floral and honey-like. Some picked the next day which was dull and cool, had no high top note at all; in fact it smelled like peas or lupins. Both lots kept in water in a warm room developed in the evening a strong musky note; it was not quite like musk, but was like enough for three people asked to smell first the flowers, and then some natural musk in a bottle, to say that there was some resemblance. But once again the dog was not interested in the flowers, although he took a lot of interest in the bottle that contained musk.

There must be many smells that interest humans that leave dogs cold—and the converse is true. Out walking, Spindle catches a scent, runs it to earth in some herbage, pushes his long nose in, and keeps it in rooting round for some considerable time; occasionally in high summer he may pull out a grass snake, but nearly always he pulls out nothing. Sometimes, too, the turf in which he noses so assiduously and with such fascinated interest, is so short that it seems impossible it could harbour a sizable creature; to what then is the fascination due? To the urinary calling card of another dog that has passed that way? Possibly, but not usually likely for, for that purpose, they choose not the flat turf, but posts, shrubs and plants that stand higher or at corners. On occasion when something of surpassing interest has enraptured Spindle, the author has got down on the turf too, and started where Spindle left off, nose to the same existing inch of turf. But it is no good, the author can smell nothing more than the usually herbaceous smell of all the turf around. For Spindle it is something highly significant and very exciting, but for the human it is nothing; his nose is not built that way. Spindle watches, but he knows it is a waste of time and that the human will not smell it. Finally it is a mystery.

And, as well, of course the dog rolls in things that to the human are most unsalubrious. On the short cut through the field where horses are kept he is always sorely tempted and sometimes gives way and gets the horrid stain round his neck. He knows his human companion dislikes it and this worries him so that he threatens to build up a neurosis. He attaches great importance to smell. There was an occasion too, when a clutch of eggs failed and some were broken; the smell was abhorrent until the remains were decently covered with earth. But Spindle went and dug them up and rolled in them. Our common ground is very limited. Olfactorily we are often poles apart.

Pet foods

In our affluent society there is money to spend on tins of cat and dog food, and a huge industry has grown up to supply them. A few of the products are good; most of them are assessed on the percentage of cats or dogs that will eat them at all, the acceptability it is called, and if it is 90 per cent, if nine cats out of ten will eat a product, then that is fine.

It is odd that the manufacturers do not pay more attention to the olfactory attraction, which is the basis of acceptability, than they do. Probably most of the materials that go into the cans have some significant nutritional value, but the contents often smell revolting to the human nose and apparently they do to the animals' noses too. Products which depend largely on their fish content can be enormously improved in odour by the addition of a little (say 1 per cent) of cod-liver oil. Such an addition seems good from every point of view and certainly results in much better acceptability by the cat. Some of the canned foods are not complete diets, and if an animal is fed exclusively on them, it loses weight and eventually develops deficiency symptoms; the manufacturers do not worry unduly because, as they say, most cats and dogs get supplements: milk and caught sparrows or field-mice for the cats; left-overs and bones for the dogs. And, of course, many animals get fresh meat. The addition to the pet foods of something that smells good and is good such as cod-liver oil, is fine and not impossibly costly; the addition of powerful flavouring materials, such as lactones, even in quantities of 5–10 parts per million is more debatable. They are attractants and their addition can raise the acceptability of a food to animals. Whether they are desirable or undesirable physiologically may not be known, but they may be useful, because as a rule animals if they have a choice, will select the diet that will be best for them (cf. Rule 68). The writer had a cat which was fed for a time on a fish preparation that was deficient in fat, and to which various fats were added experimentally. If the cat was offered any two of the following on separate dishes, it made its selection reliably.

(A) Fish preparation deficient in fat

(B) A+ butter

(C) A+ a well-known margarine equal in quantity to the butter in B.

If the cat was offered A and B, it ate B and left A alone; if it was offered A and C it ate C and left A alone; if it was offered B and C, it ate C and left B alone. It made its choice quite definitely and reliably and seemed to find it easy to distinguish between the butter and the margarine, although it preferred the latter. The odd thing is that the lactones that are used to flavour the margarine are supposed to give it a butter flavour; they certainly smell to the human nose like butter although, of course, very much stronger indeed i.e. as the pure chemicals. To the cat there are clearly different kinds of butter flavours and it knows which it prefers.

But cats vary in their likes and dislikes and it might be that other cats could not make this fine distinction. The difference between two cats was brought home to the author in some work that was being carried out on the development of seaweed products. The gum, sodium alginate, that is extracted from seaweed can be used to make very firm gels, and one outlet that was successful was to make a brawn with minced meat dispersed in the alginate gel; brawns of this kind were fairly widely sold at one time, for animal feeding. It was desired to put in a preservative, and formaldehyde was used in such small quantity that it was undetectable to the human nose. Two cats were ordinarily used to test the brawns; they were of similar age, both males, and had been brought up together: one of them, a long-haired black and white, Bimbo, would have none of the brawn that contained the formaldehyde, although he was very fond of the unpreserved brawn; the other cat, black and short-haired, Sambo, was less fussy: he did not seem to notice the formaldehyde and ate the brawn, preserved or unpreserved, indiscriminately. The fastidious Bimbo eventually outlived his companion by some years; this had probably nothing to do with the formaldehyde-preserved brawn which was only offered for a week or so, but may have been due to more careful conduct generally. Animals vary quite significantly one from another in their odour preferences, and where to draw the line about what is edible.

Animal dislikes

There are some smells that animals dislike intensely. In the high-class suburban areas twenty miles from New York gardening can be difficult; a small patch is induced at great cost of trouble and money to grow some brownish grass and not very vigorous shrubs, and these are finally at the mercy of animals, domestic and wild (racoons) who foul and ravage them. The Americans go to great pains to protect their shrubs; one device consists of a ball of string heavily impregnated with a tar or pitch-like composition; this is draped round the bushes about six inches above the ground and is said to repel the animals which dislike the creosote-like smell. One such product is called K9.

Bitches in season will attract dogs from some distance, even from a mile or two away, and these by their constant barking cause some annoyance; furthermore, it is almost impossible to exercise the bitch without male followers coming along. The trouble can be mitigated by the application to the genital organs of the bitch of a highly odorous material which has also the property of counter-acting or masking the natural animal attractive odour of the in-season bitch. In America one such preparation had the apt name "No Sir"; in the U.K., there have been various products, perhaps Anti-Mate and Skipit, being the best known. This last was formulated by the author in collaboration with a biologist and a veterinary surgeon after a good deal of careful testing; it received a good notice in the *Veterinary Record*.[81] Such a preparation that would be effective with female cats is obviously needed; the difficulty is that these animals are likely to stay away for two or three days at a time and the efficacy of the spray wears off. If they return home each day one of these sprays can be effective. One cat-owner who sprayed her cat when in season before letting it out, found after a little time that when she reached for the tin of spray, the cat went back to bed and gave up the idea of going out. It had probably had some frustrating experiences and was wise enough not to invite more.

Smell discrimination more important to animals than to man

Everywhere that one reads about smell, the discouraging statement is encountered that the sense, so important in primitive creatures, has lost its importance and its sensitivity in man. It is perhaps still true to say with Vonderahe[82] that for all animals "the first emotional state, that of being attentively alert and ready for action, in the pursuit of food or for flight or mating, appears to grow out of olfactory perception". Bull[28] draws attention to this, but then adds that the role of olfaction in initiating and directing animal activity is much reduced in man. Human beings are not like dogs, who are guided by the simple sense of smell in the majority of their daily acts, but they are nevertheless guided by like and dis-like (so spelt to emphasize the negative character of dislike) and Bull thinks this has its roots in olfactory behaviour. Undoubtedly, one cannot deny that with the coming of the erect stature, the usefulness of vision increased greatly, so that it really displaced smell as the distance receptor system. True it is, too, that in civilized communities, the individual does not have to hunt for his food, he rarely has to fly for his life, and in some ways mating is less dangerous than it must have been in a primitive society; the corollary is that man can get along pretty comfortably without placing much reliance on his smell sense. Is the butter rancid? The bitter "off"? The petrol mixture too rich? These are the questions that one asks the nose to help with nowadays; they are not really vital. But the sensitivity is still there, although we do not often use it. With a little practice the ordinary person can distinguish by smell alone with eyes closed between pure water and water that contains 1 part of mercaptan in 200 million parts, he can detect the trace of acetone that there is in the effluent of the factory across the estuary. In sensitivity man can still do very well indeed, and in terms of quality discrimination the number of smells is legion; we do not know how many.

But the sensitive area, the olfactory epithelium, the yellow sensitive patch of skin, is much bigger in some animals than it is in man. According to Neuhaus[83] who has done a great deal of work at Erlangen on the olfactory acuity of dogs, the sensitive area in a fox-terrier is 83·5 sq. cm., in a sheep dog it is 150 sq. cm. and in man it is only 5 sq. cm. The number of cells will probably vary in very much the same ratio, perhaps 10 million in man and 300 million in a sheep dog. Here, then, we are presented with a state of affairs in which the smell sensitive area is 30 times as big in a sheep dog as it is in a man. A similar state of affairs exists with other animals such as the deer. What is its significance? It is the same as that of a larger canvas, there is room for more detail in the picture. There is no *a priori* reason to think that an animal with a large receptor area should be more sensitive to smells than one with a small receptor area. It is, however, reasonable to anticipate that it will enjoy a greater variety of smells, and probably that it will be able to analyse and define more sharply its smell sensations. Man can see with extraordinary definition of detail; a badly-shaped letter in a page of print stands out boldly; man smells rather more diffusely and our smell sensations blend into one another so that we may have some difficulty in identifying even familiar fruit smells which we may tend to confuse. Animals probably can see only diffusely, but they can smell in great detail with fine definition. It is not, however, easy to be sure of what an animal's sensations are. If the animal has an anatomical apparatus that is similar to our own olfactory equipment, and if it behaves as if it can smell, then it is reasonable to think it senses smells roughly as we do. But how to go further? One way that has been used by Adrian[84] is to put an odorant in front of the nose of an anaesthetized animal (a hedgehog) and record the electric currents in the brain by passing electrodes through the skull. The method is difficult. An earlier version used by Adrian & Ludwig[85] was to use the removed head of a catfish which would continue active for half an hour after the decapitation. This procedure showed, for example, that the fish was sensitive to a rotting earthworm in water, but not to oil of cloves, whereas the hedgehog could smell more or less what we could. Another method, one that has been used by the author, is to remove the pigmented olfactory tissue from a recently killed animal and see what it will adsorb, what odorant–air mixtures it will deodorize. It was shown[35] in this way that the olfactory tissue of the wild rabbit will adsorb the smell of grass and of violets (methyl octine carboxylate) but not that of almonds (benzaldehyde). It seems to be a fair inference that a rabbit can smell violets but not almonds.

Nevertheless, however fascinating it may be to explore the sensations experienced by different animals, none of these methods throws any light at all on their preferences, on liking or disliking, on pleasantness or unpleasantness. All that we can do to learn of this is to watch the behaviour of an animal. Some people, for example, put down little heaps of food, one not odorized, and the others odorized with different oils and watch which heaps the animal, perhaps a rat, will eat. It is doubtful if anything of much interest has come out of these trials; usually the animal avoids what is likely to harm it most, and eats the unodorized food in preference to any of the others. One is reminded of the beautiful prayer[86] of the Abbot of Iona, dating from the time of St. Columba. "Praised be thou, O Lord, who hast made every animal wise in the instinct thou hast given it."

The whole field of olfactory preferences in animals is almost unexplored and might well prove to be a rewarding one to till. On the other hand knowledge of animals' likings might throw light on their physiology and nutritional needs; the emphatic nature of their responses to odours that have strong emotional connotations might be of great help to psychologists and might pave the way to a better understanding of human emotional responses. From the commercial point of view, the money spent on pet food continues to increase and probably runs well in excess of £100 million in a year. From the standpoint of the animals themselves, a better understanding of their olfactory preferences might go some way to improving the unsavoury nature of some of the canned material that is sold for their consumption. But in the end it will probably transpire that the olfactory likes and dislikes of an animal are determined by what it needs: good nutritious meat smells better than farinaceous material however adeptly it is flavoured; smells that spell danger: chemicals, gases, even excessive moisture are disliked; smells that might lead to mating are liked, smells indicative of rivals are disliked. It is much the same with humans, but here there are indications that aside from our bodily requirements, we have emotional needs and that odours can go some way to satisfy these (Rule 69). It would not be surprising if it transpired that animals too have emotional needs that can be partly satisfied by odours: the responsiveness of horses and dogs to the display of affection and their own affectionate behaviour cannot be doubted.

Being an unexplored subject, this is one that can be investigated by almost anyone who keeps an animal. Perhaps emphasis should be placed on essays to find what the animal really likes, rather than what it dislikes; this is more pleasant for all concerned and the results are more likely to be interesting and useful. Scientists can extend our knowledge by exploring the electric pulses in the brains of animals exposed to different smells, and by comparing the adsorptive properties of their olfactory tissue. At present, there is no known relation between physical phenomena such as these and pleasantness or unpleasantness of sensation, but it is likely that such relations exist and that they could be brought to light by comparing such physical observations with the animal's behavioural patterns of like and dislike.

Rules

Those rules that may be derived from the contents of this chapter are:

Rule 104. The reactions of an animal to smells are much more emphatic and may be more violent than those of a man.

Rule 105. There are some resemblances between the olfactory preferences of a dog and a man e.g. a liking for the smells musk and lavender. But the differences are far greater than the similarities; dogs show no interest in the fruit and flower smells that humans like so much, and they appear to like smells that the human cannot even detect.

Rule 106. There are some smells that animals greatly dislike that can be used in the formulation of repellents to keep them off shrubs and plants and to reduce the number of visitors to an in-season female.

Rule 107. The sensitive receptor surface of the olfactory equipment of some animals, such as the dog and the deer, is much larger than it is in man; this provides the animals with the means for smelling in greater detail and with more delicate discrimination.

REFERENCES

81. C. G. Hopson, An aerosol for bitches in season, *Veterinary Record*, 21 March 1959, **71**, No. 12, 243.

82. A. R. Vonderahe, The anatomical basis of emotion, *Ohio State Med. J.*, 1943, **39**, 325–330.

83. W. Neuhaus, Unterschiede in der Riechschärfe bei Hunden, *Zeit. fur vergleichende Physiologie*, 1957, **40**, 65–72.

84. E. D. Adrian, Olfactory reactions in the brain of the hedgehog, *J. Physiol.*, 1942, **100**, 459–473.

85. E. D. Adrian & C. Ludwig, Nervous discharges from the olfactory organs of fish, *J. Physiol.*, 1938, **94**, 441–460.

86. B. Greene & V. Gollancz, *God of a Hundred Names*, p. 93, 1962, Gollancz, London.

CHAPTER 19

OLFACTORY PREFERENCES IN FOODS

FOOD DEPENDS for its acceptability and desirability on flavour. "Flavour is a complex sensation", so the author[87] wrote in 1944, "It comprises taste, odour, roughness or smoothness, hotness or coldness, and pungency or blandness. The factor which has the greatest influence is odour. If odour is lacking then the food loses its flavour and becomes chiefly bitter, sweet, sour, or saline." So much is basic and the same words were used in a 1961 publication of the Agricultural Research Council.[88] It is smell that counts: if the smell is wrong the food will be rejected before it reaches the mouth. It is smell that will determine the preferences for one food over another. Sweetness, too, is an important component. Who would guess that sweetbreads eaten raw really are sweet, meat with a sweet malty taste? Or that raw clams straight from the Ayrshire fishing boats have also a sweet component in their wonderful flavour? Both are usually cooked before they are eaten, and their flavour is changed; the cook breaks down by using heat those same flavour principles that the body could break down more easily, at body temperature too, and more usefully so that the nutritive value would be greater. From the standpoint of flavour there is much to be said for eating raw what you can. With some foods cooking brings out the flavour: roast beef, mutton and pork; who wants to eat a raw potato? But the flavour of raw cabbage is indescribably superior to that of the cooked vegetable, although raw it is tough enough to be difficult to eat in quantity. And bread is the outstanding example; was it Wellington's soldiers who marched on wheat alone? Wheat is not easy to eat in quantity, it needs a lot of chewing, but if the effort is made, it is soon apparent that there are flavour principles in the grain that never survive in the bread. There are good reasons why most of our food is baked, roasted, boiled or fried, but there are still some foods that can safely and conveniently be eaten raw, and often the flavour in the raw is different from and better than it is in the cooked state.

Transfer of the flavour

The best flavour is in the foodstuff itself. Sometimes as in fruits, raspberries, strawberries, blackcurrants, apples, pears, bananas and oranges, we enjoy it as we find it. Other times we develop it by cooking; probably most people prefer the flavour of cooked tinned pineapple to that of the raw fruit and the same might be said of peaches and apricots. The connoisseur will find nuances in the raw peach flavour that are missing from the tinned peach, but the bulk of the populace will like the tinned variety better. Cooking develops the flavour of meats, which when raw have not much smell to the human nose, although they are evidently very attractive to many animals.

Transfer of flavour from one food to another is often attempted. There are four general ways of doing this: comminution, distillation, expression and extraction.

Comminution. The whole naturally-flavoured material is finely divided and the resulting powder is incorporated into the material that it is desired to flavour. Finely-ground vanilla beans have been used very successfully to flavour ice-cream; such a method is really much to be preferred to that of using isolated flavouring material or synthetic flavour. It ensures that the whole of the natural flavour is used including the trace modifiers (cf. Rule 2). The same method is used in the spice mill which comminutes pepper, ginger, cinnamon, allspice and so on, the finely divided spice then being included in buns, cakes and in some instances in bread itself.

Distillation. Sometimes the essential oil is obtained from a natural odorous product by distilling it in steam. The distillate consists of two phases, one oily and one aqueous; the two are separated and the oily phase is clarified and is what we know as the essential oil. This is much the commonest method of extracting odorous principles e.g. of lavender, cloves, and roses, and its wide use testifies to its simplicity and cheapness, but it does have some drawbacks, notably:

(1) The distillation process with its inevitable heating may change some of the natural odorous constituents; thus caryophyllene is one of the main ingredients of the clove oil which is ordinarily obtained by steam-distillation, but Naves[89] was unable to find it in a solvent extract of natural cloves and instead he found epoxydihydrocaryophyllene. Evidently the natural flavour component undergoes chemical change during the distillation process.

(2) Sometimes distillation yields an inferior product. In the case of the citrus fruits expression gives a better product than does distillation.

(3) The water-soluble odorous principles are lost and are not included in the oil. Rose water consists of the aqueous distillate that is separated from the attar of roses and is lost to it, so that sometimes the odour losses can be significant in the distillation process.

(4) Some odorous materials notably jasmine and tuberose are quite unsuitable for distillation and other processes such as extraction, maceration or enfleurage (extraction in animal fat) have to be used to isolate the odorous principles.

Expression. This is used mostly for fruit rinds which are rich in oil. The whole fruit is washed and crushed between rollers, sprayed with water and centrifuged to separate the oil. The method is good in that no heating is required so that there is little danger of chemical change, but it is obviously unsuitable when the proportion of oil is small.

Extraction. For fruits, this method is excellent. Alcohol is a good extractant and it can subsequently be removed by gentle heating under reduced pressure. There is more chance of retaining the water-soluble odorants, which are often alcohol-soluble too by this method than there is by distillation.

Experience decides which is the best method to use, but they can all give excellent products that will delight the olfactory sense. A little jasmine concrete (residue from the extraction process after removal of the extractant) can send the writer into an ecstasy of delight and he is not alone in this. As an old Hebrew poet[90] wrote: "Ointment and perfume rejoice the heart". Raspberry flavour (extracted) from the fruit will delight children when added to a sweet.

Often the transfer of flavour from one foodstuff to another has the commercial value of making a cheap unattractive food more attractive. Many patents have been filed to protect processes designed to such ends. One example is that of Forkner[91] who describes a method of treating a fatty material e.g. a corn oil, by intimately mixing it with perhaps 5 per cent of its weight of olive juice or coconut juice which is substantially fat-free, and later separating the olive or coconut juice after it has transferred its flavour to the fat. Sometimes the olive or coconut juice is fermented just prior to use. It is claimed that flavour, odour, and colour of the fatty material are substantially improved by the process. Furthermore, cheap and plentiful fats can be given the odour and flavour of olives or coconut. The necessary treatment may be carried out in about 15 minutes at about 60°C. Sometimes, on the other hand, an unwanted flavour has to be removed to improve flavour and make it acceptable. An example is provided by sugar beet.

Odour removal from sugar beets

Sugar beets, especially after they have been stored, may contain disagreeable tasting and smelling substances. If they are subjected to treatment with steam under pressure the malodorous substance is removed (steam-distilled off) but the disagreeable taste and odour can re-appear after further storage, so that the product which immediately after the treatment with steam was suitable for food purposes may become more or less inedible after a relatively short time. Cuker[92] has, however, described a process for removing the odour and taste permanently. It consists of mixing the crushed or sliced beet with a small quantity of some essential oil such as aniseed, carraway or fennel and then heating with steam until the smell of the essential oil has disappeared. Apparently the essential oil as it is steam-distilled carries away with it unpleasant impurities. Cuker suggests that the oil may combine chemically with the impurities or that they may be adsorbed on it or perhaps one might think that azeotropic mixtures were formed that enabled the unpleasant materials to distil off. Whatever the mechanism, Cuker claims that the process works satisfactorily, if for example twenty parts of aniseed oil are added to a million parts of crushed sugar beet and then the whole is steam-treated. It is true that in the text of the patent he discusses, quantities of oil of "not more than 0·0001 per cent" which is only one part per million but it looks as though his arithmetic must have gone astray. Such obvious discrepancies are by no means uncommon in patent specifications. Irrespective of the arithmetic, the process seems to be sound, and a good one. A process that is similar in principle has been used to remove the smoke odour from salvaged goods after fire damage (see Chapter 21).

Flavour assessment

The basic principles underlying perception are: stimulation of the peripheral receptors, passage of electric pulses along the nerve fibres, treatment at the synapses or nerve junctions which filter out the unimportant (like the secretary who answers the boss's phone), arrival at the cortex, and then (and only God knows how) sensation. For each and every sense it is the same; the differences appear to lie only in which peripheral receptors (hand, eyes, ear, tongue or nose) are stimulated and at which area of the brain cortex the electric pulses from the peripheral receptors eventually arrive. The particular application of this knowledge to flavour has been described by Adrian,[93] but despite the very considerable advances in the preceding twenty years in the physiology of the sense organs, "what we know of the physiology of the olfactory organ will not help us much in improving the flavour of our food". The physiologist knows a good deal about the signals that come from the olfactory receptors, but he knows very little about the treatment that they receive at the synapses in the sensory pathways of the brain and he knows nothing at all about the conversion of these electrical pulses into sensation. The time will come when, as a result of countless comparisons of the electrical currents passing in various parts of the brain, with the kind of stimuli offered for olfaction, pleasant or unpleasant, fruity or flowery and so on, a great deal will be known about the physiology of the end processes of flavour perception but that time is not yet. A start has been made: Adrian[94,95] showed the way with his experiments on anaesthetized animals; so long as odorous air was passed over their olfactory regions there was a stream of electrical pulses passing along the nerves that join the olfactory receptors to the brain. Sem-Jacobsen et al[96] have gone further; they have implanted electrodes in the brains of conscious people and have recorded the electrical pulses that pass through them when such odorous substances as coffee and cloves and lilac and onion are given to them to smell. That researches of this sort will eventually amass a great deal of knowledge relating physiological changes to kinds of flavour there can be no doubt. But so far, the physiologist can tell us next to nothing about the relation between the perceptual mechanism and the liking or disliking of a flavour. Ultimately, and perhaps not too long ahead, he should be able to, and one would think that the relationship between the nature of the nerve currents and pleasantness they induce should be one of the most fascinating studies on which a partnership of physiologist and psychologist could embark. For the present, these novel experimental approaches can tell us something about olfaction and flavour, but nothing whatever about olfactory and flavour preferences. The day when they can do so will come, and one would think that any large food organization should already have a team recording the brain currents in people (hospital patients) with implanted electrodes who can be persuaded to taste and savour their foods. That way may lie the most promising of all lines of food research, far more practical and likely to bring rich rewards than the laboured chemical, chromatographic and spectrographic analyses now in progress. The study of flavour in food should be as much a matter for the Medical as for the Agricultural Research Council. New fundamental knowledge, quick results, the possibility of transferring some of the work at an early stage from human to animal subjects, the scientific definition of pleasantness, and all with the comfortable worthwhile background of improving the lot, the health, and the food of the average citizen. What a wonderful opportunity for some post graduate medical workers. People, not spectrographs, eat food.

Variation of flavour preferences with age and sex

The real basis of flavour perception discussed above is difficult to work on; it can only be investigated in hospitals or medical clinics where there is some reason to put electrodes into subjects' heads. For other research workers it is out of the question at present. But what is not out of the question and is in fact ready to be taken up by any biochemist is the opportunity to investigate flavour preferences in relation to age and sex and possibly other parameters, too. For example, are the flavour preferences of the working classes the same as those of the board? Is the liking for fish and chips universal? Men of different races must have different flavour preferences; certainly they do and climate must condition them. The field is wide open and surprisingly little work on flavour preferences has been done and published. The world's schools of psychology should find work of interest here, and work which should give results that could be intelligible to the non-psychologist. Here is a wonderful opportunity and one so burgeoning with results of practical value that the tycoons of the food industry might be tempted to spend a little more on research and sponsor some of the work. At present the food industry is one which spends rather less than its share on research.

From the little that has been done and published we may select for consideration a study in taste preferences of a fruit juice and their variations with age and sex. This was carried out by Laird & Breen[64] and published in 1939. In this paper "taste" is synonymous with "flavour". Their subjects numbered:

Age	12–18 years	25 boys	35 girls
Age	20–40 years	25 men	25 women
Age	50–68 years	25 men	25 women

Pineapple juice was prepared in five degrees of sweetness, varying from sweet to tart. Each taste was separately judged in comparison with only one other taste strength at a time and each was serially compared with the other four (method of paired comparisons) so that for each one of the subjects there were four chances that any particular degree of sweetness would be preferred or chosen. In the two younger groups 12–18 and 20–40 years, the preferences were very similar. This can be seen graphically when sweetness is plotted against the number of times a degree of sweetness is chosen. Fig. 47 shows the curves for the two sexes for the 20–40

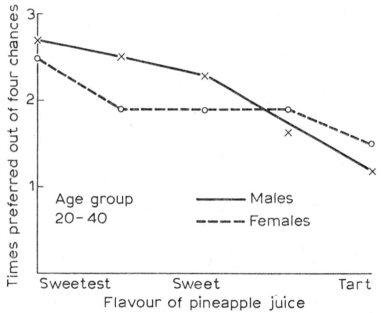

FIG. 47.—Preferences for sweetness in pineapple juice in the age group 20–40 years.

years age group. Those for the 12–18 group are not shown, but were similar. The corresponding curves for the oldest group (50–68 years) are shown in Fig. 48. In this, the oldest group, it can be seen from Fig. 48 that there is a shift from the sweet taste preferred by

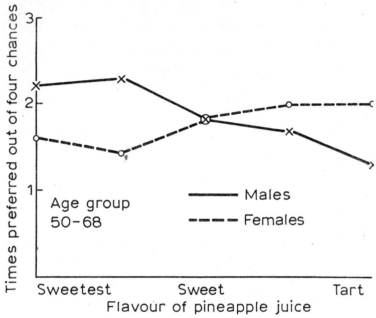

Fig. 48.—Preferences for sweetness in pineapple in the age group 50–68 years.

the younger group to tart fruitiness. In this group, 50–68 years, there is an increasing liking for the sour taste. The women at most ages had more preference than the men for the tart; and less for the sweet taste than the men. For example, the broken line in Fig. 47 is for the most part lower than the solid line.

It is known from anatomical and physiological studies that as we get older taste buds disappear; thus in early childhood the buds are present on the insides of the cheeks and in the throat, in addition to being abundant on the tongue. There is a decrease from childhood to maturity. Thereafter, there is little change during the span of adult life, but in the later years of life there is again a decline, both structural and functional in the taste buds. Apparently, in view of the results of Laird and Breen the initial loss of taste buds is complete by the age of twelve. It is an odd finding that women's taste preferences incline more in the direction of the preferences of the ageing group—a lower appreciation of sweetness *per se* and more appreciation of fruitiness. We have previously found (Rules 21, 52) that children like fruit smells much better than adults do, but now we must add that in fruity flavours they like their fruitiness very sweet. Not too much must be inferred about olfactory preferences from this work of Laird & Breen; the pineapple smell was the same throughout and the only variable was the sweetness. Their tests really investigated the variation of liking for sweetness in a fruity flavour with age and sex.

Identity of flavour chemicals

The identification of those chemical entities that are responsible for the flavour of a foodstuff is no easy matter. There is a certain amount of almost legendary material.

Bread. For example, it has been widely accepted for a very long time that diacetyl and furfuraldehyde are largely responsible for the flavour of new bread. It seems odd that the basic article of our diet has not been investigated thoroughly and its flavour chemistry finally elucidated, but there are still many uncertainties. An investigation by Maiden[97] in 1936 came to some unexpected conclusions. He started his experimental work on the basis that there were three important factors contributing to the flavour of bread and that they were: the strength of the smell, the desirability of the smell and the desirability of the taste. In order to make breads of different flavours he added various amounts of ground up crust to the doughs; it seems to be rather an indirect approach. Surprisingly, he found that 0·015 per cent acetyl methyl carbinol or 0·0019 per cent diacetyl on the weight of flour used had no effect on the bread flavour, but that if the amounts of these supposed flavour principles were doubled then the flavour of the bread was definitely spoiled. At 0·0075 per cent diacetyl spoiled the flavour hopelessly. This hardly supported the view then current that diacetyl was responsible for the pleasant flavour of bread. These results were obtained in experiments with plain doughs. Enriched doughs gave rather different results; those which contained:

4 lb. fat

4 lb. skim milk powder

1 lb. malt flour

per 280 lb. flour were sensitive to either 0·075 per cent acetyl methyl carbinol or 0·00047 per cent diacetyl, either of which had a detectable effect on the smell of the bread. The effect of the acetyl methyl carbinol was desirable and that of the diacetyl was also desirable (although later Maiden said that it caused a foreign smell in the bread) at a concentration of 0·0075 per cent. But although the enriched breads were sensitive to acetyl methyl carbinol and to diacetyl, ordinary breads were not and Maiden concluded that: "There is no hope therefore of improving the flavour of English bread by increasing its acetyl methyl carbinol or diacetyl content . . . it can be concluded with a fair degree of certainty that neither of these substances is responsible for the normal flavour of our bread". Perhaps the flavour of bread still presents difficulties. Bread was not one of the foodstuffs discussed at the Food Group (Society of Chemical Industry) Symposium[98] in 1963. Most kinds of food were discussed, but not bread.

The Low Temperature Research Station

Basic work on the identification and measurement of food flavour principles is carried out at Cambridge by the Low Temperature Research Station of the Agricultural Research Council. This is a large and costly organization which employs nearly 100 workers and is bursting with the most up-to-date and expensive electronic analytical equipment; all of which needs a lot of maintenance to keep it in reliable working order.

Gas chromatography is probably the most important single method used to analyse the chemical components of food aroma. It is extraordinarily sensitive and it gives its information in the form of an ink line drawn on squared paper; peaks on the ink line correspond to the presence of chemical entities which boil at the temperature indicated on the record. Only very small quantities of the initial foodstuff which contains the flavour and aromatic material need to be used. At first, when the method was tried on familiar essential oils and isolates it was not uncommon to get thirty or forty different peaks; what most of them represented nobody knew. Thereafter, years of laborious work were necessary with authentic samples of known chemical composition to correlate gas chromatography peaks with chemical identity. This calibration has been done so well that the majority of peaks in a record can be identified from existing knowledge. What the method does and does very well is to indicate the chemical nature of the volatiles from a foodstuff. A typical example of its use is as follows: the flavour of one kind of potato is preferred to several others; all are boiled under reflux for a defined time, then the refluxing is reduced and the volatiles no longer being returned to the boiling vessel are allowed to pass to a condenser where they are collected; then the condensate is analysed by gas chromatography. Ideally what one would hope for is that the preferred potato gave a chromatogram which showed a unique constituent, something the other potatoes did not have; or, alternatively, some one constituent was common to all the potatoes except the preferred one. But the results do not usually turn out to be so simple and clear-cut; ideal cases are few and far between. Most likely, all the kinds of potatoes, liked as well as less-liked, will have the same main constituents showing up in their chromatograms, but probably in slightly different proportions. Are these differences in proportions significant? Can they be adjusted by addition of the pure chemical entity of the kind that seems to be deficient? Can the aroma of the preferred potato be built up that way? Does the potato flavour change with the time of gathering, the locality where it has been grown, the season wet or dry, the kind of fertilizer used, the duration of storage, with the amount of peel removed and with other similar variables? Usually it is likely to change with some of the variables. To say that a great deal of work is required to sort out why one kind of potato has a preferred flavour is a statement that no one will quarrel with; how much hard work is needed none but those who do it can imagine. Progress is slow, but scraps of new knowledge turn up occasionally; they have to be carefully checked, but every item helps to build up a background of pure knowledge of the relation between flavour and chemical entity.

Some of the uses to which gas chromatography has been put in connection with flavour by 1961 are described in the Annual Report of the Low Temperature Research Station for that year[88]; they also concern flavour liking or flavour amelioration so that they have a close association with olfactory preferences. They were:

(1) The contribution of methylamines to the fish-like off-flavour of whalemeat.

(2) Collection and concentration of the aroma of boiled vegetables. It was shown that they nearly all of them produce the same group of low-boiling volatiles, i.e. substances boiling lower than 100°C and including sulphides, mercaptans, ketones and aldehydes; probably they are breakdown products of amino-acids; certainly they come from some non-odorous precursor.

(3) Rancid off-flavours in fats due to storage; the specific chemical

change that gives rise to them is cleavage of the fatty molecules in the carbon chain and formation at the points of scission of carbonyl groups.

There are other analytical methods besides gas chromatography that are used. For example, the determination of infra-red and ultra-violet spectra often enables chemical identity to be defined. The mass spectrograph is another tool, expensive but very sensitive, that has found its way into the Low Temperature laboratories, into the Tarrytown laboratories of General Foods and doubtless into many others. The picture which the reader may envisage is of a mass of new analytical apparatus, costly and requiring a lot of upkeep, but capable of great sensitivity, in the hands of young chemists and physicists who try to sort out and interpret the mass of information that these instruments offer, and who try also and this is the most difficult of all, to correlate their findings with olfactory and flavour preferences. The approach is logical; it has met with a little success and will meet with a lot more, but such work is still difficult and laborious, and it is always uncertain whether it will yield the answers to any specific flavour problem.

It has always to be remembered that any process that involves heating the sample, as gas chromatography does, may quite easily change the chemical structure of some of the flavour constituents. In any work that involves smell quality, heat should be avoided like the plague. As an assessment of this approach one can say that one must admire the courage and dedication of those workers who embark on such analytical methods to illuminate the subject of flavour. It can be added that the work has to be done, there being no adequate alternative; but one can hope that something simpler will come along soon to save such immense labour and provide a correlation between chemical constitution and flavour more quickly. It is true to say that the most likely place for the new approach to be found is amongst the men who are carrying out so assiduously the tedious analytical work with existing equipment. But there is a danger in modern research of equipment becoming too complicated, so that its own maintenance takes too much attention; the research direction must not become the slave of its own equipment, must not lose sight of the main issues, must not allow itself to get into the position that it can't see the wood for the trees. There are some scientists whose philosophy is that detail is the only reality; they are not the sort to make research station directors, but they can become able and assiduous operators of their complex equipment. A realistic appraisal of the methods being used and a broad look round for alternatives are necessary occasionally. A visitor to the Low Temperature Research Station cannot fail to be impressed by the analytical installation and the hard work that is put into its application, but he may perhaps feel that more use could be made of organoleptic appraisal and testing and of a more sustained effort to link it (flavour) with the analytical results.

The flavour profile

If the aroma of coffee is investigated by methods such as those outlined above, more than thirty chemical entities which may and probably do play a part in building the coffee aroma can be detected and identified. This information is interesting and will eventually be useful, but perhaps not just yet. Certainly it provides no more immediate help to the food technologist than does the physiologist's knowledge of the sense stimulus and the nervous pathways. What can the food manufacturer do? A firm of consultants, Arthur D. Little of Boston, for whom Dr. Crocker worked until his retirement, tried hard to give the manufacturer something useful and practical. They would take some important and useful aroma such as coffee and identify in it the main odour characteristics; they would try to separate mentally say six characteristics. The food manufacturer would send some young people from his staff to Little's laboratories for a few weeks and there they would be taught to recognize and assess the six characteristics; then trained, they returned to their employers, where they would be found to be very useful in maintaining the aroma of the coffee at a high standard. The author has seen the team of trained assistants working in the General Foods laboratories at Tarrytown and was favourably impressed by the confidence with with they did their work.

For other flavours more than six characteristics may be necessary. It has been stated[99] that the component sensations relevant to the flavour of beer are salt, sweet, sour, fruity, bitter, yeast, malt, phenylacetic acid, skunk, metallic, astringent and there may be others that may be detected.

This attempt to match language to experience, to describe the component parts of a flavour in language that anyone can understand, by association with well-known flavours, is known as the Flavour Profile method. It has been described thus: "The Flavour

Profile presents a descriptive analysis of flavour expressing in common language terms the characteristic notes of both aroma and flavour, their order of appearance and intensities, and the amplitudes of total aroma and flavour". It is a step forward.

Flavour appraisal

There are several methods of appraisal. The quickest is that in which one person does the work; next in speed is the technical flavour panel, then the non-technical panel and slowest of all, the home testing; the more people who are involved in the work the longer it takes. The advantage of having several people instead of only one is to discriminate between and appraise different flavours in order to decide which is likely to be the most popular; after that non-technical panels can follow up the work: sometimes, such a panel may consist of six or eight people; often this in turn is followed up, if in a big works and the circumstances seem to justify it, by engaging the opinions of perhaps 100 or 200 of the employees; ultimately, the manufacturers may try to get the results of a home test. Experts invariably give results quicker and better than lay people who are too often diffident and uncertain and the main use of a large lay panel is to decide between different products which the technical people think are both good but different. What are the olfactory preferences of the public likely to be? Wherever possible the few experts, the technical panel, will be used. There is some truth in the statement that the public expects the experts to know what is best and to provide it. Simultaneously, there is too often a tendency for the expert to try to give the public what he believes it wants, instead of giving it the best. If both expert and public were faithful to their convictions, we might do better. There are products offered for sale today: notably fruit concentrates, canned orange juices, tasteless tomatoes, deep-freeze turkeys, and packeted teas, that are neither more or less than a monument to the tolerance and repressed condition of the consumers. The nursery-man selling a few tomato plants says that Ailsa Craig and one or two others are fine for flavour, and that Moneymaker is "like water". But it is Moneymaker that he grows and sells: fairly early, prolific, red and round and eight to the pound. Some packets of tea bearing a world-famous name give neither the colourful tasty brew that the British people are supposed to like, nor an aroma that is more sophisticated than that of wet hay. Cheap teas are one of the richest sources of fluoride (good for teeth) in our diet, but there is not much else that can be said to their advantage. The expert tasters and blenders seem to be doing rather badly and the consumers are too complaisant. One does not need to be a connoisseur or anything at all out of the ordinary other than being capable of forming an opinion of one's own, to realize that much of what is offered for sale is poorly-flavoured. Much of what is on sale is good, some of it is marvellously good, but there is still a lot that is very poor for flavour. And yet people keep on buying it.

The expert taster. Some commodities, notably wines, whisky, tea and coffee have their dedicated tasters; such men are artists like the perfumers. Gas chromatography may not mean much to them, but they are expert at their speciality. Probably their main attributes are an interest and professional pride in their work, constant practice and a good memory. These add up to art, sometimes almost to magic. An article that appeared recently in the daily press[100] described how a coffee taster sips 400 times a day, and how having once made up his mind he has the coffee roasted, ground, tinned and sealed within four hours. Freshness is essential; if roasted whole beans are exposed to atmosphere for four days, that is long enough; if they have been ground too, twenty-four hours is long enough. To preserve the flavour after tinning, all air is drawn off and replaced by carbon dioxide, so that there will be no oxidative changes. Imagine a panel trying to get through work at this speed! Crocker's description of coffee tasting runs as follows[101]: "the coffee is drawn back into the mouth slowly until the full flavour and character is appraised, after which the liquid is expelled . . . (it) is not swallowed. In cup testing, some of the properties looked for in coffees are richness of body, 'acidity', thickness of brew, flavour, wininess, sirupy character, smoothness, and mellowness. There are certain undesirable properties which must be guarded against, such as sourness, woodiness, 'Rioyness' (a crude rawness often found in Rio coffee), mustiness, 'hidiness', bitterness, and earthiness." Each quality is looked for separately and is appraised by direct comparison with a standard.

Technical panel. Routine testing is usually done by a single operator, but a referee board or technical panel is used to select what is desirable, to give the routine operator his criteria to work to. The referee board works slowly and carefully; often it finds no difficulty in picking out what the consumer will like and can see its way clear to brief the routine tasters. There are times, however, when products that are different, but both acceptable and apparently equally so, are encountered. Which will the public, or that section of it that is a possible consumer, like better? Sometimes the products are then submitted to the opinion of lay panels. One way in which the technical panel can be of great help is in classifying the results; a large number of different flavour descriptions that inevitably come from a lay panel can often be condensed into a few without much loss of precision; thus Bate-Smith[102] has related that war-time taste panels for dried egg described the off-flavours they encountered in seventy ways, but that further study by a technical panel reduced this number to a dozen.

When careful discrimination is required a small technical or at least informed panel may be the quickest and best to get reliable results. It has, too, the big advantage that a large number of samples can be tested, so that if there are say three variables, odour, taste (for example, sweetness) and texture, these can be altered one at a time. Thus, in ice-cream, texture and odour (flavour) can be kept constant and half a dozen samples with different degrees of sweetness made up; two of the six may well be the same in sweetness as well so providing a reliability check. The six samples are tested "blind" by a panel of three or four or six people interested in the subject so that they give it their best attention, and each person rates the six samples, the one he likes best, the next best and so on. Then the results are examined. Do the results of the four or six testers agree? Are the two samples that are of exactly similar composition rated almost equally? With people who are trying hard, the point of optimum sweetness can soon be determined. Then samples with this optimum sweetness and with five quite different flavours are made up (but two of them again may well be the same as a reliability check). These are tested not only "blind" in the sense that the tester does not know what is in each sample, but literally blind with eyes closed, so that the panel members can concentrate exclusively on the smell. The first results may point to a particular flavour as being most attractive; the vanilla flavour made by manufacturer X is preferred to those of his rivals V, W, Y and Z. Fresh samples are made up with different quantities of flavour X and the panel soon gets the best formulation. Then with taste and odour (or flavour) both at their best, texture is varied by altering the type or quantity of colloid stabilizer present. Carried out informally and with good will, these tests can be extremely informative. Of course, they have their dangers; perhaps one member of the panel quite honestly thinks that Z's vanilla flavour is the best, the most reliable and the best value for money, and he may try to identify that sample which he thinks has Z's flavour in it. But the other members of the panel know him well and probably his idiosyncrasy too and they watch for its appearance. Most people can smell very well indeed and there is very great uniformity from one person to another; it goes without saying that anyone who has some affliction that interferes with his sense of smell, even a temporary head cold, should not work on the panel. Usually, the members will know from previous work and experience that they can all smell normally. Tests are best made before the day's first cigarette. With patience to perform enough repeat tests to satisfy oneself that the results are real, this method is the best of all.

There is one reservation to be made and it can often be important. We have seen that the odour preferences of children are very different from those of adults and if a product is being prepared with the idea of selling it to children, it would be madness to make the flavour adjustments without reference to children. They are usually very sensible and helpful and provided that they are dealt with singly, and not in groups where they may feel it incumbent on themselves to follow the leader, they will give trustworthy opinions.

Market research in foods. Whilst there are several factors that can contribute their part to the liking or disliking of a food, there is no doubt that the two that play the biggest part are odour and taste. A great deal of attention has been given to the consumer rating or market testing of foods and sometimes the testing extends to a large body of the general public, some thousands of whom are asked to give their opinions on particular foods or to express their preferences for one over another. Usually, the testers receive no reward other than the gift of the samples that they have tested, for their work, but this state of affairs, which is perhaps happy for the manufacturers, cannot be expected to continue indefinitely. But so far people have been surprisingly co-operative. The housewife when she answers the door-bell may be so relieved to find she is not being asked to buy something that she willingly undertakes to be a guinea-pig and to make other guinea-pigs of her family and test the products as asked to do. Sometimes, the possibility of a local factory being enlarged and so bringing more employment and money to a town may be an incentive for the local residents to co-operate. At one time when the author was doing his best to find new uses for alginates, he found that the Scottish people would do anything in reason to help to develop Scottish seaweed. The lightest of touches on the string of patriotism and one had full support from housewife, hairdresser or sausage manufacturer. That was perhaps a special case, but there is usually some good reason to be found for people doing constructive work, even although they may not be paid directly for it.

A symposium entitled "What the Manufacturer Can Learn from Consumers about Foods"[103] has discussed the subject of going direct to the ultimate consumer instead of relying on a works panel. Some of the recommendations to the manufacturers who contemplated such an investigation that were put into it by the various members of the symposium and that came out of it with some seal of approval were:

1. Do not make the first approach by ringing the door-bell. Better to get in touch with some local society or organization of women, and offer a donation graded according to the number of tests that are completed.

2. Make sure that the testers are a representative cross-section of the community or of that part aimed at as a market. Avoid the wealthy, they can't be bothered; avoid the poor, they may not be able to fill in a questionnaire properly. If many tests are to be made, change the people frequently otherwise they develop a professional attitude which is not what is wanted.

3. Fairness and freedom from bias are essential; without these the work would be better not done. Samples should not be coded by colour or anything else that might provoke an affective reaction but by fairly large and uninteresting numbers such as 351, 472, 607 and so on. Source, or name of maker, should never be divulged. Production and formulating staff who may have their enthusiasms and indiscretions are better kept away from the testers.

4. The simplest method of test is a comparison of two samples; this avoids the danger of the courteous answer "Yes" if asked of a single sample "Do you like it?" One member recommended three straight questions about a pair of samples:

(a) Is there a difference between these two products?

(b) If so, which one do you prefer?

(c) Why?

The result of such a test may be that 60 per cent of the people preferred product number 351 and 35 per cent preferred product number 472, and 5 per cent had no preference. If guessing is suspected, it can be identified by new tests in which the same two products are coded differently.

If the differences in odour, taste e.g. sweetness, colour or texture are very evident, the preferences will probably be definite and a small group will give a reliable answer. But if there are fine shades of difference of odour or taste that are being tested, then a large panel may be necessary. It is evident that with very large panels or groups of consumers, the number of products tested must be kept to a minimum. One way of cutting down the work of the manufacturers is to use a postal questionnaire. This was also described in considerable detail by another member of the symposium and has apparently been used successfully, but it might be thought that if used frequently, the testers would become bored and might return careless answers. Some sort of personal contact seems to be desirable to satisfy oneself that the work has been fairly done.

Market research, going directly to the public, is one way of determining olfactory preferences, but it is laborious, tedious and costly. It is one of the extravagances of an affluent society and in the author's view, it is not usually necessary. And unless some sort of supervision can be given, it can give misleading results.

Effect of colour on flavour preferences

It is so easy to taste or to smell and to say "I like this better than that". Yet experience shows that some sort of supervision is necessary, when unpractised people are asked to do just that. What is so simple, they tend to make difficult; they try to analyse the reasons for their liking or disliking; they allow associative ideas to come right into their mind and they entertain them there. How dangerous this can be, in its bearing on getting a straight answer to a straight question is well shown by some work carried out by Moir[104]. It shows strikingly the effects of association on recognition of odours and through that on their pleasantness. Moir's paper had as its purpose to record some observations which threw grave doubt on the ability of observers to recognize flavour. Four ordinary fruit table jellies were prepared but they were given unusual colours as indicated:

Vanilla	Yellow	instead of cream
Orange	Green	instead of amber
Lime	Amber	instead of green
Lemon	Red	instead of yellow

K

The subjects who were asked to identify the flavours of these jellies just from their taste and smell included people of different kinds, directors, salesmen, factory girls, bakers, and storemen. Out of the sixty people tested, only one gave identifications that were quite right; only 22 scored more than 50 per cent of the possible marks, that is identified the flavour correctly in half the tests. It seems incredible and so too the Editor of the journal in which it was published appears to have found it judging by his Editorial comments in the same issue.

Next the subjects were asked to identify the flavour of sponge biscuits all chocolate *coloured* but flavoured (1) with 7 per cent cocoa powder (2–4 per cent is usually recommended for a chocolate flavour) and (2) with vanilla. When the flavour used in the chocolate-coloured biscuits was in fact cocoa, twenty-eight people said the biscuits had no flavour, seven identified a "wrong" flavour that was not present and only twenty-five gave the correct flavour. When the real flavour was vanilla, thirty-five people said the biscuits had no flavour, eight gave a wrong flavour and only seventeen gave the correct flavour. Moir concludes that the majority of people have little discriminatory power for flavour, and that they are mostly ignorant of their disability. But it may be thought that all he really found was that there was a powerful association between colour and flavour and that when he deliberately contradicted this almost instinctive association by using green orange and red lemon, he frustrated the faculty of flavour identification. Flavour does not ordinarily rely much on colour for identification and if the tests had been made in the dark or blindfolded, much better results would have been forthcoming. But clearly the "wrong" colour can upset flavour identification. Lies are destructive of time, effort, and thought; Moir's samples were lies and it is not really surprising that they confused and misled the subjects. It is probably true that the nose is more easily deluded than the eye or the ear; one may feel less certainty that a smell is lemony than that a picture is of a lemon or that a succession of sounds is "Tipperary". The ease with which the olfactory sense can be deluded is due not to intrinsic inadequacy in the design of the olfactory equipment, but rather to neglect of its use and lack of practice. Ask it: Do you like this smell better than that? and if the subject does not allow his thoughts to wander, he can nearly always give a clear and definite answer. But if he starts to think about it he may soon be lost. Colour vision varies in its sensitivity to slight changes of hue in different parts of the visible spectrum. The physicists and engineers who have studied the subject have found that it is most sensitive and able to detect very slight changes indeed of hue in the reds that are characteristic of raw meat. Slight changes in the colour of meat may indicate unfitness for eating and here the eye can play a significant part in helping the chemical senses in their assessment of doubtful food material.

Contemporary flavour research

Flavour research has its justification in the existence of olfactory preferences. What is preferred by the nose in a foodstuff is a good flavour, and it is to improve flavours that in the main, flavour research is carried out. A look at some of the projects that are being carried out contemporarily will perhaps indicate the state of the art. This can conveniently be taken by reference to a report[98] of the London symposium held by the Food Group of the Society of Chemical Industry on September 18–20, 1963. There is not quite so much about flavour in the report as one might have expected, but there are numerous references to it. Some of them are:

Meat. The trend today is for lean meat and tenderness with an earlier age for slaughter, but with a certain accompanying loss of flavour. Ionizing radiation (U.V. lamps which prevent bacterial action) has been used for the long-term preservation of meat, but the dose required produces marked off-odours and off-flavours (these may be due to oxidation as U.V. lamps liberate a little ozone). "Irradiation may be combined with mild heat treatment to prevent the off-flavours produced by irradiation alone."

Fish. "The spoilage of frozen fish is not necessarily accompanied by deterioration in odour or even in flavour; thus, sea-frozen fillets may sometimes possess ideal odour and flavour yet have an unacceptable tough texture." It is pointed out, too, that the increasing sale of packed fish means that the fish is judged at the table rather than on the fishmonger's slab; and provided that the cooked odour and flavour are satisfactory that is all that matters.

Jam. Vacuum-processed or "new" jam is gaining favour. The fruit e.g. strawberries, is sliced to release the flavour, and to make it easier to spread (there is less pulping than usual). The fruit is very gently cooked in sealed pans, so that the volatile flavour principles cannot escape. Either fresh or deep-frozen fruit is the raw material. The flavour of "new" jam is said to be better than usual, but the difference is not very great. The general use of SO_2-preserved, fruit pulp for jam is falling away; when deep-frozen fruit is used the aroma is better and there is no need for artificial colouring.

Tinned fruit. The substitution of 20 per cent of the sugar by a high quality glucose syrup can be effected without adversely affecting the taste or flavour.

Fruit drinks. Citrus fruits, principally oranges, are disintegrated and put through colloid mills to convert them into liquid oranges (the quantities of peel and pulp are varied) a combination of peel, pulp, peel oil and juice, which is added directly to sugar syrup to provide a base for a fruit drink. That way, the consumer gets everything and it must be said that the drink after dilution is refreshing and wholesome. The bitter principles are at first a little obtrusive, but one soon learns to appreciate these niceties. If a little of such a lemon or orange crush is added to tinned pineapple, it gives it a very sophisticated and attractive tang. Concentrated fruit aroma distillate is a new development; "the aroma is concentrated 100–200 fold and can be stored for long periods before adding it to juice or other products. The process has been used successfully on apples, pears, blackcurrants, grapes, and cherries." The aroma concentrate is obtained by a process that is essentially one of distillation. "The use of aroma distillation has greatly improved the quality of fruit juices made partially or wholly from concentrates."

How often, especially in America, is canned fruit juice not quite what it should be, although it is drunk unquestioningly by the millions. To the author it is often spoilt by a hint of a metallic taste. Ask an American, even an American chemist, about this and he looks surprised. Quite evidently he thinks the juice is fine and the question frivolous. And yet now we hear that "bottled orange juice is much more acceptable in Germany than canned orange juice, due to the infinitely higher quality of the bottled product. The difference is so great that the suitability of tin sheet for juice packing should be reconsidered." To the author it has always seemed that glass is the ideal container for anything where odour and flavour are important.

Low calorie soft drinks. These are for slimmers; the fattening sugar is replaced not by saccharin as formerly, but by cyclamates. Saccharin has a notorious bitter after-taste and the cyclamates are thought to have a purer all-sweet taste.

Pickles. Preference has swung towards less acid than hitherto pickles. In order to prevent microbial spoilage, 3·6 per cent acetic acid is necessary, but today the acid may be reduced to 1 per cent so that pasteurization becomes necessary. Even so, enzymic activity can introduce off-flavours. Furthermore, pasteurization tends to destroy the crispness of pickled onions and to introduce a cooked flavour; also, unless care is taken, the process can make the pickles too spicy because more flavour is extracted (as a result of the heating) from the red and black peppers used as a garnish. It seems a long way from the implantation of electrodes in the nerve fibres to considerations of this sort, but there is no reason why these two approaches to flavour problems starting so far apart should not be contrived to meet.

Tomato powder. A new development. Forty lb. of fresh tomatoes yield about two lb. tomato powder with no loss in colour, flavour, vitamin content and with good reconstitution properties. It sounds too good to be true. The secret is a "no-heat" drying (Birs) process, in which concentrated juice is sprayed counter-current against pre-dried air. It is just one more illustration of the damage that heat can do to odour and flavour, and how advisable it is to avoid it.

Chocolate flavour profile. The Cocoa, Chocolate and Confectionary Alliance had a flavour profile panel for assessing chocolate. When the same samples were distributed to different tasters, it was common to find appreciably different responses. The representatives of different manufacturers tended to score highly (and differently from each other) for those factors which they valued; a floral flavour, a strong cocoa flavour etc.; furthermore, fermentation by moulds could give rise to occasional foreign flavours. Different manufacturers attached importance to very different flavour factors.

The future for flavour research

The examples just discussed are those that were thought to be of most interest by the experts of the European food industry. The most evident conclusion that can be drawn is that flavour in food is still an empirical subject, but that those who make the foods are doing their utmost to improve it. Probably within the next five years or so, gas chromatography will be making significant and practical contributions to the industry and in another five or ten years what is nowadays an art, may become a fairly exact science. There are three essential approaches:

(1) The empirical, illustrated by the examples just given.

(2) The analytical, with gas chromatography as the most useful

tool, to identify and estimate the chemical entities responsible for flavour in natural products.

(3) The psychological with more panel work on basic (not necessarily commercial) olfactory preferences and with development of experimental neuro-physiological methods to record the currents passing along the nerve pathways.

The appreciation of flavour

It was the flavours that the children of Israel remembered and regretted when they reproached Moses[105]:

> "We remember the fish which we did eat in Egypt freely; the cucumbers, and the melons, and the leeks and the onions, and the garlick."

They soon tired of manna with its "fresh oil" flavour.

That was some three thousand years ago. Nowadays in an up-to-date economy with people and food all conforming, or at least inclining to a mean, flavour seems to be having rather a setback. It is not forgotten; lip service is paid to it. In Manhattan, steaks "broiled on charcoal" and servings of ham "cured in hickory smoke" promise a lot, but when they come, they are big and expensive and pretty tasteless. In Kansas City, renowned for its steaks, they are bigger than ever, too big for any ordinary person, but still without much flavour. Oddly, in Leningrad where we might expect uniformity to be even more evident, the food is full of flavour; wonderful borsch soup, fine fish, caviar, and meats that are full of flavour. Perhaps the Russian sheep has to work hard to find a living and a small thrifty sheep has as much absolute flavour in it as a big scientifically nourished, overfed, over-medicated and overgrown Western sheep. In Stockholm, too, the food is full of flavour. On ships, generally, food is good and pleasant to eat. Why is it so often indifferent in so many other places? Grown too big? Stored too long? Cooked too much? Served too tardily? To people who since being weaned have eaten tasteless food? Give them caviar three days running and watch learning dawn.

Flavour is important. What pleasure recurs so often and so regularly as the enjoyment of a good meal? A cigarette, of course, and not altogether because of its flavour. Even so, flavour is more important than the cigarette. We are what we eat. If the food lacks interest, so will the people who eat it. History will repeat itself and eventually the people will demand and if they demand long and loudly enough, they will get, food that is full of flavour.

Rules

Those rules that can be derived from the contents of this chapter are:

Rule 108. Raw food sometimes possesses a flavour that is lost in cooking e.g. clams and sweetbreads, cabbage and strawberries.

Rule 109. The flavour of most meats develops when they are cooked.

Rule 110. Methods of isolating flavour principles from food are seldom perfect. Those which involve the use of heat, e.g. steam distillation, may modify the flavour principles chemically with loss of some of the finer shades of flavour.

Rule 111. If a natural flavour product can be used whole without the need for isolation of the flavour principles so much the better. The less treatment natural products receive the less damage they will suffer.

Rule 112. A method of removing permanently some tenacious off-flavour or unwanted odour is to add to the material that suffers from it some pleasantly odorous material such as an oil in small quantity, and then to remove the oil either by steam distillation or ventilation. Often, the oil carries away with it whatever was responsible for the malodour or off-flavour.

Rule 113. The electric currents that the neuro-physiologist can record in the brain of a person stimulated by a smell or by a flavour have not yet been correlated with pleasantness or unpleasantness, but such correlation ought to be possible eventually.

Rule 114. Children and men like their fruit drinks sweeter than women.

Rule 115. Natural flavours usually derive from chemically complex mixtures (cf. Rules 2, 3). The identification of very small quantities of a large number of chemical entities is difficult, but new analytical methods, particularly gas chromatography, are yielding a great deal of new knowledge of the chemical constitution of natural flavours.

Rule 116. Flavour profiles have been introduced; they consist of the delineation and estimation of notes such as sweet, bitter, smoky, and yeasty in aromas such as of coffee or beer. Recognition and assessment of these constituent notes is not very difficult and can be used for quality control in the food industry.

Rule 117. Routine flavour testing is best carried out by an individual expert. Selection of the best or a new product from several and adjustment of flavour are best carried out by a small technical panel. Lay panels are slow and inconclusive. Market research, when it includes home testing, is inevitably expensive and usually unreliable unless supervision can be given.

Rule 118. Colour may not usually affect flavour preferences but "wrong" colours such as "red lemon" can confuse the person who is testing flavour.

REFERENCES

87. R. W. Moncrieff, *The Chemical Senses*, 1944, Leonard Hill, London.

88. *Agricultural Research Council*, Annual Report, 1961, of Low Temperature Research Station, Cambridge.

89. Y. R. Naves quoted in Editorial, Some thoughts on flavouring materials, *Perfumery & Essential Oil Record*, 1962, **53**, 657.

90. *Proverbs*, Chapter 27, verse 9.

91. J. H. Forkner, U.S. Patent 2,411,201 (1946).

92. K. Cuker, British Patent 618,864 (1949).

93. E. D. Adrian, Physiological background of flavour assessment, *Chemistry & Industry*, 1953, 1274–1276.

94. E. D. Adrian. The electrical activity of the mammalian olfactory bulb, *Electroenceph. clin. Neurophysiol.*, 1950, **2**, 377–388.

95. E. D. Adrian, Sensory messages and sensation. The response of the olfactory organ to different smells, *Acta physiol. Scand.*, 1953, **29**, Fasc. 1, 5–14.

96. C. W. Sem-Jacobsen, M. C. Petersen, H. W. Dodge, Q. D. Jacks, J. A. Lazarte, & C. B. Holman, Electrical activity of the olfactory bulb in man, *Amer. J. med. Sci.*, 1956, **232**, 243–251.

97. A. M. Maiden, A system of judging flavour in bread, *Chemistry & Industry*, 1936, **55**, 143–145.

98. Food Technology in Europe, *Ibid.*, 1964, 1291–1304.

99. *Some aspects of Agricultural Research No. 3.* Taste & Flavour, p. 26, H.M.S.O., 1961.

100. Sipping 400 times a day, *Daily Mail*, 18 March 1964.

101. E. C. Crocker, *Flavor*, pp. 120–121, 1945, McGraw-Hill, New York.

102. E. C. Bate-Smith, The chemistry of taste and flavour, *New Scientist*, 1961, **11**, 329–331.

103. What the manufacturer can learn from the consumers about foods, *Food Industries*, March 1941, **13**, 39–50.

104. H. C. Moir, Some observations on the appreciation of flavour in food-stuffs, *Chemistry & Industry*, 1936, **55**, 145–148.

105. *Numbers*, Chapter 11, verse 5.

CHAPTER 20

PERFUME PREFERENCES

ALL PERFUMES should be delightful and a lot of them are. Long ago, the production of simple floral perfumes must have been considered inadequate; some people wanted to be different, to express their personality through their perfume. So today we have, in addition to the simple flower scents, sophisticated blends that although not immediately recalling any one flower scent, are nevertheless unmistakably floral, and we have other scents that are not so much floral as spicy, and other again that seem to have no natural pleasantly odoriferous ancestry. Some of them are still pleasant, some are intriguing and some seem to be quite intentionally unpleasant. Those that are most liked vary with the race; Western people generally like floral perfumes whilst in the East, spicy perfumes are more esteemed. Eastern perfumes are heavy, intriguing, sleepy and mildly intoxicating (cf. Rule 81); Western ones are less languorous and often gay and uplifting with a top note that fairly dazzles.

Pleasantness changes with the times

Just as different races, especially the East and the West, vary in what they think is pleasant olfactorily, so apparently have the peoples of different periods varied. The ancients liked aloes (the powdered wood of the various aloe trees has a pleasant spicy smell) and myrrh and frankincense and cinnamon and the related cassia. In the 45th Psalm[106] (a song of loves) we read:

"All thy garments smell of myrrh and aloes, and cassia."

And in the Song of Solomon[107]

"His cheeks are as a bed of spices as sweet flowers; his lips like lilies, dropping sweet smelling myrrh."

Those odours that in Western Europe, or perhaps only in France, were most highly esteemed and were used at different periods as the basis of popular perfumes were according to Henning[108] as given below. There seems to be evidence of a relationship between the times and the scents.

Louis XIII who reigned 1610–1643 in a dissolute court. Perfumes dependent largely on musk, civet, myrtle and iris such as "Eau des anges" (water distilled from myrtle flowers).

Louis XIV who reigned 1643–1715 (The state, it is I). Perfumes containing harsh spicy resins.

Louis XV who reigned 1715–1774 and loved Madame de Pompadour. Rose perfumes.

1st Empire that of Napoleon Bonaparte from 1804 to 1815. Eau-de-Cologne and rosemary at first, and later more exotic odours.

After 1830. Mixtures of patchouli (heavy Eastern) and such flowers as lavender and wallflower.

After 1870. Strong musk and patchouli odours and later novel and floral mixtures.

Recently (written by Henning about 1914). Simple flower odours for young women and heavy novelty mixtures for older women.

And since the time of Henning what has been the trend?

Largely one might think to "chypre" perfumes, and to mixtures which have beautiful floral scents, but in which no single flower smell predominates. It is seldom nowadays that one encounters such perfumes as rose, sweetpea or wall-flower beautiful as they are. The one exception is violet; how often a smart women leaves in her wake the evanescent brilliance of the violet.

Perfume compounding in modern times calls for precision and a good memory. There is also a need to know what will be liked by potential consumers, but the days of perfumers with brilliant individual gifts for compounding wonderful new perfumes have passed. In a factory that manufactures the synthetics and isolates that are the perfumer's raw materials, there will be a compounding or matching room. This consists essentially of a "bank" in which have been deposited samples of all raw materials and also of some thousands of mixtures, perfume bases that have been prepared for one reason or another over a period of years. Then if someone sends in a perfume to be matched, one of the assistants will find which of the mixtures in the bank it reminds her of, will take that as a start and modify it accordingly. It is really very like matching colours on yarn in a dyehouse laboratory, but the work does call for a good memory. The bank stock will include not only floral and orthodox scent preparations, but such out of the way smells as

pipe-tobacco, heather, and tweeds, smells with a masculine con-
notation. All told, with plenty of practice, matching is not unduly
difficult. Ask the assistants a few questions about matching some
particular sample and the answers will reveal familiarity with the
task and confidence that a good match can be made. But ask them
whether it is pleasant, whether they like it, and they are soon in
difficulties. Ask a matching dyehouse laboratory assistant if she
likes a shade she is matching and she will be nonplussed; she has
never thought about it and in order to answer the question she has
to pull herself out of the everyday working level in which she is
expert to the lay level of the girl at home. "Yes, it's not bad."
But she could have talked for five minutes about the technicalities
of matching that particular shade. The whys and wherefores of
liking and disliking, of pleasantness and unpleasantness, are much
more difficult. So it is with colour vision; even more it is with smell.
That was where the artist-perfumer used to rule, but his day is
over. It will not be long before a computer is doing part of his work.
It is a dreadful thought, but mercifully, it will not be able to do the
creative part as well. No artist-perfumer will like to become a
humble programmer. Head dyers are perhaps not the overlords
that they once were, but they are still very highly valued men.
And so are perfumers. Perhaps fashion will be their salvation. It
will be a good computer that can follow fashion. Shades of colour
are limited; they must fall within the visible spectrum and there is
no room for any shade that is much different from what we have
already seen. But what are the limits of the olfactory spectrum?
We do not know. There is no known reason why a smell, quite
different from anything yet experienced, should not be discovered
tomorrow.

Perfumes for men

Tweedy, pipe-tobacco, heather and fresh air are the smells for men
who want an out-of-doors atmosphere. No harm in that. Even to
build up a he-man atmosphere for the under-dog. No harm in that
either. And so one proceeds to copying the smell of honest toil,
the sweat and body smells that are said to have some sex-attraction.
The ethics thereabouts are more doubtful. And ultimately to the
erotic complexities of the homosexual where pity must nudge
judgement out.

Where is one to stop. A lot of people would say "at the beginning". But most men, if they come to think about it, are already

well past that stage; most of them have peppermint in their tooth-paste, and lavender in their shaving soap. Some use after-shave lotion, talc and hair oil, all of which are perfumed. There may be eau-de-Cologne on the handkerchief, a rose in the buttonhole, a spray of balm in the pocket, all for one's own delight. In America, the use of perfumes by men is more common than in the U.K. and American men spend more than £20 million a year on scented brilliantine, shaving lotions and astringents and perfume for their own use. There have been reports recently that Russian men are using increasing quantities of perfumed toiletries. Why? It is difficult to say. Probably the simplest answer is the best—that they like them.

An investigation of the relative liking by both men and women of different odours for men's use was reported recently. It was carried out in Italy by Rovesti[109] with the collaboration of the Italian Committee of Aesthetics and Cosmetology and the School of Aesthetic Dermatology and Cutaneous Hygiene of Milan. It is amazing to what authorities the sense of smell reports today. There was a panel of 100 men and women and another of 100 women all aged 18–50 and taken from several social classes. Each person was asked to smell a paper slip dipped in a 10 per cent solution of a perfume in alcohol and then asked the question: "Is this odour note suitable in your opinion as a masculine perfume? Answer frankly Yes or No." Some of the results of this survey are to be seen in Table 84.

TABLE 84

Suitability of various perfumes for use by men

Perfume	Percentage of subjects who considered it suitable for use by men	
	Men	Women
Eau-de-Cologne (classic type)	90	76
Lavender	94	88
Pine	90	85
Bergamot	80	89
Violet leaf	74	80
Fern (fougère)	38	67
New mown hay	25	58
Tobacco	26	25
Russian leather	18	25
Sandalwood	10	12
Musk	9	12
Jasmine	5	7

The preference shown by the men themselves for pine, lavender and eau-de-Cologne is well-marked and is supported by the opinion of the women, four out of five of whom thought these odours were suitable for men to wear. The feminine notes based on musk, jasmine, and sandalwood with a high(?) aphrodisiac index were not much favoured. The use of cosmetics by men is growing largely because of the high-pressure advertising that is being applied. In newspapers and magazines these are inoffensive enough, but on TV they can make the viewer squirm. But in Russia this is certainly not due to advertising, because there is very little of it there. To the author, it seems that if men use lavender and eau-de-Cologne because they like their lovely and refreshing smells, if they put bits of lavender and Lad's Love in their pockets because they are made happier by their smell, then that is unexceptionable. If it is a bit of nature that they love and admire that is delightful. But if they use cosmetics containing powerful odorants so that they will smell pleasant or attractive to other people, then that is a very doubtful business indeed. There are very many of course who hold a different view; the question is probably more of an ethical one, than one of olfactory preferences.

Russian perfumes

Do different ideologies bring about differences in olfactory preferences. They hardly should, if preferences are spontaneous, but they might have some effect through associations of ideas. Are Russian perfumes thereby different from ours? There are four recognized groups of Russian perfumes:

(1) Flowery, imitating flower scents e.g. White Lilac, Carnation and Sweet Pea

(2) Spicy and containing fatty esters e.g. Chypre and Sandalwood

(3) Based on methyl ionone e.g. *Red Moscow* (first made 30 years ago) and *Moscow's Own* (or *Native Moscow*)

(4) Based on isoeugenol and hydroxycitronellal e.g. *Black Casket* which is described as a romantic evening perfume.

In 1962 a range of Russian perfume materials was shown in London and in Glasgow at the Soviet Exhibition of Essential Natural Oils and Synthetic Aromatic Products and Perfumery Goods.[110] Some of the best selling perfumes in Russia are *Stone Flower* for evening, *Springtime* light and fragrant for day time, *Lelj* a light scent used by young girls and *Queen of Spades*, a favourite in Sweden to which it is exported. There are vast flower farms in the Southern parts of the U.S.S.R. and oils of rose, lavender, peppermint, fennel and other odorant materials are manufactured. They make large quantities of perfume annually and some 20,000 workers are employed in the industry. It is probably fair to say that Russian women use less perfume than the British, French or Americans, or at least they wear it less frequently. There is no evidence of which the author is aware that in olfactory preferences the Russians are different from the Western European. Their perfumes are fairly cheap and they smell much the same as some of ours. There are one or two, notably *Black Casket* and *Stone Flower* (fragrant of blooming bergamot trees, of musk, and oak-tree moss) that are expensive (about 5 guineas, only one size made) and sophisticated, but one or two women who have used them have expressed the view that they lack some of the subtlety and richness of French perfumes. There are, however, some new ones just (1964) arriving e.g. *Romeo & Juliet*, the former with a rich tenacious fragrance, the latter a gentle fragrance; they are packed in one casket and used together, are claimed to "glorify the everlasting power of love". Then there is *Sputnik* whose "fresh woody note pleasantly harmonizes with faraway cosmic space". *Red Moscow* is said to be the best perfume in the Soviet Union and to have a note of orange flowers, but to the author it smells mainly of methyl ionone. *Kremlin* is based on roses grown in the Crimea. *Queen of Spades* "conceived under the influence of Pushkin's famous story" is a good one with a spicy (cinnamon) note. *Red Poppy* is alluring and has a spicy fragrance. *Ballet* and *Gayane* are new ones. *Leningrad* has a cold and austere aroma. *Moscow Nights* is spicy, *Firebird* is heavy and exotic, *Springtime* or *Spring* is delicate and refreshing and suitable for a young girl. *To Space*, a new one, is claimed as a "daring novel creation specially suited for slender sportive women". *Pearl* has a complex spicy aroma of jasmine and lilac and is suitable for temperamental people. *Evening* is exciting and strong. One must give the Russians full marks for their appreciation of the power of smell over the emotions. Their catalogue descriptions may make one smile and it may be that women who ordinarily use French perfumes may find some subtle note lacking, but by and large the Russian perfumes are very pleasant; some are soothing, some are arousing and all told they are a good lot at prices from around 5/– to 5 guineas. A few that have come from Riga are said to be interesting, heavy and musky, but they are not always easy to get. A critical review of Russian perfumes by Lozzi[111] suggests that in Russia the eau-de-Cologne made in Leningrad is much preferred to that made in Moscow and both are much preferred to that made in Riga, but this applies only to eau-de-Cologne. Prices in Russia range from 50 kopecks (3s. 6d.) for straight floral perfumes to 8 roubles 50 kopecks (£3) for *Native Moscow*.

The Russians themselves attribute the good qualities of their perfumes to three factors:

(1) The suitability of the climate in Southern Russia for growing the odorous plants

(2) The highly effective processing technique used

(3) The skill of their perfumers.

In the author's opinion *Stone Flower* is streets ahead of their others. Most of them can be inspected or bought at the Russian shop in London between Chancery Lane and Holborn tube stations. It would be misleading to leave the reader with the impression that Russian perfumes are better today than French or British preparations, but they are good, and technically they are advancing rapidly. Soon they will be very good indeed.

Prices and preferences of perfumes

Are very expensive perfumes to be preferred to less costly products? Jewett[112] at the University of California made an investigation of perfume preferences. Saleswomen had ventured the statement that the average person probably could not differentiate between an inexpensive and an expensive perfume. Was this true? It was agreed that qualities that were desirable in a perfume were odour appeal, smoothness, and lasting quality, but it was doubted whether the desirability of a perfume was inextricably bound up with a relatively high cost.

Six perfumes were selected for study: two Lilacs costing $16 and $50 an ounce respectively; two Gardenias $8 and $50, two Apple Blossoms $8 and $50. These prices were in America in 1945 and would probably be higher today. But they are all, even the cheap ones, what we should think of as expensive in Britain. But even if the experiment resolves itself into answering the question: "Are perfumes that are prohibitive in price to be preferred to those that are merely expensive?", it is still interesting. It might be even more interesting to carry out similar investigations with the inclusion of some of the very good perfumes that are obtainable quite cheaply in the chain stores.

Sixty-nine subjects, all psychology students and mostly women took part in the tests. Perfumed blotters were put in small screw-top bottles and the perfumes were presented to the subjects in pairs. The preference for the inexpensive or the expensive perfume varied somewhat according to which was offered first, and sometimes the fact that one perfume was offered first of the two was favourable to it. A summary of the expressed preferences is shown in Table 85.

TABLE 85

A comparison of the expensive and inexpensive perfume

Perfume	When the expensive was offered first		When the inexpensive was offered first	
	Percentage of subjects preferring		Percentage of subjects preferring	
	Expensive	Inexpensive	Expensive	Inexpensive
Lilac	52	48	61	39
Gardenia	44	56	47	53
Apple blossom	82	18	54	46

The expensive apple blossom was clearly better than the inexpensive; there was less difference between expensive and inexpensive in the other two cases. Apparently many of the subjects found some difficulty in distinguishing between the two (expensive and inexpensive) and thought they were being tricked: "What are you doing, giving us the same perfume in both bottles?"

Persistence or lasting quality of a perfume is often considered important. Usually a period of eight hours is thought to be long enough for quality maintenance. Tests were made by putting a drop of perfume on a blotter and leaving it for eight hours in an open bottle. The subjects were then asked to say if they could detect fragrance, and as a reliability check, similar blotters, to which a drop of water had been added, were offered to them. Twenty-six students took part in the tests and could find no difference between expensive and inexpensive perfumes. The test was therefore repeated after twenty-six hours (instead of eight hours) exposure, although this time is more than long enough. Differences were then noticeable and were as shown in Table 86.

TABLE 86

Lasting qualities of expensive and inexpensive perfumes

Perfume	Percentage of subjects who detected fragrance in exposed		
	Expensive	Inexpensive	Water control
Lilac	100	81	0
Gardenia	100	100	0
Apple blossom	88	69	0

The general conclusion that Jewett arrived at is that there is not a great deal to choose between expensive and inexpensive perfumes either from the point of view of lasting quality or in the matter of "subjective estimate" i.e. pleasantness. But there is one important factor that seems to have been overlooked and that is whether the quality of the perfume persisted. That almost any perfume can still be smelled after eight hours exposure is understandable, but it would be a very good perfume indeed that after eight hours exposure smelled like it had done to begin with; usually a perfume will consist of a mixture of different odorants often of very different volatility and those that are most volatile—usually those responsible for the top note of a perfume—are quickly lost, and then the quality of the perfume suffers. A really good, and presumably expensive, perfume will have been compounded so that as nearly as possible the components volatilize at equal rates, thus maintaining practically unchanged the special quality of the perfume. This point seems to have been overlooked and it is one in which one might look expectantly for a return for costliness.

The composite smell of a perfume

Reference has already been made (Chapter 12) to the difficulty or impossibility of identifying two odours at the same time; one and then the other so that they alternate can be identified all right, but the mental pathways cannot carry the two separate sets of messages from two odorants simultaneously so that the perceptive area can recognize both. In a perfume there will usually be at least eight or ten chemical entities and quite possibly twenty or thirty. It is a characteristic of a good perfume that the individual odorants cannot be picked out and recognized by the nose. All twenty or thirty combine to send a message to the perceptive areas of the brain that causes a pleasant sensation, but it is not one that can be analysed by the perceptive area into its component parts. The practised perfumer will be able to recognize some of the components, but the layman will not. Knowing the composition of eau-de-Cologne it is possible to identify some of the constituents by smelling, provided that one is practised and is familiar with the smells of the separate chemical entities, but the layman will be quite unable to pick any simple smell with which he is familiar out of the olfactory complex that is eau-de-Cologne.

Rules

Those rules that can be derived from the contents of this chapter are:

Rule 119. What has been considered pleasant in perfumes has changed with the times. Perfumes are subject to fashion.

Rule 120. Whether men should use perfumes is still debatable, but there is agreement by men and women that if men are to wear perfume, the preferred scents are eau-de-Cologne, lavender and pine; the two last are reminiscent of air-fresheners.

REFERENCES

106. *Psalms*, 45, verse 9.
107. *Song of Solomon*, Chapter 5, verse 13.
108. H. Henning, *Der Geruch*, p. 179, Leipzig, 1916.
109. P. Rovesti, reported in Perfumes for men, *Perf. & Essential Oil Record*, 1962, **53**, 619–620.
110. Russian exhibition of essential oils, synthetic, aromatic products and perfumery goods, *Perf. & Essential Oil Record*, 1963, **54**, 15–16.
111. C. Lozzi, Pattern of the demand for perfumes in Moscow City, *Perf. & Essential Oil Record*, 1964, **55**, 184–187.
112. G. M. Jewett, A note on the relation between subjective estimates of the desirability and the lasting quality of certain perfumes and their cost, *J. gen. Psychol.*, 1945, **33**, 285–290.

CHAPTER 21

INDUSTRY'S SERVICE TO ODOUR PREFERENCES

A SIMPLE and cogent question is whether people will buy more if they like the smell of what is offered for sale. The short answer is yes, they will if the smell is noticeable, but that the question of smell does not enter into the great majority of transactions. Correspondingly, they will buy less or none of a product which carries a smell that they dislike. Probably the most obvious application for odorant addition is to artificial flowers. These have become much more popular, probably because they look much better than they used to do; they are often made of plastic and are sometimes made to smell natural by the addition to the plastic of a suitable perfume, and sometimes this is done very well indeed.

Making fabrics odorous

Most fabrics, whether scarves, dresses, underwear, bed linen, curtains or furnishings are quite inodorous. The careful housewife may have put a few sprays of lavender in the bedlinen store, but that is about all, and when the linen was bought, it probably had no special smell. One inventor, Pichlmayr[113] by name, thought that it often appealed to the housewife to impart fragrance to such fabrics as apparel, underwear, draperies, curtains, cushions, and scarves, and he suggested that this could be done by incorporating a suitable oil in a stiffening finish that is often applied to fabrics by the manufacturer. The odorant e.g. oil of lavender, or synthetic attar of roses is dissolved in 2–5 parts of dibutyl phthalate, a little wetting agent is added and this solution is dispersed in 5–8 parts of an aqueous 50 per cent dispersion of polyvinyl acetate. The milky dispersion that results is used as a dip for fabrics or garments which are then dried and ironed. The fragrance is fairly lasting, much more so than that obtained by keeping lavender bags in the linen chest, and will survive several washings. The dibutyl phthalate has two functions (1) to act as a solvent for the odorant, (2) to plasticize the polyvinyl acetate. The polyvinyl acetate has two functions:

(1) to stiffen the fabric; (2) to be the carrier or vehicle for the odorant.

Exact information on the effect of such devices is not easy to come by, but such reports as are available, suggest that a sales advantage can be derived. It has, for example, been reported[114] that two boxes of women's hosiery of identical grade were placed on a store counter. The contents of one box was delicately perfumed, the other was not. Customers in the store overwhelmingly picked the scented hose. The sales appeal of brassières can be stepped up by perfuming them. The judgement of quality can be influenced by the scent; looked at differently, a suitable smell improves the quality of merchandise.

Preventing fabrics becoming malodorous

A pleasant perfume can sell something, an unpleasant one can stop a sale. Many fabrics, especially those made of cotton and rayon, are given a resin finish. Two substances such as formaldehyde and urea which will combine to give a plastic, are applied to the fabric along with a catalyst and then when the fabric is heated, a plastic polymer is formed on the fabric, one which confers on it crease-resistance or drip-dry and non-iron properties. Resin finishes are excellent, but they do have a drawback in that they are not always very stable chemically and under some conditions, particularly when heated in the wet state (when the fabric is being washed in hot water or ironed damp) the resins may undergo partial chemical decomposition. If they do so, then two of the chemicals that are likely to be liberated and evolved have quite strong smells: one is the original formaldehyde; the other is trimethylamine or some closely associated amine. Trimethylamine has a strong fishy smell, reminiscent of spoiled herring. Sometimes if the resin-treated fabric is kept in store for a long time, it may be found to have developed a fishy odour when taken out for sale. The real difficulty has been that fabric received by a merchant from a finisher may have been quite odourless, but on storage has developed an odour that is very detrimental. So long as this odour development was unpredictable so long was the trouble serious. However, simple tests discussed by the author[115] have been developed which will reveal before storage the likelihood that any batch of fabric will develop an odour during storage. If the tests do indicate a danger of odour development sometimes all that is needed is an extra scour; sometimes it is more difficult and the fabric may have to be disposed of as seconds, smell and all. But, at least, the danger of unexpected odour development has been eliminated.

Of recent years non-woven fabrics have become better-known; they can be made without the traditional, but very laborious, weaving or knitting processes and they are therefore cheap and for some purposes, e.g. linings and hangings, they can be reasonably satisfactory. The thousands of fibres in a warp are bonded together often with acrylic and nitrogenous resins; the resin or bond constitutes a main part of the fabric and it is a potential odour-developer. The fabric, therefore, requires odour control and this is effected according to a recent patent[116] by adding a little bisulphite which picks up any unreacted formaldehyde and then drying and curing at 135°C to give a product effectively free of odour. It goes without saying that consumer preference would be shown for an odour-free fabric over one that had a haunting fishy reminder. Prevention of potential odours is one of the factors that has received a lot of attention in the manufacture of non-woven fabrics.

Fabric treatment to reduce sweat smell

The moisture that we lose as sweat is inodorous; it is only after bacteria have worked on it that it becomes odorous and offensive. There are substances known as bactericides and bacteriostats which will kill bacteria or at least stop them multiplying. Bacteria are not animal, but vegetable; they are very small plants, so small that a gram of soil usually contains hundreds of millions of them; they are everywhere and they abound on our skin. To avoid the danger of sweat becoming malodorous, the bacterial population of the skin must be greatly reduced. One bactericide that will inhibit both gram-positive bacteria such as those that cause a sore throat, and gram-negative bacteria such as those that cause intestinal upsets and which was produced by American Cyanamid was given the name Cyana Purifying Agent. It has been described by Salsbury[117] who has reported that if 10 per cent is applied to cellulosic (cotton and rayon) fabrics, it will inhibit the growth of bacteria on the skins of people who wear next-to-the-skin garments of this fabric. On test, men who ordinarily developed a strong offensive sweaty smell remained odourless, because there were insufficient bacteria present on their skins to decompose their sweat and give it the usual unpleasant odour.

The fabric treatment was most effective on cotton and related fibres; on some of the others, such as nylon and wool, the bactericide was inclined to wash out on repeated home laundering. Nevertheless the production of such a substance is an interesting new development and one that will doubtless be followed by similar products to suppress or prevent body odour, to serve olfactory preferences. A more usual method of preventing body odour is to apply some substance that will stop locally the body sweating, such as aluminium chloride or sulphate. It does not sound a very safe method (and theoretically at least one might prefer the treated fabric), but the fact is that millions of women use these perspiration inhibitors made up by the pharmacists into creams, or lotions or sprays and seem to come to no harm.

Plastics. Many plastics have intrinsic unpleasant smells and their acceptability is often improved by the addition of a masking agent such as amyl butyrate which has a powerful not unpleasant ester odour. Cheap plastic handbags can even be made to smell like real expensive leather; men's plastic wallets can be given a good leather smell. The upholstery and the floor mats of second-hand cars in America are often sprayed with odorants to give a "new-car" smell; it costs about 25/– to spruce up a car in this way, to cater for the general olfactory preference for a new-car odour. This, incidentally, is one odour that can hardly be much liked on its own merits, but only apparently through associations with prosperity and good living. The new-car smell can thereby become a fine odour and one that is greatly appreciated, although in other circumstances, e.g. on a frock or in a dining room, it might well be considered repellent.

Cleaning materials. Polishes generally are perfumed; the lavender in the furniture polish is liked and lends a hint of good housekeeping. But when perfuming extends as it has done of late to the abrasives that are to be found near the kitchen sink, the soul revolts. Firstly, why perfume them, scouring powders as they are, at all; their job is simply to remove dirt; secondly they are so cheap that the odorant materials themselves have also to be cheap. The author has asked a good many people what they think of them and it has to be admitted that usually the answer is "not worried" or "don't mind" with a few expressing marked disapproval and none expressing a liking. If ever there was a case where no smell is the best smell this would seem to be it. Perhaps it may be that one and the same industrial combine makes both scouring powders and industrial perfumes and the old-established scouring powder department is expected to give the younger perfume department a leg up, even to the tune of buying perfume materials, that it would rather not have, in order to satisfy some quite imaginary olfactory preferences.

Masking and counteraction

The meanings of "odour masking" and of "odour counteraction" have varied from time to time, largely because of the quite honest doubts that many people have had about the genuineness of odour counteraction. However, the meaning seems now to have settled down somewhat as follows:

Masking is the overpowering of one smell usually unpleasant by another which is stronger and more pleasant. Rubber manufactures may have their rather unpleasant rubbery smell overpowered or "masked" by including some fatty ester or some other very strong and unobjectionable odorant. Sometimes this is called reodorizing, the idea being that the old odour is masked and a new one takes its place so that it is reodorized. The masking agent is then called a reodorant. Paint is a commodity whose odour is often masked; ordinary oil paint and high gloss enamel often have a tenacious smell and the smell of paint may hang around a newly-painted room for several days; most people dislike it and some are quite genuinely nauseated and sickened by it, so that painting and decoration have to be done during their absence from home. Mrs. Beeton's famous treatise on Household Management recommends standing a bucket of water with some hay in it in a newly-painted room so that the smell will disappear overnight; this recipe is a splendid one and anyone who tries it will be delighted. It probably is so effective because the damp hay adsorbs the volatiles from the drying paint. Painters and decorators sometimes add a powerful odorant such as vanilla extract to their paint to mask the paint odour; there are sixpenny plastic balls of masking agent that the amateur can buy at paint shops. These devices (not the bucket of hay which relies on adsorption) are pure masking. The masking of paint odours has been discussed in the Givaudan house magazine[118] "You send us a quart of your paint and we'll return it to you smelling better than ever. We'll select the odour modifier best suited to your product", so say Givaudan and this approach is typical of the excellent technical service that is often available nowadays from good manufacturers. Emulsion paints are less liable to have tenacious and objectionable smells than oil-based paints.

One method of masking that can be very successful is by modification to a more pleasant odour by aromatic materials which are sometimes associated naturally with the odour that is causing the trouble. Thus if the odour of acetic acid is troublesome it can be built up into a fruity complex by adding bergamot oil; fruity complexes naturally contain acetic acid. An odour of tar can be suitably masked to resemble Russian leather. Phenolic odours can be built up into carnation. The approach towards masking should be to consider in what natural and pleasant products the unwanted odour of the material is a component and then to build up to that natural product. If the unwanted odour is really unpleasant it has to be swamped; castor oil with raspberry or vanilla essence, and petrol smells with oil of orange, or benzyl acetate or amyl butyrate. The fruity esters are especially valuable because they reduce any nauseous component that may be present. Another useful approach is to avoid the unwanted odour by using a better quality material, e.g. a refined wax (nearly inodorous) base, instead of a cheap and odorous wax as a base for a cosmetic formulation. The flavouring of yeast extracts, so rich in vitamins but so uninteresting, to make them pleasant really comes into the same category—that of masking.

Counteraction is the use of one odorant to reduce the smell of another, so that the total odour of the two together is less than that of either of the two separately. Under suitable conditions this is quite effective, but usually it operates only when odours are slight and not intense. Some of the aerosol air-fresheners that have been sold depend in part on counteraction for their ability to freshen the air in a close or oppressive room, although usually there is a good deal of masking and reodorizing as well. Olfactory preferences have to be handled very gently with such devices and the new odour that is introduced should not as a rule be a noticeably beautiful one; not for example rose or jasmine, but should be clean and unobtrusive, e.g. pine, fir, or reminiscent of green vegetation (one of the best has had the very descriptive name of Glade). The original Air-wick was another of the best; it consisted of many odorants and had a characteristic not unpleasant fresh smell. It is important that the smell of such products should be one that can be endured for a long time without arousing revulsion; and to this end it must not be sweet or honied. Anyone contemplating the formulation of an air-freshener could do worse than play the citrus fruit smell against that of pine forests; both are pleasant, both fresh and both can be lived with; the trick is to make a mixture that is still pleasant, but that does not smell decidedly of any single type of constituent; it is practically the same trick as was used by the perfumers in the formulation of eau-de-Cologne. A great deal of work has been done in the formulation of these space refreshers, but most of it has been very empirical and there is certainly room for improvement by a more systematic and logical approach to their compounding.

Removal of unwanted odours

Sometimes an unwanted odour can be removed without introducing another odour which is going to be present permanently. The usual trick is to introduce another odorant, then to remove it and surprisingly and almost magically, it is found that it has taken the original unpleasant or unwanted odour with it. An example was given in Chapter 19 of the permanent removal of off-flavours from sugar beet by adding an essential oil and heating with steam; if the essential oil was not added, then the removal of the off-flavour by steam was not permanent.

It has been found that smoke-odour damaged goods can often be put right by a similar process. After a fire at a warehouse or store there is sometimes a large quantity of valuable merchandise which is not otherwise damaged but which is contaminated with a smoke odour, which ordinary ventilation will not remove, so that the value of the merchandise is considerably reduced. If, however, the damaged merchandise is first sprayed with a fine mist of odorous materials similar to the basic constituents of an air-freshener and then later is ventilated with a current of air, not only are the odorants which were applied removed by the air, but they take with them the smell of smoke and leave the goods in much better condition.

There have been many industrial applications of odour suppression or removal. One such was at Stornoway in the Hebrides; the trawlers bring in very heavy catches of herring at certain seasons and a factory was built to process the surplus fish and convert it to fish meal. Unfortunately, the smell of the factory was very evident and was not at all pleasant, but it was later greatly improved by the injection into the exhaust ducts and smoke-stacks of suitable odorants. Industrial odour problems of many kinds, in sewage plants, at paper mills, fertilizer factories and fat rendering plants have been suitably overcome by the addition usually to the exhaust or effluent of pleasantly odorous materials; their detailed consideration hardly falls within the scope of this book, but the author[119] has already given some indications of the lines along which such treatment is made.

Rules

Those rules which may be derived from the subject matter of this chapter are:

Rule 121. It is becoming more common to odorize merchandise of the kind that is ordinarily inodorous to make it sell better. For underwear, bed-linen and so forth this practice if used temperately may be desirable. Discretion must be used to ensure that the perfumed product will be olfactorily preferred to the unperfumed.

Rule 122. Manufactured articles that have a disliked odour are usually masked or reodorized. Some new material, the mask or reodorant which has something in common with the unwanted odour is added, e.g. an acid odour can be built up to a fruity note. The odour of the mask overcomes that of the acid note.

Rule 123. There are some off-odours that can only be masked by overwhelming them with relatively large quantities of powerful but reasonably pleasant odorants, notably the citrus oils.

Rule 124. Odour counteraction is an established phenomenon but for the most part it is only applicable to faint odours; a weak malodour can sometimes be removed by counteraction with a suitable odorant, e.g. butyric acid can be compensated with juniper oil.

REFERENCES

113. H. Pichlmayr, *Method of imparting a permanent fragrance to fabrics,* B.P. 735,684 (1955).

114. Selling by smell; sweet scents invade industry and business; steady increase of use of aromatic chemicals, *Perf. & Essential Oil Record,* 1957, **48,** 349–350.

115. R. W. Moncrieff, Odour in resin-treated fabrics: simple tests to ensure absence, *Textile Weekly,* 1963, **63,** 475–478.

116. West Point Manufacturing Co., *Preventing odours in filamentary or sheet material treated with thermo-setting aldehyde resins,* B.P. 890,515 (1962).

117. J. M. Salsbury, Something new in finishes, *Modern Textiles Mag.,* 1957, **38,** No. 4, 82–86, 103.

118. Sindar Corporation (associated with Givaudan-Delawanna), The sense of smell as a marketing tool in *The Sindar Reporter,* No. 3, 1961 and Personal observations on the odour of paint, *Ibid,* No. 1, 1964.

119. R. W. Moncrieff, Industrial odours, *Industrial Water & Wastes,* 1961, pp. 107–110, 131–132, 195–199.

RULES OF ODOUR PREFERENCE

A T THE END of each chapter those rules that could be derived from the chapter's contents were enunciated. They are grouped together here to facilitate comparison and reference. Where it seemed to be permissible, the wording has been fined down. The 124 Rules given below include the best contemporary knowledge of the subject of odour preferences.

1. Natural materials are liked better than synthetics.
2. Trace constituents contribute to the pleasantness of natural materials.
3. It is still impossible to synthesize products that are as good as the natural materials.
4. Dilution of an odorant usually increases its pleasantness.
5. People of all kinds agree unanimously about really bad smells.
6. Most people agree well about really good smells.
7. If children are excluded, people agree even better about good smells.
8. Preferences are more confused in the middle range of odorants, those that are neither greatly liked nor disliked.
9. As even a little unpleasantness creeps in, agreement between observers improves sharply.
10. To most odours people are relatively indifferent, only a small number are greatly liked or disliked.
11. Men and women agree well (Rules 5, 6) about good and bad smells, but there are sex differences in the intermediate range (cf. Rules 44, 45).
12. Men's preferences are surer than those of women in the fairly pleasant range of odours (cf. Rule 19 relating to children).
13. Women's dislikes of slightly unpleasant odours are surer than men's.
14. Both sexes like flower smells; women like their flowers simple, but men can enjoy sophistication.
15. Fruity smells appeal equally to the sexes.
16. Most essential oils appeal fairly equally to the two sexes.
17. Musks are generally ranked better by men than by women.

18. Culinary odours are ranked higher by women than men.

19. Children are surer than adults of their preferences in the fairly pleasant odours (cf. Rule 12).

20. Children do not appreciate sweet flower smells nearly so much as adults.

21. Children are much more appreciative of fruity smells than adults (cf. Rule 52).

22. Children are more appreciative of some nutty smells than adults.

23. Children dislike oily smells.

24. Simple flower smells are greatly liked by all adults.

25. Sophisticated flower smells are liked much better by the over 25's than by the young adults.

26. Musky smells are liked better by the over 25's than by the young adults.

27. Fruity flavours are rated better by the over 25's than by the young adults, but not nearly so highly as they are by the children.

28. Alliaceous smells, chives and onions, are most highly appreciated by young adults.

29. Age is a more powerful determinant than is sex of olfactory preferences (cf. Rule 50).

30. Synthetic flavours, unattractive to adults, are considered quite passable by children.

31. Young adults give the best (but not a very good) rating to alcohol. Children dislike it most.

32. Children tolerate faecal odours much better than adults (cf. Rule 57).

33. Temperament has little effect on the liking or disliking of most odours.

34. Among the pleasant odours, the extroverts' preferences, when they differ significantly from those of the introverts, are more like those of children.

35. Among the unpleasant odours, it is the introverts' preferences which, when significantly different from those of the extroverts, are more similar to the children's.

36. Anything unusual or strange in an odour is more acceptable to introverts than it is to extroverts.

37. If there is a big difference between the sexes in their ranking of an odour, it will probably be the males who like it the better.

38. If there is a big difference between the two temperaments in their ranking of an odour, it will probably be the introverts who like it the better.

39. Reproducibility of order of preference of a small number of odours by one person is good.

40. Reproducibility, and therefore reliability of preferences, is best in the 20–40 age group.

41. Males are a little more reliable than females in their odour preferences.

42. There is no difference in reliability or reproducibility of odour preferences between people of introvert and extrovert temperaments.

43. When two preference arrangements of ten dissimilar odorants are made by a group of people of eleven years and over, about 40 per cent of the placings will be the same in the two arrangements, about 30 per cent will only be one place removed and the other 30 per cent will be two or more places removed.

44. Some of the differences between the two sexes in respect of odour preferences are very marked (cf. Rule 11).

45. Those odours which the sexes rate differently are in the intermediate range, in line with Rules 8 and 11, and the differences are biggest between the ages of fifteen and forty.

46. Muskiness appears to be a sex attractant for males (cf. Rule 17).

47. Females rate the almond and naphthalene smells much better than males do; these preferences become less marked after age forty.

48. Odour preference differences between the sexes persist into old age if the preference is shown by males, but die away soon after forty years of age if the preference is shown by females.

49. Sex differences in odour preferences are evident at a very early age. They are already detectable before eight years.

50. Olfactory preferences may change very considerably with age (cf. Rule 29).

51. Sometimes the changes in preferences with age are different for the two sexes; examples are provided by almond and musky smells (cf. Rules, 22, 26, 46, 47).

52. At all ages the fruity smell is liked, but the liking is very much greater in children than it is in adults and is at a maximum at ten or eleven years (cf. Rule 21).

53. The liking for some odours, changes very little with age.

54. Occasionally there is a very sudden change in liking for an odorant. The liking for lavender increases enormously from fifteen to eighteen years.

55. Odours which have sex significance evoke two changes in preference among the subjects; the first at adolescence and the second at the end of the reproductive period (cf. Rules 47, 48).

56. Odours which are unique evoke responses that are more irregular than most odorants.

57. Odours which are commonly disliked are tolerated very much better by very young children (cf. Rule 32).

58. Generally the biggest changes in olfactory preference take place in youth, in the first twenty years of life (cf. Rule 54).

59. The young (not the very young) are the most emphatic in their olfactory likes and dislikes.

60. When preference placing is plotted against age, curves can result which are mirror images of each other. Identical, or at least simultaneous, physiological changes can both enhance and diminish liking for different odorants.

61. Examination of the proportion of subjects who place any one odour first, yields preference age curves generally similar to those obtained by plotting average placing against age.

62. Differences in olfactory preferences that are due to temperament differences are much less frequent and much smaller than those due to age or sex differences (cf. Rules 11, 29, 33, 66).

63. The liking for the fruity odour lasts longer through life in the introverts than it does in the extroverts.

64. The biggest differences between the two temperament groups occur towards those odorants which one sex likes better than the other.

65. Intelligence differences have little or no effect on olfactory preferences, with the reservation that intelligent children exhibit preferences more in line with those of normal children who are a little older.

66. The most powerful determinant of olfactory preferences is age; next comes sex which also has a powerful effect; then comes temperament which has only a slight effect and finally intelligence which has practically no effect.

67. Liking or disliking when it occurs of a smell is involuntary, and immediate, but to many odorants the reaction is one of indifference.

68. Liking or disliking of an odour, especially of food, is partly determined by the requirements of the body. The smell of what will be good for the body will usually be liked.

69. Liking or disliking of an odour may be partly determined by the emotional requirements of the subject, either transient or long term.

70. Association of a particular smell with some former experience may play a part in determining whether it will be liked or not.

71. Most often there is no apparent reason for liking or disliking a smell.

72. Liking and disliking of odours are not strong emotions like anger and fear; they are gentler reactions that are referred to as "affective states".

73. Two separate smells, e.g. one pleasant and one unpleasant, cannot be simultaneously perceived separately; but only in alternation due to a shift of attention.

74. Two or more separate smells may be perceived simultaneously as a composite whole as in a perfume.

75. The sensations of pleasantness and unpleasantness cannot be experienced simultaneously.

76. A smell sensation and the pleasantness or unpleasantness that it arouses can be experienced simultaneously.

77. Some pairs of odorants present in small and suitable proportions in air may, when mixed, give an air in which neither odorant is recognizable and of which the odour is weaker than that of either component separately. This is known as odour counter-action (cf. Rule 124).

78. Reactions to pleasantness or unpleasantness of odours can be very marked, particularly in children. Generally, a contraction of the facial muscles indicates dislike, whilst their relaxation indicates liking.

79. Reactions to unpleasant odours are more violent than to pleasant odours.

80. Reactions that belong properly to olfactory unpleasantness are frequently used to signify dislike of any disorderly situation or person even although no smell is present.

81. The different races of mankind show some, probably minor, differences in olfactory preferences.

82. People of different races have different body odours; usually those of their own race are the least objectionable.

83. Olfactory pleasure is unlikely to continue for long, because fatigue ensues rapidly. Unpleasantness also fades but more slowly.

84. Even very unpleasant odours lose their apparent intensity in time: the subject becomes habituated and eventually unaware of the olfactory unpleasantness of his environment.

85. Many relations between chemical constitution and type of odour, often pleasant or unpleasant, have been enunciated, but it has not yet been possible to weld them into a general theory.

86. There are indications that pleasant odorants may stimulate receptors of different kinds fairly uniformly, whereas unpleasant odorants have high specificity of stimulation so that they excite some receptors and hardly affect others.

87. The most successful odour classifications are based on a division of several odour properties into their pleasant and unpleasant aspects.

88. There is sufficient agreement between different people of the same sex and age group in their olfactory preferences to justify making an average assessment as a "general affective value" (cf. Rules 5 and 6).

89. The apparent pleasantness of an odorant is appreciably increased by just-prior smelling of unpleasant odorants. Conversely it is apparently reduced by just-prior smelling of pleasant odorants.

90. Recognition of an odour enhances its pleasantness.

91. Ease of recognition after previous experience of odours is nearly independent of pleasantness or unpleasantness.

92. An adult individual's odour preferences are very constant over a period of years.

93. Often-repeated testing on one adult individual reveals excellent consistency of preferences amongst the liked and the disliked odours, but considerable variability amongst the indifferent odours (cf. Rules 5, 6 and 8 for *groups* of people).

94. Constancy of preferences in one individual at different times is greater than that between several individuals.

95. There is a tendency for young children to give higher coefficients of pleasantness (to say "Yes, I like" more often) to odours, than older people would.

96. Old people are prone not to notice smells, even unpleasant and dangerous smells.

97. A small minority of people are very susceptible emotionally to odours, and can be upset by their presence.

98. The play of odours on the emotions can be measured as changes in the electrical resistance of the skin.

99. Some odours will affect the emotions beneficially, soothing anger and uplifting the downcast.

100. Odours probably have an important part to play in healing the sick; especially in diseases of the breathing apparatus and in mental illness.

101. Cigarette smoking greatly depresses the sensitivity to odours that resemble tobacco smoke, but has no marked effect on sensitivity to odours of other kinds.

102. It is difficult to recall a smell in abstract (that is without the smell being present). Those smells that are the most liked are those that present the least difficulty to recall.

103. Knowledge of a person's olfactory preferences may give clues to the sex, age and temperament of that person.

104. The reactions of an animal to smells are much more emphatic and may be more violent than those of a man.

105. There are some resemblances between the olfactory preferences of a dog and a man, but the differences are far greater than the similarities.

106. There are some smells that animals greatly dislike that can be used in the formulation of repellents.

107. The sensitive receptor surface of the olfactory equipment of some animals, e.g. the dog, is much larger than it is in man; this provides the means for finer discrimination.

108. Raw food sometimes has an odour or flavour that is lost in cooking.

109. The flavour of most meats develops when they are cooked.

110. Methods of isolating flavour principles from food are not perfect. In particular those which involve the use of heat may cause chemical change.

111. If a natural flavour product can be used whole, without the need for isolation of the flavour principles, so much the better.

112. A method of removing permanently a tenacious off-flavour or odour is to add to the material that suffers from it some pleasant odorous oil and then to remove the oil either by steam distillation or ventilation.

113. The electric currents that the neuro-physiologist can record in the brain of a person stimulated by a smell or a flavour cannot yet be correlated with pleasantness or unpleasantness.

114. Children and men like their fruit drinks sweeter than women.

L

115. Natural flavours are usually complex mixtures (cf. Rules 2, 3). New analytical methods, particularly gas chromatography, are yielding a great deal of new knowledge of their chemical constitution.

116. Flavour profiles have been introduced; they consist of the delineation and estimation of notes such as sweet, bitter, smoky, and yeasty in well-known aromas.

117. Flavour testing on a routine basis is carried out best by an individual expert. Selection of one new product from several and adjustment of flavour are best carried out by a small technical panel. Lay panels are slow and inconclusive.

118. Colour can affect flavour preferences.

119. What is considered pleasant in perfumes changes with the times. Perfumes are subject to fashion.

120. The use of perfumes by men is still regarded doubtfully, but there is agreement by men and women that if men are to wear perfume, the preferred scents are eau-de-Cologne, lavender and pine.

121. It is becoming a more common practice to odorize merchandise of the kind that is ordinarily inodorous to make it sell better. Discretion must be used to ensure that the perfumed product will be olfactorily preferred to the unperfumed.

122. Manufactured articles that have an unpleasant odour, are usually given a masking or reodorizing treatment. Some new material, the mask or reodorant which has something in common with the unwanted odour is added, e.g. an acid odour can be built up to a fruity note.

123. There are some off-odours that can only be masked by overcoming them with relatively large quantities of powerful but reasonably pleasant odorants, notably the citrus oils.

124. Odour counteraction is an established phenomenon, but for the most part it is only applicable to faint odours. Sometimes it can be used to remove unpleasant industrial odours (cf. Rule 77).

Author Index

L*

Subject Index